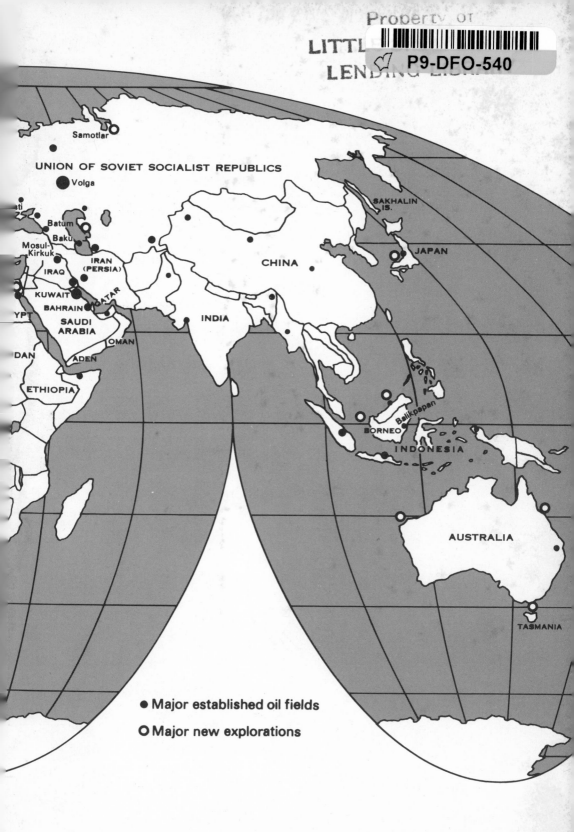

Samotlar

UNION OF SOVIET SOCIALIST REPUBLICS

Volga

SAKHALIN
IS.

ati
Z

Batum

Baku

JAPAN

Mosul-
Kirkuk

IRAN
(PERSIA)

CHINA

IRAQ

KUWAIT

QATAR

INDIA

BAHRAIN

YPT

SAUDI
ARABIA

OMAN

DAN

ADEN

ETHIOPIA

Balikpapan

BORNEO

INDONESIA

AUSTRALIA

TASMANIA

● Major established oil fields

O Major new explorations

Books by Richard O'Connor

Fiction

Guns of Chickamauga
Company Q
Officers and Ladies
The Vandal

Nonfiction

Thomas: Rock of Chickamauga
Hood: Cavalier General
Sheridan the Inevitable
High Jinks on the Klondike
Bat Masterson
Johnstown: The Day the Dam Broke
Hell's Kitchen
Wild Bill Hickok
Pat Garrett
Black Jack Pershing
Gould's Millions
The Scandalous Mr. Bennett
Courtroom Warrior: The Combative Career of William Travers Jerome
Jack London: A Biography
Bret Harte: A Biography
Ambrose Bierce: A Biography
The German-Americans
Pacific Destiny
The First Hurrah: A Biography of Alfred E. Smith
O. Henry: The Legendary Life of William S. Porter
The Oil Barons

The Oil Barons

The Oil Barons

Men of Greed and Grandeur

Richard O'Connor

Little, Brown and Company — Boston - Toronto

Illustrations and endleaf map by Dick Sanderson

PRINTED IN THE UNITED STATES OF AMERICA
*Published simultaneously in Canada
by Little, Brown & Company (Canada) Limited*

Acknowledgment

I am indebted to the American Petroleum Institute for the use of its excellent and expertly staffed library in New York City; to the Manuscript Division of the Library of Congress for making available the Admiral Mark Bristol papers and war diary; to H. E. Tolle of Humble Oil for explaining certain oil industry economic problems (from the industry's viewpoint); to Dale L. Walker of El Paso for obtaining certain rare books about the oil industry; to Robert Woodward, head of the Bangor, Maine, Public Library for a similar service; and — not least — to Ruth Sheldon Knowles and Christopher Tugendhat for an overview of the subject not readily available elsewhere.

For permission to quote, I am indebted to Harold Ober Associates, Inc., agent for Ralph Hewins, *Mr. Five Per Cent*, 1958; to Crown Publishers for Glyn Roberts' *The Most Powerful Man in the World*, 1938; to Doubleday & Co. for John Bainbridge's *The Super Americans*, 1961; to McGraw-Hill Book Co. for Ruth Sheldon Knowles' *The Greatest Gamblers*, 1959; to Charles Scribner's Sons for Allan Nevins' *A Study in Power: John D. Rockefeller, Industrialist and Philanthropist*, 1953.

RICHARD O'CONNOR

Contents

CONTENTS

The Oil Barons

Introduction

A collection of tear sheets assembled from newspapers and magazines during 1969 suggests that the international oil industry is in serious trouble with the public, under fire on a number of fronts ranging from tax favoritism to despoliation of the environment. It also suggests that, short of changing its methods and thereby reducing its profits, it might explain itself more fully. There has been a convergence of angry opinion on the subject of conserving what's left of our environment, growing in vehemence from right and left and center, that forecasts a devastating time ahead for the oil industry.

Many works on the industry have been encouraged or financed by the oil companies with predictably pleasing results. This book was undertaken independent of such influence. It is intended to be a realistic reappraisal of the lives of a small number of men who have changed the history of the past century while tapping the world's oil deposits and enormously enriching themselves; a not overly pious narrative of the interaction of those men and its effect on our lives.

Unfortunately, from their standpoint, the results of their endeavors are plainly visible. Wars have started over the possession of oil resources and possibly will again. Even if the quest for oil could be conducted peaceably, humanity would still be confronted by the pollution of air and water caused by petroleum and the internal combustion engine. No one writes songs about "merry Oldsmobiles" anymore; more likely

3

books about "insolent chariots." One expert, without striving unduly for sensationalism, has warned that within the next twenty years the earth will be enveloped by a carbon-dioxide blanket from automobile exhaust, largely, that will choke all life on this planet. It seems that humanity unwittingly has cast itself in the role of Count Frankenstein, with a century-old monster about to descend on the global village in a final outbreak of destruction.

The Bible allowed us "a little oil in the cruse" to light our homes, but now our cruses are overflowing. During the early months of 1969 — an unfair sampling of oil history, perhaps, but the period that coincided with the start of this book — there was abundant evidence that mankind may have struck a Faustian bargain in accepting the conveniences provided by petroleum and its by-products. In the middle of that period a newspaper columnist declared that "it was a very bad day at some black rock or other when somebody discovered that petroleum made a dandy fuel. If you stop and think for twenty consecutive seconds about the oil business, you end up in a swamp of evil . . . Look at the trouble oil has caused the world . . . a physical, social and moral pollutant. The splendid philanthropies of the Rockefellers and others loom small when viewed against the years of savaging the landscape and exploiting the land and its people."[1]

It was indeed a bad time for those responsible for the industry's image-polishing, a field incidentally pioneered by a genius of propaganda on behalf of John D. Rockefeller, Sr. But even full-page ads in the *New York Times* and *Wall Street Journal*, along with less obvious endeavors, could not paper over the disturbing news of what oil was costing the human race. In February, an offshore oil well in the Santa Barbara Channel had been ruptured, a thousand gallons of oil an hour oozed into the water, and the beaches for miles around were covered with the black slime. The damage oil can do to beaches and wildlife already had been demonstrated two years earlier when the *Torrey Canyon* spilled one hundred

4

thousand tons of crude oil into the English Channel and onto the English beaches.

A short time later American relations with Peru disintegrated to the breaking point when that nation seized the holdings of the International Petroleum Company, a subsidiary of Standard Oil of New Jersey, which had been operating in Peru for almost forty-five years. In the Middle East, there were greatly heightened tensions between Israel and the Arab alliance, in the background of which was the long underground war for the oil resources of that area, which indirectly were subsidizing the terrorist activities against the Israelis. Iran, though not allied with Israel's enemies, was reported in mid-April considering the seizure of a large part of the oil production within its borders because the international consortium operating there had not increased its production to keep pace with the demands of the Iranian $11 billion development program, a rather grandiose scheme conceived through the over-expectations that oil invariably arouses.[2]

Domestically, too, an oily sludge had seeped into American social and political and economic affairs. One contentious issue, significant largely because it showed the political clout wielded by the oil industry, was the proposed establishment of a huge oil refinery, storage facility, and foreign trade zone at the deep-water port of Machiasport, Maine. Occidental Petroleum wanted to build the facility as a means of importing cheaper Libyan oil, refining it, and distributing it in New England, which has been victimized by the rigged prices enforced by the major companies. Large sums were contributed to the Nixon presidential campaign fund by Texas oil barons in the hope that the Machiasport project would be killed off and the integrity of the domestic market, which has always been jealously guarded against cheaper foreign oil, would be preserved.[3]

At the same time the American consumer was contemplating the cheap-jack "contests" which were supposed to lure him into the gasoline service stations. Every station had taken on the aspect of a miniature Las Vegas, with banners and

5

billboards proclaiming alleged giveaways such as Tigerino, Dino Dollars and Presidential Dollars. The Federal Trade Commission investigated the nationwide lottery and found that the player had 3.4 chances in 1,000 of winning an average prize of $3.87. The odds of winning a thousand-dollar jackpot were 1 in 1,200,000.[4]

In various parts of the nation, from the North Slope of Alaska southward, Americans during this brief period were experiencing anew the mixed blessings of oil discovery and exploitation. Not only were they concerned by the dangers to coastal waters from offshore drilling, but far inland they were learning at first hand that an oil derrick bears a certain resemblance to a crucifix. Late in December 1968, development operations began in the Blue Creek field of West Virginia. Within a few months West Virginians were appalled at the side effects. Drillers slashed through miles of field, forest and farmland. The people living around the field itself found that their water supply was fouled by salt from the wells; they were receiving no benefit from the oil being sucked from the land beneath them because they did not own the mineral rights to their holdings. In addition, the purity of Charleston's water supply, the Elk River, was endangered by the drilling operations and a member of the state pollution commission reported, "It's rape. Rape of the land, rape of our water resources, rape of the people. There is hardly any virgin land left in West Virginia."[5]

And in this same period — when the major oil-producers were congratulating themselves on Alaskan discoveries that will bring them billions of dollars, not to mention a controversial shale-oil deposit in three western states which some estimate to be worth $8 *trillion* — millions of American taxpayers were borrowing money to pay their income taxes on April 15, 1969, while brooding over the disparity, the inequity and the undoubted iniquity of tax loopholes through which billions in oil revenue was happily gurgling away from the U.S. Treasury and into private exchequers. The sacred oil-depletion allowance, always irksome to the vast majority of non-beneficiaries, now assumed the proportions of a national scandal. On that black-letter day itself, April 15, bemused taxpayers could read the denunciation of the oil companies by Representative Bertram Podell of Brooklyn. "Did you pay an average tax rate of 25 percent of your income last year?" Representative Podell asked in Congress. "Shed a tear, ungrateful wretch, for persecuted Shell Oil Co., which paid 13.1 percent of $342,-000,000 in 1967 in the form of federal taxes. Weep for Union Oil Co., which paid 6.3 percent tax. Or how could we forget the terrible fate that overtook Getty Oil Co. in 1967? It earned $132,762,000. Shall we expand the food-stamp program to include starving oil company executives and their ragged families huddled in pitiful groups on the Riviera and in the Caribbean? How can they keep polluting our beaches, killing our wildlife, keeping out cheap foreign oil, and taking that 27½ depletion allowance on a pitiful diet of filet mignon, pâté de fois gras and ten-year-old whiskey?"[6] Even more inspiring to the average taxpayer were tales of multimillionaires, sheltered by the depletion allowance, who paid no tax at all.

Those first several months of 1969, atypical period though it may have been in a hundred years of oil history, certainly did not endear it to the rest of humanity. In that century a handful of men have become enormously rich, immensely powerful, and increasingly arrogant over the privilege they have monopolized, the right to suck oil out of the earth, refine, and market it. They have influenced the world's geopolitical balance to an incalculable degree; just how much is seldom admitted by national leaders because oil is as strategically necessary to power politics as a ballistic-missile system or an atomic-powered submarine fleet. And oil is not only where you find it, but how well it can be protected by diplomacy and the threat of military or naval power (thus the Sixth Fleet in the Mediterranean is as much an adjunct of the oil industry, or more so, than of NATO's "southern defenses"). Oil as the lubricant of civilization is second only to food as the most important commodity in the world, the indispensable means of victory in war and the principal source of prosperity in peace. In the past century no nation has been able to become a major power without assured sources of petroleum. Oil won the battle of Verdun and thereby saved the Allies in World War I and was a principal factor in bringing down the Axis war machines in World War II. The greatest present threat of World War III appears over the oil domes of the Middle East, imperfectly concealed by the Arab-Israeli struggle.

The oil kings are more than mere purveyors and entrepreneurs engaged in finding and selling a commodity. At times they almost seem to form an unofficial super-government. In this book they will be examined as individuals, no less than the hard-hatted men who drill their wells, and as a collective which has engaged in the subsurface war, the incessant intrigue, the political and corporate infighting, the historic drama that marks every episode in the tightening grasp of oil on the world's affairs. They are the men who, more than dead Hitlers, replaceable Nassers, fleeting kings and sheikhs and messiahs, have made the world what it is today and will determine what it may be tomorrow.

I.

The Lamplighters

1.

"Strong Men Go Mad"

In the American marketplace, oil has always possessed a special quality, an excitement, which has attached itself to no other commodity. It is as much a part of legendary America as gunfighters and clipper ships. From the beginning it had what Santayana called the "ideal essence" of American business; it offered vast opportunities and equally large risks, it was hotly competitive, it was filled with the speculative tension of a bookie joint on Kentucky Derby day, and it acquired a mystique all its own. An oilman is no ordinary fellow. He is inclined to swagger a bit and talk a little louder. He comes from a long line of folk heroes. He is Clark Gable in *Boomtown*. Even the corporate process has not entirely tamed him.

There is a drama about the oil business that attends no other. It has all the elements of a well-made play of the old-fashioned sort, with a plot, a rousing second-act curtain, well-defined heroes and villains — and plenty of critics in the audience. The discovery and exploitation of an oilfield has all the suspense of a well-ordered drama and the pictorial aspects of a film epic in Panavision and Technicolor. The drilling of the first well. The suspense of waiting to find out whether it is a dry hole or a producing well. The black plume shooting sky-ward and showering the countryside as a gusher comes in. The rush for leases and mineral rights. The building of a boom-town. The process of small operators being engorged by the men who depend on money rather than luck . . .

All the standard ingredients were present in the first oil boom in this country (and the world), the opening of the western Pennsylvania field during the 1860's.

Not the least of those ingredients is the seemingly omni-present oil thirst. Until refined petroleum came along, the oil of the sperm whale was used for filling lamps. In a nation that was expanding and industrializing itself at a galloping pace, however, the supply of whale oil was running short by the time of the Civil War. Whaling, in fact, had already peaked out. The U.S. whaling industry reached its peak in 1848 when 738 vessels were engaged in killing whales, rendering their fat (two hundred gallons of oil extracted from a ton of blub-ber), and keeping American lamps burning. By the 1860's the whale herds had been decimated and longer and less profit-able voyages had to be undertaken by the whaling fleets of New Bedford, Sag Harbor and New London.

Mankind had long suspected there might be a wholesale use for the "rock oil," sometimes called Seneca oil, known to be stored in pools below the earth's surface. For centuries, in various parts of the world, petroleum was regarded as a medi-cine, a specific to be used against various ill-defined aches and pains which physicians had thus far failed to sort out. In the fourteenth century Marco Polo reported that oil seeping out at Baku on the Caspian was being used for curing "cutaneous distempers in men and camels." In western Pennsylvania, on Oil Creek and in Venango County, the Seneca Indians smeared oil on themselves as a liniment and mixed it with their war paint. White settlers in Pennsylvania stole the idea, called the substance Seneca oil, and used it medicinally — as a presumed cure for arthritic joints, though not for war paint.

Finally some local promoters became obsessed with the possibility that petroleum, after being submitted to a refining process, could be employed as a lamp fuel. They formed the Pennsylvania Rock Oil Company, with headquarters at Titusville, and engaged Benjamin Silliman, Jr., a professor of chemistry at Yale, to analyze a barrel of petroleum they shipped him and determine whether it could be used as lighting fuel. After experimenting in his laboratory for about six months, Silliman announced that he had made astonishing discoveries but refused to submit his report until his fee of $526.08 was paid in full. "I have submitted the lamp burning Petroleum," he reported late in 1857, "to the inspection of the most experienced lampists who were accessible to me, and their testimony was, that the lamp burning this fluid gave as much light as any which they had seen, that the oil spent more economically, and the uniformity of the light was greater than in Camphene. As this oil does not gum or become acid or rancid by exposure, it possesses in that, as well as its wonderful resistance to extreme cold, important qualities for a lubricant. In conclusion, gentlemen, it appears to me that there is much ground for encouragement in the belief that your Company have in their possession a raw material from which, by simple and not expensive process they may manufacture very valuable products."[1]

The promoters of the company for some mystifying reason, possibly connected with the $200 they persuaded him to invest in the company's stock, then selected one Edwin L. Drake, a thirty-eight-year-old conductor on the New Haven Railroad, semi-invalided by neuralgia, to take charge of field operations. He had no technical qualifications, but then neither had anyone else. They might, however, have been expected to pick an able-bodied man for the exhausting tasks ahead. Nevertheless they chose the frail, soft-spoken Drake, appointed him "general agent" of the Pennsylvania Rock Oil Company, gave him a thousand dollars, and sent him to their holdings in western Pennsylvania with instructions to get that oil out of the ground — somehow — and into barrels.

Drake, a quietly stubborn man, hired a number of farmers, mostly German and Irish immigrants, to dig for what he called an oil spring around the place where seepage had created a pool. Learning on the job, he realized that a hole of sufficient depth would have to be drilled rather than dug, and he proceeded to assemble the necessary equipment, a twelve-foot derrick, a walking beam to drive his drills into rock and earth, a steam engine to supply the power, cast-iron pipe to be pounded through sand and clay until it struck rock at thirty-two feet. All that summer of 1859 the sickly Drake, with his tortured spine, labored with his crew to dig a well deep enough to tap an oil-bearing crevice. At sixty-nine feet they stopped drilling. The story of their discovery was told in a three-paragraph dispatch of the New York *Tribune*, the only newspaper even slightly aware of what that event might mean to the world:

SUBTERRANEAN FOUNTAIN OF OIL DISCOVERED

"Perhaps you recollect," the dispatch started in leisurely fashion under the dateline of Titusville, September 8, 1859, "that in 1854 there was organized in the City of New York a Company, under the name of the Pennsylvania Rock Oil Company, which for some good reasons, passed into the hands of some New Haven capitalists, and was by them removed to New Haven. In 1858 the directors leased the grounds and springs to Mr. E. L. Drake, well known on the New Haven Railroad. He came out here, and in May last commenced to bore for salt, or to find the source of oil, which is so common along the banks of Oil Creek. Last week, at the depth of 71 feet, he struck a fissure in the rock through which he was boring, when, to the surprise and joy of every one, he found he had tapped a vein of water and oil, yielding 400 gallons of pure oil every 24 hours (one day).

"The pump now in use throws only five gallons per minute of water and oil into a large vat, when the oil rises to the top and the water runs out from the bottom. In a few days they will have a pump of three times the capacity of the one now in use, and then from ten to twelve hundred gallons of oil will be the daily yield.

"The excitement attendant on the discovery of this vast source of oil was fully equal to what I ever saw in California, when a large lump of gold was turned out."

The story was signed Medicus and contained almost as many factual errors as a patent-medicine-man's spiel, but it did manage to convey the fact that a large supply of petroleum was available and Drake was the first man to extract it from the earth in a regular and sizable quantity. A rush for Oil Creek started, with ex-whalers and gold-rushers among those in the vanguard; derricks sprouted on the landscape; leases on land suspected of bearing oil were frantically acquired and traded, and overnight a crop of "experts" sprang up. Drake's first well was drilled between the creek and a bluff, so it was taken for granted that oil would be found only under those circumstances (mistaken though the belief was later proven to be). From the beginning the process of finding oil was surrounded by considerable superstition, fraud and guesswork, with such amiable fakers as doodlebug men, oil-witchers, oil-smellers, and other diviners in immediate abundance. J. H. A. Bone, who wrote the first book on the subject, noted the presence of "a new class of people which has sprung into existence under the cognomen of 'oil smellers,' who profess to be able to ascertain the proper spot by smelling the earth. Some of them practice considerable mummery in order to mystify their employers."[2] The Oil Creek field was soon overrun by sniffers, hazel-switch diviners and practitioners of second sight. Oilmen have never scorned them, though more scientific methods are now in use. "More oil has been found by doodlebugs," a prominent petroleum geologist has said, "than by regular geologists."[3] Possibly the most eminent of all oil geologists, the late Everette Lee DeGolyer, discovered a huge Mexican field while working his way through college and always attributed that find more to luck than science.

15

Expertise would always be haphazardly acquired in the oil business. The most scientific and knowledgeable explorations of the earth's contours often yielded nothing. On the other hand Abram James, who tapped a new Pennsylvania field in 1867, claimed that he was guided to the spot by the spirit of a Seneca Indian.

Promoters and speculators moved in behind the adventurers and "experts," and a determined effort was made to capture the attention of investors throughout the country, particularly through such effusions as a pamphlet titled *The Wonder of the Nineteenth Century: Rock Oil in Pennsylvania* and authored by one Thomas Gale, who spattered his prose with exclamation points: "A splendid thing is the Crossley well! A diamond of the first water! Enough of itself to silence the cry of humbug; to create a sensation among rival interests; to inspire hope in many toiling for the subterranean treasure, and to make every son of Pennsylvania rejoice in the good Providence that has enriched the state . . . with *rivers of oil!*" In a more sober passage Gale had to admit that "One is almost constrained, from his intuitive notion of the natural world, to suspect such a theory is a *whopper*; and that the man who talks in this manner of oil flowing up, has been drinking poor whiskey. But good vouchers are at hand."

Titusville and the surrounding villages were soon bursting with people intent on getting rich in a month or two, including an old whaling captain from New Bedford who propounded the theory that a huge shoal of whales had been stranded in western Pennsylvania during the biblical flood and that the oil now being removed was actually a gigantic deposit of blubber. So many whalers showed up, in fact, that one reporter commented, "Now they have come to harpoon Mother Earth."

More than eight hundred wells were producing thousands of barrels daily, but the growth of the industry was temporarily stunted by the Civil War and its demands on the oil-field's manpower. Before the war ended, Edwin Drake, receiving the reward usually reserved for discoverers and setting a pattern for many others who struck oil, was shunted away by his corporate partners; he eventually died in bitter and abject poverty. In belated recognition of his contribution to the industry that made so many millionaires, a Standard Oil partner later had his body removed to Titusville and placed under a $100,000 monument.

The oil industry in western Pennsylvania marked time during the war, its wells producing enough for export to bolster the northern economy and build up foreign exchange for the purchase of munitions. Oil had seeped into the national consciousness, however, to the extent that when a Methodist bishop itemized the Union's hopes for the future in a wartime sermon, President Lincoln reminded him of an omission on his list, saying, "Bishop, you didn't strike ile."[4]

Another man who was fascinated by the prospects of the oil industry was John Wilkes Booth, assassin of the President. The erratic and alcoholic actor made a spectacular appearance, as he did everywhere, in the oil region. Between tours he invested about $6,000 in various dry holes, drank, and brawled in the oil towns and harangued various saloon audiences on the virtues of Robert E. Lee and the Confederate cause. He spent most of the summer of 1864 in the oilfield towns, but unfortunately for Mr. Lincoln and the nation he became more obsessed with politics than with making a fortune out of his oil interests. After the assassination, the Venango *Spectator* noted, "The supposed assassin, J. Wilkes Booth, spent several months in this place last summer and is well known to many of our citizens. He was engaged in the Oil business, and we understand had large interests here now . . ." Booth left his worthless Venango County oil stock to a brother and sister before plunging into his last reckless venture.

The Pennsylvania oil boom really got under way after the war ended and gushers shot up around the town of Pithole, which became the wildest of all the boomtowns. Within a few months fifty hotels had been built, and the raw new streets were thronged with speculators, drillers, lease-grabbers, prostitutes, ex-soldiers, desperadoes, and hellions of all varieties. Journalists from New York and Philadelphia came to investigate and pronounced Pithole the wickedest city on earth. "A person in Pithole is indeed placed between fire and water," wrote a man from *The Nation*. "To drink water is to drink a solution of salts. To drink whiskey is to drink poison. Every glass of water I took I foreswore water, and every glass of whiskey, I foreswore whiskey . . . Every other shop is a liquor saloon. It is safe to assert that there is more vile liquor drunk in this town than in any other of its size in the world. Indeed a bar is almost the invariable appendage to every building . . ."[5]

Aside from producing oil, Pithole was printing oil stock in carload quantities and even the chambermaids in those fifty hotels were speculating on their $3-a-week salaries by buying 25- and 50-cent shares. Many who had struck only sand in their drilling operations sprinkled a few gallons of oil around their dry holes and sold shares in their "oil-bearing property."

The first man to engage in oil-stock promotion in a big way was Colonel William D'Alton Mann, recently commander of the Seventh Michigan Cavalry and future inventor of the Mann sleeping car and publisher of the scandalmongering *Town Topics*. The colonel was one of the liveliest opportunists cast up in nineteenth-century America. A man of genuine innovative talent, he might have piled up millions legitimately, but had a kink in his psyche that made one dollar swindled preferable to a hundred honestly earned.

The doughty, mustachioed colonel was seized early in 1865 by what he later called a golden inspiration. He owned a hundred-acre farm in Ohio, worthless for anything but the scheme he had in mind; that, combined with one acre he bought in Venango County, Pennsylvania, near Titusville, plus a bottle of lubricating oil and his persuasive manner, were the total assets of what became the U.S. Petroleum Company. After having letterheads printed and establishing himself in New York offices, he was ready for what the newspapers later called "The Celebrated Oil Bubble" and "The Great Petroleum

Swindle." Using his colonel's eagles and his share of the glory of Gettysburg, where his regiment had participated in a bloody but futile charge, Colonel Mann persuaded Major General Winfield Scott Hancock, a Union corps commander, to accept the presidency of U.S. Petroleum with Mann himself as vice-president, general superintendent and money-handler. To prospective investors his brochure promised that "Successful drilling will be completed in sixty days"; it dwelled enthusiastically on the oil that would come bubbling up from his acre near Titusville and his farm in Ohio "just across the Pennsylvania line." Actually the Ohio farm, near Grafton, was a hundred miles from the Pennsylvania border.

The colonel took a suite at Owen's Hotel in Washington, where he announced that his old comrades in Union blue would be given preferential treatment in being allowed to buy one hundred thousand shares of stock in U.S. Petroleum at $1 a share, though the par value was stated to be $3. Many a ranking officer contributed to the $57,500 which Colonel Mann collected in Washington. No one, including General Hancock, ever saw a penny of the investment.

Mann's stockholders became restive late in 1865 even though the colonel kept brandishing a telegram from the caretaker of the Ohio farm stating that drilling was just about completed and a tremendous gusher was expected. The stockholders, disillusioned with Mann's promises, appointed a former governor of Dakota Territory to go out and inspect the farm. "Crack everything up high," Mann wired his caretaker, meaning the latter was to start digging a well and pretend the drilling machinery was elsewhere. "Rush things for God's sake."[6]

The stockholders' investigator was undeceived, however, and shortly after his return to New York the colonel was arrested on a warrant charging that he obtained money under false pretenses. A lengthy front-page trial followed, but the case against Colonel Mann was dismissed on the grounds that the court did not have jurisdiction over a swindle perpetrated in

19

Washington. From then on the oil-stock promoter, following in Colonel Mann's pioneering path, doubtless encouraged by his escape from any penalties, took his place in American folklore beside those who salted gold mines and sold shares in the Brooklyn Bridge.

A more legitimate offshoot of the industry, the pipeline, also made its appearance in the early years of the Pennsylvania fields. Pithole and other centers were producing more oil than could be carried away in tank wagons. So pipelines were laid from Pithole to the railhead at Titusville, where the oil could be shipped out of the region in the new wooden tank cars. One entrepreneur, using steam pumps to force oil through his two-inch pipeline, was netting $2,000 a day from the enterprise.

In the oil towns, too, there soon appeared certain stigmata characteristic of boom times — the wholesale caterers of vice and the playboys dazed by sudden wealth and intent on disbursing it as rapidly and foolishly as possible.

The premier vice-king was one Ben Hogan, a large stolid man dressed in deacon's black broadcloth, who proudly advertised himself as "the wickedest man in the world." Hogan started his career as an orphan boy in upstate New York by stealing books from a clergyman who had befriended him; he was a prizefighter of sorts in New York City, drifted to New Orleans, joined the Confederate Army one day and deserted the next, killed two gamblers in Mobile over a card game, and came north at the end of the war to investigate the possibilities of the Pennsylvania oil boom. In Pithole his advancement was spectacular, starting as "business manager" of French Kate's whorehouse, opening his own Hogan's Lager Beer Parlor (with the girls upstairs), and branching out (with French Kate as his partner) with sporting houses in other oil towns.

To the ex-prizefighter the term "sporting house" was something to be taken literally. Once during an upsurge of civic feeling Hogan was arrested and charged with running a house of ill fame. He was fined a mere $200 after explaining to the judge that his establishment was actually "a gymnasium where members of both sexes may enjoy wholesome exercise, using the different parts of the body in such a way as to bring all the muscles into play."[7] During the later stages of the boom he and French Kate bought a riverboat, the *Floating Palace*, outfitted it with gambling tables, staffed it with gymnastic girls and, operating out of the reach of reform-minded citizens, made $210,000 in three years cruising off the boomtown of Parker's Landing.

Another orphan boy, who might easily have claimed the title of "foolishest man in the world," was John Washington Steele, better known as Coal-Oil Johnny, the first of the oil-rich playboys. His career was short but spectacular. Steele had been adopted by a widow, Mrs. Sarah McClintock, who owned a 200-acre farm strategically located on Oil Creek, when his parents died of diphtheria shortly after he was born. Johnny was a handsome, happy-go-lucky youth who worked as a teamster in the oilfields until Mrs. McClintock died in 1864, when Johnny was a few months short of his twenty-first birthday.

A fortune tumbled into his lap, and the only thing the Widow McClintock had not left him was a sense of discretion. He inherited $200,000 in gold and currency found locked in the widow's safe, $100,000 deposited in a bank, and the farm which had sprouted oil wells and was paying more than $2,000 daily in royalties. That growing fortune presented a challenge to its inheritor, who managed to disperse it, against all the odds, considering its growth rate, in about one year. Since Pennsylvania did not offer a wide enough field for his endeavors, he moved to New York where he would not be bothered by Mrs. McClintock's importunate brothers-in-law and their lawsuits to have the widow's will nullified. He toured the New York streets in a huge carriage with his "coat of arms," an oil derrick and a flowing well, emblazoned on the doors. He signed various disastrous documents under the influence of brandy and champagne, walked around with ten-dollar bills stuck in his buttonholes so anyone could help himself without asking, bought a minstrel show, took over the Continental Hotel and threw its doors open to any who wanted to join his monumental spree. A reporter described Coal-Oil Johnny's suite as having its carpets soaked in spilled champagne, silk stockings hanging from the chandeliers, girls dancing on marble table-tops or being suspended from the windows by their ankles. Outside a placard read: OPEN HOUSE TODAY. EVERYTHING FREE. ALL ARE WELCOME.

His timid little wife back in Oil Creek sent relatives to beg Johnny to sober up and come home, but he ordered more pickled oysters and champagne and said he was having too much fun in New York. Several false friends bilked him out of sizable sums, and then suddenly the vultures began to circle overhead. The oil-soaked McClintock farm, and Johnny's royalties, were tied up by court actions and agents of the Internal Revenue appeared to demand the ten percent wartime income tax and other assessments.[8] Coal-Oil Johnny's monumental bender came to a grinding halt, one oil-country newspaper reporting, "Wine, women, horses, faro and general debauchery soon made a wreck of that princely fortune."[9]

The sobering-up was manfully undertaken. Steele announced that he'd been a damn fool, went back to his wife, moved out west, and became superintendent of the freight yard at Kearney, Nebraska, where he died in 1920 with a savings account and a highly respectable name. His whirlwind year as Coal-Oil Johnny could have served as a cautionary tale to be told in the nurseries of all oil heirs and heiresses.

Sermons and soda water were in prospect for the whole industry, in fact, which was producing so rapidly that there was an occasional glut on the market. Actually it wasn't an industry yet — it awaited an organizational genius — but a sector of free enterprise running wild. The U.S. tax collector in Venango County reported that production at Pithole and Oil Creek was running to ten thousand barrels a day and the market, even including the European demand, simply wasn't geared as yet to absorb large quantities. During one spell of panic, six Titusville banks closed and one New York banking firm specializing in oil went broke. A postwar deflation caused another tumble and prices fell so precipitously that the government had to remove its dollar-a-barrel tax. The market recovered, however, and construction began on the oilmen's palaces on Millionaires Row in Titusville, the first mansion being that of Jonah Watson, with its mansard roof and $50,-000 conservatory blooming with orchids. Oil wealth was becoming respectable and Millionaires Row was visited by such authentic celebrities as Henry Ward Beecher, President Ulysses S. Grant and the Emperor of Brazil, but there were sportive types like Jesse Heydrick who took $300,000 to New York to speculate on Wall Street (he said) but turned up a year later, broke, blandly explaining that he had been shanghaied to Cuba. There was a considerable investment in racehorses, gold dinner china, gowns from Worth's of Paris, and fake ancestral portraits.

It was time for a man of firm business principles, one whose head did not ache at the sight of a long column of figures, to take the oil industry in hand. The stage was set for a man who could organize oil as Vanderbilt had organized railroads.

Toward the end of the 1860's, according to Ida Tarbell and Henry Demarest Lloyd, the operators of the Pennsylvania fields were on their way to solving their problems, largely those of disorganization and cutthroat competition. "But suddenly," Miss Tarbell observed, "at the very heyday of this confidence a big hand reached out from nobody knew where to steal their conquest and throttle their future."

The "big hand" was that of John Davison Rockefeller, a Cleveland merchant still in his twenties. In 1860, barely twenty-one years old, he had been dispatched to the Pennsylvania oilfields by a group of Cleveland businessmen to investigate the possibilities of the infant industry. For two months Rockefeller toured the oil towns on Oil and French creeks and the Allegheny River, observing every detail of the operations, asking questions, making notes, and totting up columns of figures. Shaking his head, Rockefeller, who had made a poor impression on the roughnecks of Titusville and Pithole ("that bloodless Baptist bookkeeper," was one of the kindlier estimates of a young man who priggishly refused to take a drink with them), told his associates that investing or becoming involved in the oil business would be near-suicidal. All he could see, he said, was "chaos and disorder, waste and incompetence, competition at its worst."

Statistics, it would seem, bear out the young Rockefeller's conclusion and tend to negate Miss Tarbell's claim that the infant industry would have managed to solve its problems without the big hand of John D. Rockefeller. It was chronically in trouble through overproduction, and few small producers were able to survive for long. As early as 1866 there was discussion of combining forces to obtain better prices for crude oil from the refineries, the Oil City *Register* reporting that "Producers at Titusville and other places are clamoring for a Convention of interested persons to take some action looking for better prices for oil."[10] Crude-oil prices were on a continual roller-coaster ride. Shortly after the Pennsylvania fields were discovered the price was $20 a barrel, two years later it was 10 cents a barrel. In July 1864, it was $14 a barrel, a year later $4. The fluctuations continued after the war ended, with $1.35 quoted in December 1866, $5.75 in July 1868, $7 in January 1869, and $2.70 in August 1870.

So a Rockefeller was probably inevitable. Despite his initial reaction to the "chaos" of the oil industry, in any case, John D. Rockefeller himself decided that the industry was worth a try. But only after mature, longheaded consideration. Young Rockefeller had his own father's career to contemplate as an example of the results of profligacy; his whole life, in fact, might be seen as a reaction to that of William Rockefeller, who was his opposite in every respect.

A big, hearty, put-'er-there type, with a glib tongue and a footloose disposition, William Rockefeller frequently disappeared from the family home — first at Richford and Moravia, Cayuga County, New York, later Oswego — and left his wife and children to fend for themselves. In 1849, when John was ten years old, William had to take to his heels when the Cayuga County grand jury indicted him on charges of rape brought by Anne Vanderbeak, the Rockefellers' hired girl.[11] The family then moved to a farm near Oswego, where he stayed with them for a spell. A neighbor traveling in Ohio came across a poster announcing that "Doctor" William Rockefeller, "the Celebrated Cancer Specialist," was coming to town to dispense his remedy for the disease. The memory of the senior Rockefeller would haunt the family from then on.

Joseph Pulitzer, possibly the most virulent of the Rockefeller-haters, assigned reporters to tracing old William for years, and in 1908 his New York *World* published a rather cruel and needless exposé. The old quack had died in 1906 and was buried in an unmarked grave in Freeport, Illinois. The *World* charged that William Rockefeller had led a double life for thirty-five years and was married to a woman in Freeport without having divorced his legal wife.

His son John moved to Cleveland at the age of sixteen to attend Folsom's Commercial College and work for a commission house at a salary of $3.50 a week. Out of that small salary he contributed $1.80 monthly to the Baptist Sunday school he attended. At the age of eighteen he and Maurice Clark established the commission house of Clark & Rockefeller on the Cleveland waterfront and at the end of their first year had collected commissions on a gross of half a million. Weedy, polite and pious John D. Rockefeller made an excellent impression on his fellow businessmen, and his analytical powers, combined with a native talent for cost accounting, made him the logical man to send to Pennsylvania in 1860 to determine whether the oil boom was something to be taken seriously or a case of mass insanity.

The more John D. thought about it, the better the oil business looked. As he surveyed the situation, it could be divided into three parts: production, refining, transportation. For the moment (1862) it seemed to him there might be a decent profit in the refining process. It cost only 30 cents to refine a barrel of crude oil while kerosene made from shale oil cost a dollar a gallon. The tricky factor, of course, was the fluctuating price of crude oil.

That year Rockefeller became physically as well as economically aware of the oil-refining business. A number of small refineries had been established on Walworth Run, which flowed into the Cuyahoga River, on which Rockefeller's establishment was located. The river was soon polluted from the refineries' wastes, with an oily smelly scum floating on its surface.* From that scum Rockefeller scented the possibility of growing profits. He and his partner invested several thousand dollars in a small refinery operated by Samuel Andrews, a former candlemaker, who was handicapped by his plant's tiny daily output of ten barrels. In 1865 he decided to make the plunge into the oil business and did so in a characteristically canny way. One partner would have to be dumped. His association with Clark had been longer, but it was Andrews' skills as a refiner — he had perfected a process by which he extracted more kerosene from crude than rival refineries — that were more necessary to the business. The new firm was styled Rockefeller & Andrews.

Once in, despite the panicky ups and downs of the oil market, which often caused him to lay awake nights worrying about "the oil fields giving out," he expanded with the calculated recklessness of an expert gambler. During the oil panic of 1866, he refused to hedge his bets but established a second Cleveland refinery, the Standard Works. A year later he opened a New York office to handle the European export trade with his brother William (who took after their father in his hearty, outgoing manner, as John resembled their pious hard-working

* By the summer of 1969 the Cuyahoga was so oil drenched that a flash fire broke out on its surface and it took several days for the Cleveland fireboats to extinguish it.

26

mother) in charge of that operation. All the while he indulged his passion for cost accounting, for reducing the outlay on extracting kerosene and following the adage quoted by his mother, "Willful waste makes woeful want." Frugality had been imprinted on his character by both sides of his ancestry, German on his father's, Scottish on his mother's. From the beginning his formula for success, given anyone who asked for it, was frugally expressed: "Attention to little details."

To pare down the costs of his refining operations, he built his own cooperage to manufacture barrels and bought wagons to transport the crude oil to his refineries and the kerosene to the freight yards. He saved a few cents on each barrel by buying crude direct from the producers in Titusville and Oil City instead of through the jobbers. Soon Rockefeller kerosene was on sale as far south as New Orleans, as far west as Chicago, and was making inroads into the export trade which hitherto had been monopolized by the eastern refiners. In his empirical fashion he had determined that the modern industrialist must keep expanding — or lose out to the competition — and must command as many of the processes and facilities as he can to operate economically. The less he spent in manufacturing his own product, the cheaper he could sell it — and the more of his rivals' business he could capture.

With all his passion for detail, he saw that he would need able executives to help him run a rapidly growing business. Rockefeller was a man with a firm sense of proportion, and knew that while he might be the guiding genius of his operation he had to parcel out responsibility. One of the major facets of his success was his ability to pick men who could carry out his design, work together whatever their individual differences, stay with Rockefeller rather than striking out on their own. Each Rockefeller executive was a satrap rather than a minion. Without his striking ability to select the right men at the top, and keep them by his side, he could never have been able to dominate the industry within so few years.

H. M. (Henry Morton) Flagler was one of his early finds.

Like Rockefeller an upstate New Yorker, Flagler had left home at the age of fourteen with the traditional bundle on a stick, four pennies and a nickel. He still had the nickel when he died. Working on the Erie Canal earned him a stake to enter the speculative salt-mining business at Saginaw, Michigan, where he married the niece of Stephen V. Harkness, a Clevelander who made his first million in whiskey-distilling. Flagler made and lost a small fortune in salt, then moved to Cleveland to be closer to his uncle-in-law's millions and became a commission merchant. Flagler was not the Rockefeller type; he was a bold-eyed swashbuckler with "an eye for the ladies" and no out-standing record for church attendance. But Rockefeller liked his energy, his enterprising ways, and the fact he might be able to induce Stephen Harkness to invest in Rockefeller & Andrews. Uncle Stephen came up with the money, and the new firm was styled Rockefeller, Andrews & Flagler.

That move gave Rockefeller the capital to initiate the first stages of a breathtaking plan. His vision was that of a monopoly. The key was transportation. He could eliminate his competition, he saw, if he could bulldoze the railroads operating in the oil region into giving him rebates, shipping his oil cheaper than that of his competitors. His first target was the Lake Shore Railroad. In 1868 he and Flagler presented themselves at the Cleveland offices of the Lake Shore, a part of the Vanderbilts' New York Central System, and demanded — and received — a rebate of 10 to 15 cents a barrel on crude oil shipped from the oilfields and another on kerosene shipped to New York. This enabled him to knock out the local competition, reducing the number of Cleveland refineries from thirty to ten inside of a year, with their owners given the choice of joining Rockefeller & Company or going out of business.

On January 10, 1870, with everything moving along splendidly, he and his associates incorporated Standard Oil of Ohio and issued a million dollars worth of stock, with himself, his brother William, Flagler, Andrews, and Harkness the major holders. At the age of thirty-one he was dedicated in unequal proportions to business, church ("the most diligent Christian in Cleveland") and family. He had married and was the father of four-year-old Bessie. His deeply religious mother lived nearby, but his father appeared only at long intervals, the well-fleshed skeleton in the family closet.

The senior William Rockefeller's heartiness evidently preyed on his son's mind, for the latter would lecture his Sunday school class endlessly on the perils of boozy good-fellowship. "Don't be a good fellow," he instructed his pupils. "I love my fellow man and take a great interest in him. But don't be convivial . . . don't let good-fellowship get the least hold on you . . . It is my firm conviction that every downfall is traceable directly or indirectly to the victim's good-fellowship, his good cheer among his friends, who come as quickly as they go." Good fellows, he said, were responsible for the overflow in "our asylums, our poorhouses and the very gutters of our streets."[12]

If he took any "great interest" in his fellow men, aside from teaching Sunday school, it was not visible to others. He had nothing to do with civic affairs, politics, social life, or clubs. Whatever joy of living he exhibited was on display when he brought off a business coup; then he would clap his hands, throw his hat in the air, hug the nearest person. Money, or the power of money, the thrill of success, momentarily transformed him. His pale features literally glowed. In one triumphant moment he cried out, "I'm bound to be rich! *Bound to be rich!* BOUND TO BE RICH!"

So it seemed with the new setup at Standard Oil, with John D. himself as the strategist, Flagler as the energizer, and brother William as the genial frontman in New York seeing to it that Standard got its share of the booming export market. Another refinery was acquired in Brooklyn, giving Standard a total output of fifteen hundred barrels of kerosene a day. John D. Rockefeller had to insure a steady flow of his product to the markets because storage cost money. To insure that flow, he conceived a master plan calling, as one authority has described it, for "first, an end to refining competition in Cleveland. Next, the big refineries in other regions must join Standard — or be eliminated. The railroads must make more favorable rebate arrangements with Standard and its allies than with others. The railroads must also refuse shipments of crude oil for export, for Standard planned to refine oil for the world. Lastly, there were those wild fellows, the oil producers. They had no sense of order, much less of the dangers of unrestrained competition. They would have to be educated. This might call for harsh measures. Producers were pigheaded men of no vision."[13]

By grabbing higher rebates on his shipments than the independents received, he intended to monopolize the industry. He had a tight grip on refining, now he planned to throttle the producers. The instrument (or garrote) he would employ was a conspiracy titled the South Improvement Company. It was formed by Rockefeller and his associates, including a number of large refineries which saw that they either had to cooperate or go under. South Improvement Company then signed contracts with the three major railroads catering to the oil region, the Erie (controlled by Jay Gould and Jim Fisk), the New York Central, and the Pennsylvania. The railroads were to raise their freight rates by a hundred percent and more, then give South Improvement enormous rebates not only on what it shipped but on its competitor's shipments. (The regular freight rate, for instance, was 80 cents a barrel from the oil region to Cleveland, $2 a barrel for kerosene from Cleveland to New York, for a total of $2.80. South Improvement's collaborators would pay a total of only $1 a barrel, allowing them to undersell the outsiders.)

Oddly enough, the scheme was as legal as it was ruthless and amoral. Each refiner who joined the South Improvement conspiracy was forced to sign a pledge reading, "I do faithfully promise upon my honor and faith as a gentleman that I will keep secret all transactions which I may have with the corporation known as the South Improvement Company; that, should I fail to complete any bargains with the said company, all the preliminary conversations shall be kept strictly private; and finally, that I will not disclose the price for which I dispose of my product, or any other facts which may in any way bring to light the internal workings or organization of the company . . ."[14]

Despite all its hush-hush maneuvers, perhaps because of the unwieldy size of the conspiracy, word leaked out that the cruncher was about to be applied to independent refiners and oil-producers, with a Cleveland newspaper warning early in 1872 that "a gigantic little game" was to be played by South Improvement.[15] As Commodore Vanderbilt once remarked, a secret shared by three persons meant that one hundred eleven were in on it.

Five days later the rise in freight rates was made known to the oil-producing region. The news was greeted with rage and consternation. Refiners paid the freight on oil shipped out of the region, but the producers knew that South Improvement Company meant a powerful combine had been formed which would grind down the price of crude oil. In the Titusville Opera House a mass meeting attended by three thousand registered its roaring protest under banners reading, "Don't Give Up the Ship," "Down with the Conspirators," "No Compromise." The only humor of the occasion was provided by a telegram from Erie's Jay Gould declaring that he had signed the South Improvement contract "only after it was signed by all the other parties." On March 1 a second mass meeting was held in Oil City at which a speaker whipped up the producers' indignation when he declaimed, "In the South they enslave blacks. And this is an *improvement* on the South since it is intended to enslave whites."

Until now the producers had preferred to stay unorganized and operate on the old dog-eat-dog principles which had been traditional in the oilfields. Now they formed the Petroleum Producers Union. Its secretary was twenty-four-year-old John D. Archbold, an independent refiner, who later became one of

Rockefeller's chief associates. Its battle cry was "No oil for the Ring," meaning South Improvement. Most of the region's wells were shut down and drilling of new wells halted. Feeling ran so high that Joe Seep, a good-natured German, and Dan O'Day, a fast-talking County Clare man, were hauled before a special meeting of the Titusville Oil Exchange to face unspecified charges before a drumhead court merely because they were employed as oil-buyer and transportation manager, respectively, by a refiner who had signed the South Improvement agreement. They were saved from mob action by Archbold, who pleaded that Seep and O'Day "shouldn't be held responsible for the views or doings of their employers." Both were later rewarded, handsomely, by Rockefeller.

The producers almost to a man held to a pledge not to sell crude to any member of the South Improvement conspiracy. Ida Tarbell's father was offered a high price for a whole year's output of his wells but turned it down. Not a barrel was to be sold to Rockefeller or his collaborators, nor shipped over the Erie, the New York Central, or the Pennsylvania as long as the unfair rebate system was kept in effect. It was called the oil war of 1872, but there was little actual violence, although John D. was hanged and burned in effigy. For forty days all oil shipments out of the region were embargoed.

Obviously, with production shut off, South Improvement and the railroads would have to capitulate. Neither Rockefeller nor any of his colleagues seem to have anticipated the reaction their scheme would arouse. The nation's press was almost entirely opposed to South Improvement. The public was outraged, and the politicians, one beat behind as usual, began to echo its demands for suppression of the South Improvement Company's attempted monopoly.

Rockefeller was no bitter-ender and realized the combine would collapse under the weight of opposition, so during the furor he quietly busied himself elsewhere, by driving his remaining competitors in Cleveland to the wall. One of the victims of the Rockefeller squeeze was Frank A. Arter, who had spent $12,000 building his refinery and who later testified, "It was a hard blow when Rockefeller's appraiser valued my plant at $3,000. I had a debt outstanding of $25,000. But what could I do? When conditions were so bad in the oil business that a small refiner could not make money, his plant was worth only what it would fetch as material. So I sold out for $3,000. I had my choice of cash or Standard Oil stock. I asked Rockefeller and Flagler which I ought to take. They both spoke at once. 'If you will take the stock and hold it some day you will get back the full price you asked for your refinery.' " Occasionally Arter would be hard pressed to pay off his outstanding debts and he would ask Rockefeller whether he still recommended holding the stock. "Sell everything you've got, even the shirt on your back," Rockefeller advised, "but hold on to that stock."[16] Good advice as Arter discovered.

The rebellion in the oilfields was not so easy to deal with. It had built up so much political pressure that the Pennsylvania legislature decided to rescind the South Improvement Company's charter, and a congressional investigating committee denounced it as "one of the most gigantic and dangerous conspiracies ever conceived."

Late in March the railroads caved in, asked for a conference with the Petroleum Producers Union. Representatives of the union ranged themselves behind a table at the Grand Opera House in New York, which happened to be owned by Erie's Jim Fisk, and summoned the railroad officials to account for themselves. In the *New York Times* account the railroad presidents were thoroughly humbled. Commodore Vanderbilt of the New York Central blamed his son William H., as usual, for making a bad deal. "I told Billy not to have anything to do with that scheme," the commodore virtuously added. Thomas Scott of the Pennsylvania told the producers' committee that his line was through with the South Improvement Company and the unfair rebates were eliminated. Erie followed suit. Outside in the corridor Rockefeller and other members of South Improvement sought admission to explain themselves, but were

33

coldly told to go away, and "Rockafellow [sic] disappeared looking rather blue."[17]

The *Times* man was probably mistaken about the extent of "Rockafellow's" chagrin. He came out of the ruins of South Improvement bigger and stronger than ever, with the daily capacity of Standard Oil increased from fifteen hundred barrels to eleven thousand, thanks to the monopoly he had established in Cleveland. He had lost on one sector because he didn't have the political muscle and the ultimate financial clout to ride out the embargo and keep the railroads in line despite their losses. But he had gained on another. And he had learned a valuable lesson on the perils of overextension.

Furthermore the executive recruitment program was expanded, thanks to Rockefeller's talent for spotting a promising man and keeping his loyalty once he was recruited. Joe Seep became Standard's head oil-buyer and held the post for forty years; Dan O'Day was placed in charge of buying and building a network of pipelines in western Pennsylvania that became the American Transfer Company, an arterial system that would soon extend to New Jersey tidewater.

Two even more valuable acquisitions were John D. Archbold and Henry Huddleston Rogers, both of whom had won Rockefeller's admiration by opposing him in the oilfields. Anyone who fought Rockefeller right down the line was almost certain of a job offer. Later he would be charged with using coercion to enlist such men, to which he rightly replied, "Would it have been possible to make of such men life-companions?" He knew that he needed bold, enterprising men to carry out the plans he conceived while he presided over the books and kept track of costs. He was the first to understand the nature of corporate endeavor, the necessity of a super-tycoon to surround himself with aggressive sub-tycoons.

Archbold and Rogers were as unlike Rockefeller as Flagler. The son of a Baptist preacher, Archbold nonetheless, or therefore, loved to play poker and indulge those "convivial" tastes which Rockefeller warned his Sunday school pupils against.

34

He had come to the oilfields as a boy of fifteen, worked as a shipping clerk. Four years later he was the partner in a refining company. As secretary of the Petroleum Producers Union, he was one of the leaders of the anti-South Improvement fight and when crude prices slumped in 1871 rallied the oilfields with his cry of "Four dollars a barrel!"

A short, aggressive young man with a large head, he was one of the oil region's heroes after the fight was won. There were a score of independent refineries in the region which he persuaded, on the strength of his anti-Rockefeller campaigning, to combine with him into the Acme Oil Company. It soon became apparent that Archbold had made a separate peace with Rockefeller, and that Acme was a subsidiary of Standard Oil. Those he had conned into the arrangement were outraged at what they regarded as a betrayal. Archbold was no longer the Sir Lancelot of the oilfields, but he was consoled with a Rockefeller vice-presidency and later became president of Standard Oil of New Jersey. Because of his winning personality he was employed as the man in charge of influencing legislation. Stated less politely, as Standard Oil's enemies would, he was Rockefeller's "arch-corruptionist" and dispenser of political cumshaw.

H. H. Rogers, too, had made an early start on an oilman's career. At thirty-two he was a partner in the Brooklyn refinery which produced Astral Oil, the best lamp fuel in the country. Like most Rockefeller executives he had come up from the ragged newsboy or Horatio Alger ranks. A native of Fairhaven, Massachusetts, across the harbor from New Bedford, he sold the Boston newspapers on the streets of his hometown. One day when he was fourteen he learned how tricky and fluctuative the oil business could be. A ship with five hundred barrels of sperm oil consigned to New Bedford was lost at sea. The dealer to whom the shipment was consigned took all of Rogers' newspapers, bought all the sperm oil available in the district, and temporarily cornered the local market.

Eventually Rogers went into the oil business himself and

35

worked his way up to a partnership with Charles Pratt at Astral Oil. The partners declared war on the South Improvement Company and fought hard against the Rockefeller combination. After the dust settled, however, they accepted an offer from Rockefeller to add Astral Oil to the Standard Oil line and became vice-presidents. Rogers was placed in charge of the manufacturing division and eventually, with Flagler and Archbold, became one of Rockefeller's three top executives. John D. was shocked by his profanity, often taken aback by his aggressive personality. With enemies in the business world he was a completely ruthless infighter, but on the private side he was capable of generosity and sentimentality. It was Rogers who rescued Mark Twain from the wreckage of his disastrous essays as a businessman, Rogers who saw to it that the monument to Edwin L. Drake was constructed in Titusville long after Drake became the forgotten man of the first American oil boom.

During the decade following the oil war of 1872 Standard Oil crunched its way over the independents in the refining and transporting sectors of the oil industry as remorselessly as a newly risen Golem. Through Rockefeller's methods, as Henry Demarest Lloyd would describe them in *Wealth and Commonwealth*, "rivals are blown out of the highways, busy mills and refineries turn to dust, hearts break, and strong men go mad or commit suicide." That was certainly a melodramatic overstatement. Aside from its harsh methods of dealing with competition, the Rockefeller combine was favored by technological breakthroughs which made it difficult for the smaller refineries to stay in business. A new "cracking" process for the distillation of kerosene from crude oil had been developed; it increased the proportion of kerosene which could be distilled from crude to seventy-five percent, but the new stills were huge and expensive things with a 3,000-barrel capacity, and the smaller refineries couldn't raise the capital necessary to take advantage of the more efficient cracking process. In one decade, the cost of building an efficient refinery increased tenfold. The panic of 1873 also eliminated a number of the lesser competitors in the kerosene market.

In addition, Rockefeller had cornered most of the men with brains and enterprise in the industry. "I wanted able men with me," he later explained. "I tried to make friends with these men. I admitted their ability and the value of their enterprises. I worked to convince them that it would be better for both to cooperate . . . and if I had not succeeded in getting their friendship the whole plan of the Standard Oil Company would have fallen to the ground. I admit I tried to attract only the able men; and I have always had as little as possible to do with dull business men."[18]

The dullards, certainly, were soon cut down by the ambitious young men who had signed on as Standard vice-presidents and Rockefeller "friends."

Friend Rogers, for instance, supervised the attack on a threatening rival, the Empire Transportation Company, which was organized by Thomas Scott of the Pennsylvania Railroad. Through that subsidiary Scott planned to take over and monopolize the movement of oil from the Pennsylvania fields to the East Coast terminals. Rockefeller was the giant of the refining sector, but Empire blocked his advance toward taking over the transportation end of the business. In a few years it had pipelines, five thousand railway tank cars, a fleet of Great Lakes steamers, a warehouse and tank-storage complex at Communipaw, New Jersey.

Rockefeller declared war on Empire and the Pennsylvania Railroad, and immediately insisted that the Erie and the New York Central become his allies by granting him freight rebates, which they hastened to do. Meanwhile Rogers was superintending a price-cutting war on all refineries which allowed Empire to transport their products. With the capital he had collected for the purpose, Rockefeller was able to afford to offer his products at lower and lower prices in districts where Empire's allies operated. The kerosene-suppliers linked to Empire soon found themselves all but giving the stuff away.

Just when Pennsylvania was losing a million dollars a month to support the price-cutting war with Standard, its stock falling to half of par value, its dividend passed for the first time in its history, the railroad was engulfed by anarchic labor troubles. In midsummer of 1877 mobs of rioters, partly composed of striking railroad workers, smashed and burned Pennsylvania's rolling stock, roundhouses, depots and warehouses, and in Pittsburgh alone twenty-five persons were killed in battles with the state militia.

Almost before the smoke cleared above the Pennsylvania's ruined terminals, Thomas Scott decided to make peace with Rockefeller. He and his aides journeyed to Cleveland to submit themselves to Standard's mercy. Rockefeller informed them that he would be willing to take Empire off their hands for $3.4 million, which was much less than it was worth. Scott capitulated, and Empire's pipelines and tank cars were added to Standard's subsidiary United Pipe Lines, which quickly absorbed another rival, the National Conduit Company, unwilling to face the sort of competitive ordeal which had eliminated the Pennsylvania Railroad's offspring.

Other pipelines and refineries which had been holding out against Standard's engorging tactics also succumbed, and by 1878, when Rockefeller was thirty-eight years old, he controlled ninety-five percent of all such facilities in the United States.

Yet he still concerned himself with all those buzzing little "details," which he considered all-important. In the midst of buying up millions of dollars worth of competition, he wrote one of his plant superintendents about the disappearance of 490 bungs, used to stop up barrels and costing less than a cent apiece, and demanded to know what had happened to them.[19]

That same year, 1878, Rockefeller and his associates were

confronted by another insurrection among the oil-producers, who were rightly alarmed by the fact that Standard now controlled most of the pipelines and through its refineries set the price for crude oil. With the growing realization that they were being slowly throttled by the Rockefeller embrace, the producers made an all-out effort to combine against Standard. A somewhat grandiosely styled "Parliament of Petroleum" was convened in Titusville with guards posted at the doors to turn away anyone suspected of being a Standard agent. After seven days of secret meetings, the producers agreed to build their own outlet from the oilfield: either a pipeline to Buffalo, where the crude oil could be transferred to barges which would take it down the Erie Canal to New York, or a 235-mile pipeline from the Allegheny River to Buffalo.

To support either proposal, the Parliament of Petroleum through its representatives in Harrisburg leaned heavily on the Pennsylvania state legislature to allow it the right of eminent domain for the construction of a new pipeline independent of Rockefeller control. A formidable threat. But Rockefeller and his men reacted promptly and with trip-hammer enthusiasm; the term "overkill" had not yet been invented. They knew that they already had a stranglehold on the producers, who simply had no place to store their oil if the Rockefeller pipelines were shut off. Before the producers could build their own, the oil strike at Bradford, in McKean County, began adding twenty-two thousand barrels a day to the glut. United Pipe Lines, the Standard Oil subsidiary, announced that its storage tanks were filled and they could accept no more crude oil. The whole region threatened to drown in its own product. Mobs surrounded United's headquarters and threatened violence if the pipelines were not opened and the growing surplus drained.

In that heated atmosphere, the Clarion County grand jury was summoned to hear charges of criminal conspiracy against Rockefeller and his associates. It was charged that Standard was maneuvering to expand its monopoly from refining and transporting to producing as well. An indictment naming Rockefeller and others was returned, but John D. refused to surrender himself to the law of Clarion County. Meanwhile his henchmen were rushing around trying to make a deal to have the indictments quashed — *criminal* charges bore heavily on the Baptist Sunday school teacher — and a truce arranged with the producers. The Parliament of Petroleum, awash in crude oil, agreed to an armistice; Standard opened its pipelines again, and the indictments were withdrawn. Which left Standard still pretty much in command of the situation, since the producers never went ahead with their plan to build their own pipeline.

Despite all the lessons he administered to would-be rivals, there were still bold specimens who would challenge Rockefeller. Free enterprise was supposed to be operative still — even in the oil industry. Working on this theory, three men named Byron Benson, Robert Hopkins and David McKelvy organized the Tidewater Pipe Company to build a long-distance pipeline — with large new 80-horsepower pumps — over the Alleghenies to Williamsport. It would require an audacious engineering feat, but Tidewater hired as its chief engineer General Herman Haupt, who during the Civil War was said to have built bridges out of cornstalks and fence rails to keep the Union Army mobile. With a pumping station on every peak, the oil would be propelled over the mountains as fast as a man could walk. Once the pipeline was completed Tidewater would be able to convey crude at half the price Standard's subsidiary charged.

Rockefeller agents kept a close watch on every stage of Tidewater's construction and reported personally to their chief. The line was completed in 1879, and Rockefeller in a superficially friendly gesture offered to send ten thousand barrels of crude a day through the new system. No, Tidewater replied, the system had been built to encourage the few remaining independent refiners. Internal subversion, it appeared, would be required to make Tidewater see the light.

A former Rockefeller enemy named E. G. Patterson, who had been a leader in the fight against the South Improvement Company, popped up as a Tidewater stockholder and applied to the courts to have the company placed in receivership. Tidewater, he deposed, was being mismanaged and was close to insolvency. Investigation showed that Patterson had been "reached" by John D. Archbold, the chief fixer for Standard Oil, and given the money to buy Tidewater stock. The court not only rejected Patterson's petition but declared it was part of a "nefarious plot" by Standard Oil. But Standard kept burrowing away. Tidewater was indeed in financial trouble and had to float a $2 million bond issue through a New York bank. Rumors were spread that Tidewater was on the rocks. Later it became known that Tidewater, in its desperation, had obtained a loan from Standard in exchange for a block of voting stock.

A Tidewater stockholders' meeting was called, and the old triumvirate which had organized the company and kept it going against all of Standard's attempts at subversion was thrown out of office. It was replaced by officials more sympathetic toward a deal with Standard Oil. In the ensuing settlement Tidewater simply became a satellite of the Rockefeller interests, allowed to function at Standard's pleasure. Of all the oil conveyed from the Pennsylvania fields, Standard's United subsidiary was to be given eighty-eight and a half percent of the business, Tidewater eleven and a half.

Standard was becoming too big to have permanent headquarters in Cleveland, and Rockefeller soon moved with his family to New York City. He had quietly accumulated a sizable fortune and taken a place in the front rank of American industrialists, but he still shunned ostentation. Other tycoons had established themselves in chateaux and pretentious town houses along Fifth Avenue; Rockefeller and his family moved into a fairly modest house at 4 West 54th Street. They kept their distance from the Astorbilt Four Hundred. John D. insisted that his children must keep their feet on the ground, and his only son, John D. Jr., was kept on an allowance of nickels and dimes which he had to earn by doing chores and taking violin lessons.

Rockefeller was utterly determined not to be changed by wealth, and clung to his Baptist faith as unwaveringly as when he had been a $3.50-a-week clerk. H. L. Mencken was no fervent admirer of the sect, but he once conceded that "the most interesting thing about Rockefeller in the analysis is his fidelity to this rustic and preposterous faith. Most Americans when they accumulate money climb the golden ramparts of the nearest Episcopal Church where the crude Yahveh of the backwoods is polished and refined and speaks to the vulgate with an English A. But the Rockefellers cling to the primeval rain god of the American hinterland, and show no sign of being ashamed of Him. The Hell of the Bible is Hell enough for them."[20]

Family, faith and money were the fixed stars of Rockefeller's life, which for many years in New York would be bounded by the house on 54th Street and the modest Standard Oil headquarters at 140 Pearl Street. Its simplicity was unchanged even while Standard was stamping its brand throughout the world, a household name in the remotest village of Europe, Asia and Africa, with donkey trains carrying Standard kerosene in North Africa, camel caravans in the Sahara, elephants in India. And that was only the beginning.

2.

"Individualism Is Gone, Never to Return"

> The Land of Grease! The Land of Grease
>   Where burning oil is loved and sung;
> Where flourish arts of sale and lease
>   Where Rouseville rose and Tarville sprung;
> Eternal summer gilds them not
>   But oil wells render dear each spot.
>   — Samuel C. T. Dodd

The verse quoted above was composed by Samuel C. T. Dodd, who started out in life as a printer's devil in the oilfields, a boy with a love of classic literature, and who ended up composing the legal fiction which justified the formation of the Standard Oil Trust. The men whom Rockefeller gathered around him to build that monopoly were all strong, differing, thrusting individuals; he was certain of the power of their mutual enterprise to keep them working in harness, but all were familiar enough types in the business world.

Dodd, however, was odd-man-out in the Standard Oil boardroom. He had worked his way through back-country schools, was admitted to the Pennsylvania bar, and quickly became an

43

opponent of Standard Oil's monopolizing tendency — the sure way to attract John D. Rockefeller's attention. His real love was not the dry precision of legal prose but writing occasional magazine articles and verse. His ode to the "land of grease" was said to be the first poem ever written on the subject.

When Rockefeller urged him to join Standard as its general counsel, he accepted with the wry statement, "Well, as the ministers say as they get a call to a higher salary, it seems to be the Lord's will." Even more oddly — to the mind of a Rockefeller — he refused a salary of more than $25,000 and turned down an offer of stock that would have made him very rich. The reason, he said, was that he wanted to preserve his "independence of mind." Yet as one observer wrote, "this able and upright lawyer could invent with perfect spiritual composure the scheme which . . . enabled Standard leaders, while violating laws in fact, to tread with legal safety upon the edges of perjury."[1]

And it was the invention of the trust that persuaded John D. Rockefeller to announce with perfect equanimity: "Individualism is gone, never to return."

He meant that henceforth the country's major industries would form trusts to insure complete efficiency and perfect harmony. Competition would be eliminated because it was wasteful. What was good for the trusts was, ultimately, good for the country. Though the idea of the trust was conceived by Dodd, it was the logical outcome of all that Rockefeller had been doing for years; it was his true objective.

Rockefeller was one of the few men who realized that the old localized way of doing business was outdated. And rapid transportation was changing it more every day. Local industry was being swept aside by competitors operating on a national scale and able to offer lower prices. The name of the great god Efficiency was being invoked with increasing fervor. Rockefeller's urge to monopolize and form cartels was impelled not merely by love of money, not with his Spartan tastes, nor even an ungovernable lust for power. Partly it was a passion for order. He craved tidiness and efficiency as much as any of the German burghers from whom he was partly descended. His compulsion was also, of course, part of what has somewhat pejoratively become known as the Protestant Ethic. Money certified one as a member of God's elect, was regarded as a mark of divine favor rightly accorded.

Some way had to be found to bind the whole Standard Oil structure together, as a stockade against the constant assaults of investigating committees, jealous rivals, a largely inimical press and an unsympathetic public, some sectors of which were being influenced by socialism, anarchism and populism. Standard had become a complex of some forty corporations, fourteen of which Rockefeller and his associates owned completely, the rest controlled through majority stockholdings. The stockholders in Standard now numbered thirty-seven. No longer included was Andrews, who in 1880 sold his interests to Rockefeller for an asking price of $1 million. Because of the inordinate curiosity about Standard Oil being exhibited by various legislative committees, it became necessary to concoct a scheme by which any of its members could swear before the inquisitors that Standard did not own or control its subsidiaries.

Lawyer Dodd thus drew up the first trust agreement in the spring of 1879. All existing stock in the various corporations was conveyed to three Standard Oil employees acting as "dummy" trustees. The legal fiction invented by Dodd was that Standard's satellites no longer were owned or controlled by Standard Oil of Ohio but by the trustees.

Three years later the trust was rearranged. Nine trustees were appointed, and these were no dummies. They included John and William Rockefeller, Flagler, Pratt, Archbold, and four other stockholders. The trustees controlled every phase of those forty corporations' operations, regulated the production of petroleum, and set the price for petroleum products in the American market. In 1882, the bulk of American oil was under the control of the men who met in the boardroom of their new offices at 26 Broadway. The main objective of John D.'s career had now been attained. As Dodd truthfully explained the setup in 1888, when the details of the trust were made public, "Stockholders of the various corporations referred to became mutually interested in the stocks of all. It was a union, not of corporations, but of stockholders. The companies continued to conduct their business as before. They ceased to be competitive in the sense of trying to undersell each other. They continued to be competitive and are to this day competitive in the sense that each company strives to show the best results in making the best products, at the lowest prices."[2]

Dodd explained all this to the public in a pamphlet rather interestingly titled *Combinations: Their Uses and Abuses*, carefully refraining from styling the new conglomerates as trusts. Whatever the code word, Rockefeller and his associates had now tidied up the oil industry with no more noise being made about the process than the scratching of Lawyer Dodd's pen.*

If the sleep of a good Baptist could ever be troubled by worldly affairs, John D. Rockefeller's must have been interrupted by one recurring nightmare. That was the ever-flowing source of petroleum. Standard Oil could be ruined overnight if the producing wells dried up. Oil exploration was then in its infancy and the known deposits were severely limited.

Rockefeller had been haunted from the beginning of his career by the possibility that the Pennsylvania fields would be exhausted. It was, in fact, inevitable. In the mid-1880's there were signs that production from the western Pennsylvania fields would soon decline. The Bradford wells were going dry. Many oilmen suspected that when all the Pennsylvania producers began tapping more sludge than petroleum the long oil boom would collapse. The nimble and utterly cynical John D. Archbold sold some of his Standard stock on the strength of

* For a defense of Rockefeller's methods, see Appendix B.

those apprehensions. To the suggestion that more sizable fields might be drilled somewhere in the vastness of the American continent, Archbold snorted, "Are you crazy, man? I'll drink every gallon of oil produced west of the Mississippi."

At this critical juncture, circumstances suddenly favored Rockefeller and his worried associates. Balzac maintained that behind every great fortune there is a great crime. He might have included the element of luck.

Just as Pennsylvania was petering out, in 1885, a new "land of grease" was discovered in northwestern Ohio and eastern Indiana, the Lima field. Inside of a year it was producing a million barrels and in the next five years the yield would rise to 15 million barrels annually.

There was, however, a handicap in processing Lima oil that at first seemed insurmountable. The Lima crude assayed a high sulfur content which gave it a foul rotten-egg smell. If the sulfur could not be removed, kerosene made from Lima petroleum would cause smoking when it was used as a lamp fuel and also give off a highly unpleasant odor. Another handicap was that while Pennsylvania crude on distillation produced seventy-five percent kerosene and naphtha, Lima's produced only fifty-seven percent. On the other hand, because of those problems, Lima crude sold for only 15 cents a barrel.

Rockefeller took up the matter with his executive committee, proposing that Standard buy Lima oil in large quantities and store it until a process could be devised to eliminate the sulfur content. The other members opposed the idea. They believed that Lima crude might be collected for several years and become a dead loss when the search for the right cracking process failed. Even H. H. Rogers, who generally liked a gamble, thought it would be a disastrous risk; so did his old partner in Astral Oil, Charles Pratt, possibly because both men had made their initial mark on the oil industry by distributing kerosene of the highest quality.

But Rockefeller was obdurate. If the executive committee

47

wouldn't go along with him, he declared, he would invest his own money in the Lima venture. The committee yielded, but with the utmost reluctance.

So far Rockefeller had avoided becoming involved in production because he believed it was a boom-and-bust game which could never be tidied up as he had placed in order the refining and transporting. Now, somewhat carried away by his estimate of the possibilities of the Lima field, or just as probably determined to erase his old nightmare of not being able to procure floods of petroleum for his refineries, he also made known his intention of going into production. This too met with determined opposition from his associates, John D. Archbold in particular. It would, Archbold warned, "make food for demagogues, politicians, papers and howlers of all descriptions." Rockefeller went ahead with his plan for buying up oil-bearing properties, however, and in the next several years Standard had bought up $8 million worth of leases and owned a major share of Ohio oil production.

Now his problem was to prove that Lima crude could be processed into a marketable product. With his penetrating knowledge of every phase of his industry, Rockefeller had heard of a genius at industrial chemistry named Herman Frasch. A German immigrant of great energy and an excitable temperament more commonly found in the theater, Frasch had succeeded several years before in Ontario, Canada, in devising a process of refining petroleum which also had a high sulfur content.

In his longheaded way Rockefeller probably had Frasch in mind when he committed Standard to storing crude from the Lima field and buying up oil leases there. Anyway he persuaded Frasch to begin experiments in a Standard laboratory in 1886. The process Frasch developed — adding a metallic oxide which united with sulfur and formed a precipitate which could be removed while distilling kerosene from crude oil — was a success, though it took two years of failure and experiment to come up with the right formula. Meanwhile, to provide a temporary outlet for the Lima crude, which threatened to swamp the Standard storage facilities, Standard built a pipeline from the Ohio-Indiana fields to Chicago, where it was distributed in the western market. Standard salesmen gave away thousands of barrels in hope of inducing industry to use it as fuel, but coal was cheaper and manufacturers resisted the proposition.

Working night and day on a project that was costing his employers approximately $2,000 a week, Frasch in his laboratory at the new Standard facility in Lima, Solar Refinery, finally came up with the exact formula for removing sulfur. The patents on that process were to make Standard millions of dollars in the next seventeen years. Immediately after the news of Frasch's success flashed around, the price of Lima crude rose from 15 cents to a dollar a barrel. Most of Standard's share of Lima production was refined at Whiting, Indiana, after being conveyed there through the new Chicago pipeline.

Already there were premonitory shudders over the environmental changes that the industry could bring. Standard had intended to locate the facility close to Chicago and the terminus of its pipeline, but an uproar ensued over the sulfur-laden fumes caused by the Frasch process and the refinery had to be moved seventeen miles away and across the Indiana line. Within a few years the dunes and woods and duck-hunting bogs around Whiting were transformed into a reeking, smoke-blackened, sulfur-blighted area. Around the Standard refinery a complex of allied industries sprang up, including a barrel factory and an acid-producing plant. It all provided an example, uncomprehended at the time, of the price the country would pay for the privilege of making Rockefeller and his friends so rich.

Rockefeller's mastery of the multifaceted art of developing and then encompassing a whole major industry, dominating it as no other man would or ever could again, was strikingly demonstrated in his single-minded exploitation of the Lima field, which against the advice of his associates was undertaken to assure Standard of a source of essential supply during the long dry spell of American oil exploration.

The very self-containment which preserved him from the mistakes of other men, which armored him against the more banal human frailties, carried a built-in handicap. It made him blind to other people's view of him, insensitive to how his activities might affect them. He would never be so indiscreet as to echo the Vanderbilt public-be-damned pronouncement, but neither would he understand that the bigger a business becomes the more tenderly it must treat public opinion.

Public relations had not yet become a profession, nor had the delicate process of image-forming been developed, but it was fairly well understood by other magnates of the time that public opinion was something to be taken into serious consideration. Both financiers and politicians, toward this purpose, kept a shockingly large number of newspapermen on their payroll. On some papers it was understood that a reporter or editor, making perhaps $25 or $30 a week, would not be frowned upon for taking money on the side; the same system of subsidized journalism has prevailed through various French Republics with historic ill effects. The great Philadelphia banker, Jay Cooke, kept a score of newspapermen on his payroll. The Tweed Ring in New York had corrupted the city's press. Until Pulitzer took it over, the New York *World* had been the organ of various financial and industrial interests. Thomas Scott of the Pennsylvania Railroad had owned it for a time, until Jay Gould bought it and used it to manipulate public opinion. When the wealthy Samuel Tilden's political career was on the rise, his advisers insisted that he must pay out $3,000 to $10,000 monthly to thirty journalists to obtain a favorable press, and for a time he also published the New York *Morning News*.

John D. would have scorned such methods if they had been

proposed to him. As one biographer noted, "He had marched forward in the mechanics of business. But he lagged hopelessly behind many other men in his understanding of the new elements which entered the problem . . . He went on believing that the oil business, even though he should get it all in his grasp, was his own private business and was none of the public's business at all. He withdrew behind his righteousness and let his enemies howl."[3] He was unable to see that his corporate task was not merely to sell kerosene and other oil products to the public as cheaply as possible, but himself and his company as well.

It was not enough to be in the right, as he believed, but to make the public believe it. He should have been warned by the eruption against Standard Oil among the producers during the 1870's that he had to present himself in the most favorable light. A good public relations campaign could probably have headed off those outbreaks and made Rockefeller a hero bringing efficiency to the industry. And there was the scandal that erupted over the Widow Backus affair before he moved from Cleveland. A pioneer in the lubricating-oil field, F. M. Backus died in 1874 leaving a business that was netting about $25,000 a year. His widow operated it for several years until Standard Oil entered the lubricating field itself. Mrs. Backus "as the mother of fatherless children" asked Rockefeller to buy her out. She asked $200,000, but was forced to accept Rockefeller's price of $79,000.[4] Her complaints, loud and endlessly reiterated, made John D. appear to be a skinflint who did not hesitate to drive a ruthless bargain with a defenseless widow, and the charges were picked up and amplified by two of Rockefeller's most relentless prosecutors in print, Henry Demarest Lloyd and Ida M. Tarbell, as an example of the Rockefeller business methods.

Actually Rockefeller could have made a pretty good case for himself if he had troubled to defend himself. It may have been a hard bargain but it wasn't unfair, considering the plant was worth about $20,000 and its profits would have been

51

sharply reduced in competition with Standard's lubricating-oil subsidiary.

To all such attacks, however, Rockefeller would respond only with a dignified silence. Once he had been terribly embarrassed when the pastor of his church, during one of the periods when Standard Oil was embroiled in controversy, had declared in a sermon that "tainted money" — such as that liberally contributed by Rockefeller — was "sanctified" when it was turned over to the holy purposes of the Baptist church. Rockefeller let it pass; only a very unworldly pastor could have thought Standard's was "tainted money."

Thus Standard was unprepared for the troubles that afflicted it early in the 1890's when "hydra-headed monster" was a relatively gentle description of the company. Rockefeller refused to recognize that the day was past when a Standard Oil man could flippantly turn aside questions as Archbold did in 1879 during the Hepburn Committee investigation. (The committee was headed by a young and aggressive New York state legislator named Alonzo B. Hepburn, who was determined to find out just how the railroads and their customers worked out the rebate system. Not surprisingly, Hepburn eventually became a trustee of the Rockefeller Foundation.)

Two of Standard's top executives, Rogers and Archbold, were among those summoned to testify, and two brief passages from their examination will show the quality of their response. Rogers, referred to as "Hell Hound" in the press, was first.

COMMITTEE COUNSEL: You are a member of the firm of Charles Pratt and Company, are you not?

ROGERS: Yes, sir.

COUNSEL: That firm is one of Standard Oil's affiliated firms, is it not?

ROGERS: I don't know that I understand your question.

COUNSEL: You ship under the Standard Oil's rates, do you not?

ROGERS: I really don't know whether we do or not.

COUNSEL: Are you a member of the Standard Oil Company?
ROGERS: If I was, I think that is a personal question.

And there was Archbold's playful passage with the Hepburn Committee's counsel:

COUNSEL: Well, Mr. Archbold, what function do you play in the Standard Oil now as a director?
ARCHBOLD: I am a clamorer for dividends. That is the only function I have in connection with the Standard Oil Company.

Rockefeller was said to have chuckled over Archbold's sally, but others were inclined to view the testimony, if it could be called that, of the Standard executives as verging on insolence, as typifying the trust's attitude toward the government and the public. Complaints began to grow in number and volume that Standard's monopoly kept the price of kerosene unnecessarily high; that its marketing policies, tending to drive the stunted surviving competition to the wall, amounted to a restraint of trade. In 1887 one of Rockefeller's aides in the field frankly wrote him that the public's picture of Standard Oil was not a friendly one, explaining, "We are quoted as the representative of all that is evil, hard-hearted, oppressive, cruel (we think unjustly) but men look askance at us, we are pointed out with contempt, and while some good men flatter us, it is only for our money, and we scorn them for it, and it leads to further hardness of heart."[5]

But Rockefeller and his chief associates at 26 Broadway, well insulated from the plaints of the marketplace, could reflect that the Standard Oil Trust was only one of many inequities in the American economic system. Other trusts had sprung up, on the Standard pattern, in steel, whiskey, sugar, coal, and many other commodities, all of them sheltered by the protective tariff from foreign competition which would have forced prices down. Rockefeller and his executive phalanx maintained their attitude of icy indifference toward any viewpoint but their own. Their position appeared to be impregnable. Henry Clews, a Wall Street broker who wrote an invaluable insider's history of American finance during that period, observed that "Their resources are so great that they need only concentrate on a given property to do with it what they please. They are the greatest operators the world has ever seen, and the beauty of their method is the quiet and lack of ostentation, no gallery plays, no scare heads in the paper, no wild scramble for excitement. With them the process is gradual, thorough and steady, with never a waver or break."[6] Understandably the engineers of that perfectly running machine might have been afflicted by a touch of *hubris*. Certainly they did not seem to have been prepared for the legislative and journalistic storm gathering over 26 Broadway.

Big business itself was under growing political pressure. In 1884 the Anti-Monopoly Party was organized to press, first of all, for regulation of the railroads. The result, three years later, was the Interstate Commerce Commission. The following year the state Senate of New York appointed a committee to look into the affairs of Standard Oil, among other trusts, and managed to subpoena the elusive Mr. Rockefeller. Against the expectations of the company lawyers, Rockefeller, though inexperienced in the cut and thrust of such inquisitions, conducted himself with superb self-possession and, as the New York *Tribune* reporter at the hearing observed, "seems the embodiment of sweetness and light." Under the badgering of committee counsel, Rockefeller replied in tones "clear, melodious and deliberate." He produced a copy of Standard's trust agreement without the expected protest and answered all questions readily. Standard was now capitalized at $90 million, controlled about ninety percent of U.S. production, paid a seven and one-half percent dividend annually. He was appalled at the suggestion that Standard was a monopoly and pointed out that eleven companies were still competing with him.[7]

Though blandly delivered, his testimony provided a rather alarming picture of how Standard had obtained a strangle-

54

hold on the industry. It whetted the interest of congressional reformers, who summoned Rockefeller and all his chief collaborators before an investigating committee which took a thousand pages of testimony.

The Fifty-first Congress, 1889–1890, proceeded swiftly to act upon a bill introduced by Senator John Sherman which would "declare unlawful trusts and combinations in restraint of trade." This was the Sherman Anti-Trust Act, still the basis for governmental regulation. It was passed and signed by the President six months later.

Standard was quickly made to understand it was no longer impervious. The Ohio Supreme Court declared Standard Oil of Ohio to be a monopoly and ordered it to withdraw from the trust agreement.

Actually Rockefeller and company, with the best legal talent in the nation at their disposal, were quite undismayed. They not only voted Standard Oil of Ohio out of the trust, but dissolved the trust agreement. A loophole had been found. Standard's legal corps had read the fine print in a new law enacted by the New Jersey state legislature. Designed to bring new revenue into the state treasury, the law permitted companies which incorporated themselves in that state to hold stock in other corporations. It also allowed the formation of the first holding company, Standard Oil of New Jersey, which became the carryall for the stocks of every Rockefeller constituent company. Terminology had been changed — holding company for trust — but the effect was the same. Standard was again secure behind its bulwarks, for the time being; overnight Standard Oil of New Jersey's capitalization was increased from $10 million to $110 million.

Rockefeller, however, could not find sanctuary from the persistent enmity of the publicists, intellectuals, journalists and politicians intent in cutting his empire down to a more manageable size.

Gadflies swarmed, and the trumpets of reform sounded. The first and noisiest gadfly was Henry Demarest Lloyd, who

55

had begun his crusade against Standard Oil even before it was organized as a trust. Although he looked something like a cow-country college professor with his pince-nez and his scholarly bangs, Lloyd was well equipped for his polemical mission. He was a Columbia University graduate who had switched from law to journalism and become an editorial writer for the then antimonopolist *Chicago Tribune*. No more unstained by ambition than his chosen enemies, he explained his motive for taking up journalism in a letter to his sister Caro, who was also his biographer. "I want power," Lloyd forthrightly stated. "I must have power. I could not live if I did not think that I was in some way to be lifted above and upon the insensate masses who flood the stage of life in their passage to oblivion . . ."[8] Lloyd married the daughter of a part-owner of the *Tribune*, which considerably lifted him above the masses and allowed him to retire from newspaper work and concentrate on the writings he hoped would make him famous.

His first crack at Standard Oil was a magazine article titled "The Story of a Great Monopoly" and published in the *Atlantic Monthly*.[9] It attracted so much attention that the magazine had to be reprinted seven times and eventually made Lloyd known as the "father of the muckrakers." On the basis of research he had been gathering for five years Lloyd charged that a monopoly such as Standard Oil was organizing was actually an offense against the system of free enterprise, and he warned of the danger in the adulation of magnates such as Rockefeller, Morgan and Vanderbilt.

Despite his position as the son-in-law of wealth, he turned to populism and later socialism as a remedy for what ailed the country, even defending the anarchists convicted of the Haymarket riot murders. Populism was too tame for him, largely because it insisted on the primacy of the free-silver issue, which Lloyd considered a trifling approach to social and economic reform. He was also repelled by the fact, as he saw it, that "the People's party should be more boss-ridden, ring-ruled, gang-gangrened than the two old parties of monopoly."[10]

All his political interests, however, were peripheral to producing his masterwork, *Wealth and Commonwealth*, which was published in 1894 and immediately became a best seller. Rockefeller was his primary target, but the "captains of industry" as a class were indicted in the most corrosive and closely reasoned assault yet mounted on the super-capitalists. Something of his attitude toward this class undoubtedly was derived from Mark Twain's *The Gilded Age* and by other novels which depicted the post–Civil War magnates as the New Barbarians, rootless, uneducated and corrupt. Lloyd set forth his purpose in attacking Rockefeller and his fellow titans as follows:

"If our civilization is destroyed as Macaulay predicted, it will not be by his barbarians from below. Our barbarians come from above. Our great moneymakers have sprung in one generation into seats of power kings do not know. The forces and the wealth are new, and have been the opportunity of new men. Without restraints of culture, experience, the pride or even the inherited caution of class or rank, these men, intoxicated, think they are the wave instead of the float, and that they have created the business which has created them. To them science is but a never-ending repertoire of investments stored up by nature for the syndicates, government but a fountain of franchises, the nations but customers in squads . . . The possibilities of its gratification have been widening before them without interruption since they began, and even at a thousand millions they will feel no satisfaction and will see no place to stop."[11]

At times Lloyd seemed to be more outraged by the fact that Rockefeller and the new money kings were parvenus, that they lacked "culture" and "inherited caution," than by their visible depredations. But he was definitive when he came to detailing the exact nature of Rockefeller's operations from the moment he stepped into his first Cleveland refinery. He showed how

Standard had obtained its monopoly, not so much by enterprise and risk-taking, as by skulduggery in the railroad offices;
controlling the transportation of petroleum from the oilfields
and kerosene from the refineries had made it all possible.

The bulk of his indictment was based on facts given him by
persons who had been driven into the ground as ex-competitors
of Standard Oil, parties who claimed they had been injured
(the Widow Backus, for instance), testimony before the New
York state and congressional investigating committees. It
hardly pretended to be an impartial, objective work and made
no attempt to present Standard Oil's side of the controversies
it raked over. Lloyd saw himself, with just a touch of megalo-
mania, as David bringing down Goliath; he was not about to
wait until Rockefeller found his own slingshot. Whatever its
demerits on the grounds of unfairness, it created a tremendous stir, particularly among the people whose opinions and
attitudes counted the most. Edward Everett Hale considered
it the most important book since *Uncle Tom's Cabin*, and William Dean Howells wrote Lloyd that the facts he recited were
so "infuriating that I have to stop from chapter to chapter to
take breath. It is like a tale of some remote corruption, some
ancient oppression far from ourselves." Another who read it,
and was inspired by it, was Miss Ida Tarbell, then a history
student at the Sorbonne.

A much larger public, which did not read 500-page books,
was also being penetrated by anti-Rockefeller influences. During the later decades of the century newspaper and magazines
had grown in number and circulation; daily newspapers from
574 in 1870 to 1,610 in 1899. The newspapers thereupon
assumed a new role — a role, as Richard Hofstadter, in *The
Age of Reform*, has noted, of "creating a mental world for the
uprooted farmers and villagers who were coming to live in
the city." To capture the interest of these new readers, they
invented the "crusade," substituting newspaper gossip for village gossip. Crusades needed an object, and the newly rich
and powerful were ready-made villains. Modest as he was —

in contrast to the elder Morgan and other plutocrats — John D. Rockefeller was nominated as the No. 1 villain on the scene. The personal abuse visited upon him through the press undoubtedly had its inception in the oilfields, where every dry-holer automatically blamed Rockefeller for his bad luck. An oilfield pioneer named John J. McLaurin recalled that every man who went broke in the oil business claimed he had been crushed by the Rockefeller juggernaut rather than admitting to any mistakes of his own. "If a man anywhere in Oildom drilled a bad hole," McLaurin wrote in his memoirs, "or backed the wrong horse, lost at poker, dropped money speculating, stubbed his toe, ran an unprofitable refinery, missed a train, or couldn't maintain champagne style on a lager-beer income, it was the fashion for him to pose as the victim of a gang of conspirators and curse Standard Oil vigorously and vociferously."[12] Taking up this all too human foible, the newspapers also were inclined to blame Rockefeller for everything that went wrong in the country; not least two of the largest, Hearst's New York *Journal* and Pulitzer's New York *World*.

The same circulation-getting quality about the Rockefeller name, coupled undoubtedly in some cases with genuine social idealism, attracted the attention of the magazines which devoted themselves to muckraking. *McClure's*, a leader in this endeavor (which the *Atlantic Monthly* archly identified as "the literature of exposure") decided to wield the muckrake on Standard Oil, as its publisher later explained, for "educational" reasons. Publisher S. S. McClure recalled that in regard to the trusts the "feeling of the common people had a sort of menace in it; they took a threatening attitude toward the Trusts, and without much knowledge."[13]

Thus the publisher-editor and the writer he chose for the project, Ida Tarbell, at least embarked on their own crusade with a less polemical and radical viewpoint than Lloyd. Certainly Miss Tarbell was no Marxist firebrand. That gently reared and cultivated young woman, however, had certain personal reasons for disliking Rockefeller and his works. She was born in the Pennsylvania oil region, had been raised in Titusville and Pithole, and her father and brother both were oilmen who had fought the Rockefeller combine. Still, when McClure asked her to undertake the exposé of Standard Oil, following up her successfully serialized biographies of Lincoln and Napoleon, she hoped that the series "might be received as a legitimate historical study."

Miss Tarbell's series, later published as a book under the title *History of the Standard Oil Company*, covered much the same ground as Lloyd's, but it reached a wider audience and was more effective because it adopted a detached, scholarly and seemingly objective attitude. What Lloyd denounced in scorching phrase and diatribe, Miss Tarbell pointed to in dismay. She also provided a fairly sophisticated insight into the economics of the oil industry. Fresh from her study of Napoleon, she compared Rockefeller's genius for organization to that of Bonaparte. The impact of her nineteen-article series in *McClure's* and their collection in book form made a tremendous, worldwide impact.

Thereafter Rockefeller always referred to her as "Miss Tarbarrel," cognizant at last of the damage that could be inflicted by the published word. Miss Tarbell herself was taken aback to find herself cast in the role of a crusader against capitalism, would point out that the last chapter of her book was titled "The Legitimate Greatness of the Company," and wrote in her autobiography that she was "chagrined" to find herself labeled a muckraker. Much of the balance of her career, in fact, was devoted to writing about the achievements of big business and its leading figures — though not John D. Rockefeller — because "The public was coming to believe that the inevitable result of corporate industrial management was exploitation, neglect, bullying, crushing of labor, that the only hope was in destroying the system."[14]

No doubt she was also startled to find herself and her work the inspiration of such sensational works as the novel *Oil!* by the socialist writer Upton Sinclair. A good part of the publishing industry seems to have latched onto the "Rockefeller gang," as it was generally termed, for profitable vilification. The same year Miss Tarbell's exposé came out in book form, there were the best-selling recollections of Thomas Lawson, a Wall Street operator, published under the title *Frenzied Finance.* The bulk of Lawson's book was a recap of how the stock of Amalgamated Copper was manipulated by a group of insiders. Thirty outsiders, caught short, committed suicide, Lawson claimed. He indicated that the center of the conspiracy was 26 Broadway, the Standard Oil headquarters, which he described in chilling terms: "Solid as a prison, towering as a steeple, its cold and forbidding facade seems to rebuke the heedless levity of the passing crowd." H. H. Rogers, William Rockefeller and James Stillman, known as the "Rockefeller banker," were involved in the Amalgamated Copper conspiracy, according to Lawson. John D. himself was not implicated, but the scandal spattered him as well as his culpable associates. To Lawson, John D. Rockefeller was an operator of the same stripe, an "ideal moneymaker," which he defined as "a machine the details of which are diagrammed on the asbestos blueprints which paper the walls of hell!" Rockefeller was viewed as a hypocrite who gave to many religious charities with one hand while taking from the poor with the other by raising the price of kerosene.

Commenting on the Lawson and Tarbell books, the magazine *Arena* with an effort at fairness stated that "There are worse men than John D. Rockefeller. [Abdul the Damned was still on the Ottoman throne, after all.] There is probably not one, however, who in the public mind so typifies the grave and startling menace to the social order . . . John D. has one vulnerable point, his religious instinct. Dissimulator and hypocrite by nature, the so-called development of veneration is nevertheless plainly marked."[15] But to all such attacks, Rockefeller continued to maintain a hurt silence.

During the period known as the fuel age of the oil industry, in the years preceding Rockefeller's early official retirement as head of Standard Oil, an external threat arose and posed even greater dangers than government regulation, a hostile press, or the enmity of liberal and radical intellectuals. That menace was embodied in the discovery of huge oil deposits in southern Russia, which in turn meant deadly competition in the all-important European market. In that crisis, some saw Standard in a new light as the defender of the American economy. John J. McLaurin, otherwise not overly friendly to the Rockefeller interests in his *Sketches in Crude Oil*, wrote in the 1890's that without Rockefeller leadership against the encroachments of Russian oil the American economy would have suffered disastrous blows. "Russian competition," he wrote, "the extent and danger of which most people do not begin to appreciate, was met and overcome by sheer tenacity and superior generalship . . . Deprived of the invincible bulwark that Standard offered, the oil-producers would have been utterly helpless. The Muscovite bear would have gobbled the trade of Europe and Asia, driving American oil from the foreign markets. The oil regions would have been irretrievably ruined, dragging down thousands of the brightest, manliest, cleverest fellows on God's footstool."[16]

The Russians began their offensive for the international market around 1880. Ten years before, the field at Baku, on the Caspian, had been little more than a matter of curiosity for awed travelers. Oil was literally bursting up through the surface, but it had merely been an object of veneration by superstitious natives — the "sacred fire of Baku" — for many centuries. The American oil industry itself was only a dozen years old at that point.

In 1872, exploitation of the Baku field began. Until then Standard Oil was unrivaled in the foreign market; it boasted that its product was "carried wherever a wheel can roll or a camel's hoof be planted." The export trade increased steadily from 175 million gallons in 1873 to 367 million gallons in

1888 to double that in 1900. It contributed greatly to a favorable trade balance, bringing in $1 million in gold weekly. At first the export market was serviced by jobbers who, as one observer explained the process, "bought the refined oil from the Standard or other refiners and shipped it abroad to wholesale dealers in various countries who in turn sold it to small retail outlets. It goes without saying that these small wholesale outlets were for the most part inefficient and that they also controlled, subject to competition, the price and service of kerosene to the consumer. They could, of course, shift their business from one refiner to another at will. The whole system of distribution was sloppy, inefficient, wasteful and costly. All of Rockefeller's laboriously wrought economies were thrown away when the oil passed into the hands of the jobber . . ."[17]

Baku oil made reorganization all the more necessary. It also forced the Standard executives into another round of competition, this time far from American shores. Foreign competition until the Baku field was developed was a minor matter, limited to English producers who extracted oil from Scottish shale. The gushers which erupted on the western shore of the Caspian Sea momentarily seemed to Standard like the black plumes of a funeral cortege. The average Baku well belched up 280 barrels a day; labor costs in Russia were less than half the American, and the Baku field was compressed into a small area, five square kilometers, while American sources were dispersed from western Pennsylvania to eastern Indiana. In the European market, too, there was such a demand for the heavy oil used in industry and transportation that the Russian producers could dump kerosene on the market at next to nothing as a by-product. Europeans also were inclined to favor the Russian brand over the American when special lamps and wicks were developed that made the Russian kerosene provide a brighter, less smoky illumination.

Rockefeller agents watched the exploitation of the Baku fields closely, their chiefs at 26 Broadway with growing alarm. Standard methods were being imposed, it was apparent, with

European variations. The Nobel brothers of Sweden entered the Russian field, spent millions on building pipelines, tank ships and cars, and modern refineries, until by 1879 the Baku wells were producing 1 million barrels annually. The French Rothschilds entered the business in 1884 and built the Caspian & Black Sea Company into the biggest exporter of kerosene in the European market. In 1883 a railroad was extended from Baku to Batum on the Black Sea, where the oil could be transshipped to tankers and carried through the Dardanelles and into the Mediterranean and the European ports.

Rockefeller met the threat of Russian competition in his usual calm, deliberate, longheaded style. He sent his young men abroad to study the problems of direct marketing in Europe and Asia, determined to eliminate the jobbers and other middlemen so he could cut the price of his products. For five years the bright young men studied the foreign markets, surveyed transportation routes, studied local customs and methods of doing business. Their reports passed over Rockefeller's desk. Through his analytical mind filtered all the obvious difficulties that would have to be overcome before Standard could set up an efficient distribution system abroad: native prejudices of one kind or another, tariffs, trade barriers, local monopolies concerned with pushing their own, nonpetroleum products. In China, for instance, Standard's ambassadors encountered the opposition of the mandarins who insisted that the Chinese must burn peanut oil and of priests who excommunicated any peasant daring to use kerosene to light his hut. Similar difficulties were met in North Africa, the Sudan, the Congo, Japan and India.

It wasn't until 1885, when the dimensions of the Russian threat had fully developed, that Rockefeller was ready to inaugurate his own distribution system abroad. He had incorporated new subsidiaries in Europe, built refineries, established a network of railway transport and bulk stations. He had also found a way of reducing the costs of shipping American oil by building his first oil tanker. All these measures, reinforced by Standard cost accounting, executed by the smartest and most aggressive young men he could recruit, allowed the company to bring down the prices of its products in the foreign markets and make them competitive with the Russian companies, largely non-Russian in ownership and control.

What were the gadfly stings of a Lloyd, a Pulitzer, or a "Miss Tarbarrel" compared with the pleasures of contemplating the huge new extension of Standard Oil into every corner of the world? Or editorial sneers compared with the fact that Standard had more tank wagons (four thousand of them) retailing its kerosene and other fuel oil in Europe than it had in the United States?

In 1896 he was able to retire, officially though not entirely, from the day-to-day operations of the company he had built from a noisome shed on Walworth Run, content with the ever-growing $200 million he had piled up, and concerned mainly with nursing his various physical ailments and preparing his soul for presentation to his Baptist God.

"None of us ever dreamed," he wrote in his *Random Reminiscences* thirteen years later, "of the magnitude of what proved to be the later expansion." The years of explosive expansion were still to come while John D. puttered around on golf courses, gave dimes to small boys, and delayed meeting his maker until his ninety-eighth year.

3.

The Lessons of Spindletop

From the beginning, the history of the oil industry has been marked by one bitterly ironic circumstance. The men who hazard life and fortune, who follow their hunches into the rough country where new oil resources are usually discovered, who use up their last dollar and last unit of energy, rarely rake in the jackpot. The rewards are reserved for calculating men, comfortably removed from risk and discomfort, whose agents appear on the scene immediately after oil explodes into the sky. Rockefeller cashed in on the Pennsylvania and Ohio-Indiana fields, and when the Southwest's first bonanza revolutionized the industry another great American fortune came into the picture.

Judging from the fate of those who pioneered such efforts, and have somewhat pejoratively been shuffled into the background as "wildcatters" in the industry's official histories, with the thrill of discovery their sufficient reward, a man who drilled for oil and struck whiskey may have been the luckiest of his breed. It was a true story, or at least true enough to be recounted in a New York newspaper. The driller, in Pennsylvania, was boring into a hilltop. About two hundred feet down, he later related to a reporter, "the drill seemed to fall into a cavity." Instead of gas, he sniffed whiskey fumes. The wildcatter pulled out his drill and lowered his lunch bucket into the hole. It came up "full of the best corn whiskey I ever laid my lip to," he affirmed. The reason was that he had inadvertently drilled into a moonshiner's cave.[1]

Many an oilman who preceded and followed that lucky fellow must have wished he had struck a deposit of good corn liquor instead of petroleum. The oil kings are and were, really, the money kings. As in poker, they come into the game late, but with the most chips, and are mathematically certain to claim the big stakes. Thus the first great producing field in the Southwest was stamped with the proprietary name Gulf Oil. Whoever heard of Patillo Higgins except gossiping old-timers?

At the turn of the century the Southwest was America's underdeveloped country, baking under the sun in a semi-Mexican drowse except for a few of the larger cities and trading centers. In 1900 the population of Texas was only 2,235,-527; it was cow and cotton country. Only a little more than 8 million lived in the six Southwestern states which later produced oil, less than a million in New Mexico and Oklahoma Territory combined.

One of the drowsier trading centers was Beaumont, Texas, a rice-marketing town, which sometimes called itself the Queen of the Neches. Its streets had been built along the old paths from blacksmith shop to saloon to general store to railroad depot, and through this maze the railway tracks slashed their way into the heart of the town. Beaumont, in brief, was ill prepared for sudden progress, let alone a reverberating boom.

Just outside the town was a low circular mound called Big Hill about a half mile in diameter, rising above the swampy ground in an elbow of the Neches River, which emptied into the Gulf of Mexico a few miles to the south. It was interesting to the natives because the rotten-egg smell of sulfur and gas

67

seeped from its spongy soil. Small boys liked to set fire to the gaseous earth and watch it burn.

Eventually that bump in the terrain attracted the somewhat more scientific curiosity of a one-armed man named Patillo Higgins, the son of a Beaumont gunsmith. In his youth Higgins, a tall, loose-limbed type familiar to eastern Texas, had wandered around as a logger and jack of all trades and had acquired a reputation as the most ferocious brawler in the state. Even after he lost an arm in a logging camp accident, he was said to be capable of taking anyone west of the Sabine with two arms. Late in the 1880's he returned to Beaumont, determined to settle down and make something of himself. He worked as a draftsman and mechanic, read books on scientific subjects, and taught Sunday school in the Baptist church.

From his reading he convinced himself that an oil strike of great magnitude would be made in the Beaumont district. It would make the town an inland port shipping out something more profitable than rice and lumber. Gripped by his vision, he persuaded several of the more prosperous citizens of Beaumont to help him form the Gladys City Oil, Gas and Manufacturing Company (named for a girl in his Sunday school class) with himself as general manager. That was in 1892.[2]

His hopes were centered on Big Hill, later known as Spindletop, because of its heavy seepage. The Texas oil historian C. A. Warner credits him with being the first man to use geology in the search for oil. Higgins himself later claimed that geological data rather than the gas seepage convinced him there was oil under Big Hill.[3] A later historian isn't quite so sure, granting that "Higgins had studied a publication of the United States Geological Survey, and had perhaps identified the low mound four miles south of Beaumont as an anticline; but unless it is among his unpublished papers, he has left no detailed account of his theory. He did believe that gas in contact with sand and shale would cause them to turn to rock, and thus form a roof for an oil trap. But if the memory of one of his fellow townsmen may be trusted, he also witched the hill with a peach limb."[4]

For the next eight heartbreaking years, while most of his fellow citizens came to believe him a madman, Higgins struggled to prove there was oil under Big Hill. Attempt after attempt failed. The first hole was bored in 1893 by a Dallas driller, mostly through a heavy layer of quicksand. It went 418 feet down, with the driller using only the light equipment available to him, a seventy-foot wooden derrick, a light rotary rig powered by a 25-horsepower boiler and a 16-horsepower engine. Higgins insisted that wasn't deep enough, that they'd have to go a thousand feet down, but the attempt was abandoned. By now Higgins had become a fanatic, raised money from anyone who would listen to him, and acquired 1,770 acres in the bend of the Neches. Two more wells were drilled on the mound, one in 1895 and the other the following year, but neither managed to penetrate the quicksand.

His original backers in the Gladys Company refused to invest any more money, particularly after three geologists made independent surveys and declared there couldn't be any oil under Big Hill. Oil, they said, was always found in rock formations. Only Higgins refused to be dissuaded; he was certain that the three test borings hadn't gone deep enough. Local people with money insisted on investing it in rice-milling, and shrugged off Higgins' pleas for capital by quoting the statement of one of the geologists Higgins hired, which appeared in the Beaumont newspaper, warning the townspeople "not to fritter away their dollars in the vain outlook for oil in the Beaumont area."

Higgins was forced to sell all but thirty-three acres of the plot at Big Hill, and finally, in desperation, he advertised in an eastern trade journal inviting participation in a "great oil-bearing concession." Only one answer came, but it was from a man whose imagination and determination matched his own.

The interested party was Captain Anthony F. Lucas, his name Americanized from the original Luchich, who was born in the Dalmation province of Austria and graduated as an engineer from the Polytechnic Institute at Graz. Commissioned a naval officer, he rightly foresaw there wasn't much of a future in the Imperial Austrian Navy and migrated to the United States. He prospected for gold in Colorado without much luck and, after marrying a Georgia girl, turned to something more practical, salt mining in Louisiana. His experience as a salt miner convinced him that salt, sulfur and oil were somehow associated. On reading Higgins' prospectus he decided that there must be a salt dome — and oil — under the mound outside Beaumont.

Lucas came over to survey the Gladys City property, conferred with Higgins, was partly converted by the one-armed man's undiminished faith and partly by his own belief in the oil-bearing possibilities of salt domes. He bought out the Gladys City Company for about $10,000 down and notes on the $20,000 balance and also acquired Higgins' thirty-three acres in return for a ten percent interest of Lucas' holdings.

The supremely confident Lucas and his wife moved into a shack at Big Hill and brought over his drilling equipment from Louisiana. He was certain he would strike oil in a few weeks, disregarding Higgins' warning that he would have to drill at least a thousand feet. Six months went by, and he had bored only 575 feet through quicksand. A few traces of oil had come up, but he couldn't go any deeper with the equipment he had. Furthermore Lucas, by early 1900, was broke. He had exhausted all his savings in that 575-foot hole in the quicksand of Big Hill. Also his credit in town. He and his wife were on short rations, but she believed as much in Big Hill as he did and encouraged him to stick it out. Lucas saw that his only hope was to attract the interest, and the financial backing, of someone with greater resources.

In 1900, there was no feasible alternative to Standard Oil. He wrote Henry C. Folger, one of Rockefeller's top executives, and Folger sent down Standard's expert on production, Calvin Payne, who had surveyed fields in Borneo, Sumatra, Russia, Rumania, as well as the United States. Though not a geologist, Payne was supposed to know oil property when he saw it. Like most experts, he was obsessed by precedents. Oil had never been discovered on land resembling that of the swampy plain around Beaumont. His report to Standard headquarters was negative; "no indication whatever to warrant the expectation of an oil field on the prairies of southeastern Texas." As if that weren't strong enough, he added that the Big Hill property "has no analogy to any oil field known, as in fact there was not the slightest trace of even an oil escape."[5] It was one of the costliest bits of expertise Standard Oil ever paid for.

Payne's report, however, was contravened by the opinion of Dr. William Battle Phillips, whom Lucas called into consultation after the turndown from Standard Oil. Dr. Phillips was professor of field geology at the University of Texas and director of the Texas State Mineral Survey. After inspecting the Gladys City mound, Battle said he didn't like to disagree with so much eminent opinion, but he thought Lucas' theory about salt domes and oil was valid.

The professor's judgment tipped the balance. Lucas and his wife, still constantly encouraged by Patillo Higgins, decided to go on living in their shack and using egg crates and apple boxes for furniture while new financing was sought. Phillips gave Lucas a letter of introduction to the Pittsburgh oil-prospecting firm of Guffey & Galey, which had been highly successful in Pennsylvania, Kansas, and elsewhere and had a reputation for being willing to take a gamble.

Lucas went up to Pittsburgh to see the partners, an oddly assorted pair even for the oil business. Colonel James McClurg Guffey was a W. C. Fields type, who always seemed about to break into a patent-medicine spiel. He dressed in pleated shirts, Windsor ties and gaudy vests, and always wore a swallow-tailed Prince Albert coat. An inevitable broad-brimmed black hat added the final meretricious touch. He had dabbled in politics and had been chairman of the Democratic National Committee. The colonel was the front man of Guffey & Galey. The brains were supplied by his small, self-effacing partner John H. Galey, who had a nose for oil-bearing property.

Colonel Guffey prided himself on being a plunger, but he was cautious enough never to take a gamble until Galey had sounded out the prospects. When Lucas approached them for backing, Guffey stalled until Galey could make a quick trip to Beaumont. Galey was impressed by what he saw and the partners announced to Lucas that they were willing to go along with him, put up $300,000, under certain conditions. The first was absolute secrecy. The second was that Lucas buy up as much of the acreage around Big Hill as possible. Third, Guffey & Galey, using their own drillers, would bore a deep well and if that didn't produce there would be no more exploration. Lucas was more obsessed by finding oil than making a fortune, and accepted a mere eighth interest in the new venture (with one-tenth of that going to Patillo Higgins).

On returning to Beaumont, Lucas managed to buy up leases on about fifteen thousand acres around Big Hill and the drilling proceeded immediately on the fifth hole to be bored into the mound. The three Hamill brothers of Louisiana, J. G., Curt and Al, along with two employees, brought over the heavy rig and piping to send down a 1,200-foot well. If that didn't tap oil, Lucas knew he would never be able to find the backing for another well.

A rotary drill, unlike those used in Pennsylvania, was employed at Big Hill. That kind of rig had been developed for salt mining in Louisiana and it proved to be the most efficient in drilling for oil. Under the eastern method, using cable tools, a hole was pounded into the earth, like driving a nail. The rotary drill was comparable to putting in a screw; it chewed much faster through soft layers such as the quicksand of Big Hill. The Hamill brothers also used larger castings and telescoped pipe of various sizes from four to ten inch into the hole. Water was piped down to keep the bit of the drill cool, at first, until the Hamills discovered that if they used mud in the cooling process it plastered the sides and prevented the hole from caving in. At the 160-foot level they struck a layer of coarse sand and gravel that even the mud couldn't seal off, so they had to drive the eight-inch pipe down by hand. Two weeks of back-breaking labor were required to drive through that 285-foot strata, during which the Hamills' two employees quit in disgust. Then they hit a pocket of natural gas, which sent mud spewing up the casing and into the wooden derrick. The inventive Lucas solved that problem on the spot and overnight by devising a back-pressure valve like that used in pumping water into a boiler without allowing the steam to escape.[6]

By now Lucas, the Hamills and a new recruit Peck Byrd were working on eighteen-hour shifts. After six weeks of the most grueling labor, they were becoming more certain than ever that they would strike oil. On December 9, 1900, their hopes were rewarded, at least in part. Al Hamill later wrote in a memorandum that "On December 9, it was my turn to get up at midnight for my eighteen-hour shift. As usual, while I was on duty, I tried to make all the hole I could. At this time we had put up the evening before an additional joint of drill pipe. I do not recall which one of the boys I relieved, but he had not been able to make much hole. He left almost the full length of drill pipe above the rotary table. At about three o'clock in the morning, I noticed the pump working more freely and the rotary turning very easily, so I began to let the pipe down. Still both pump and rotary worked freely. I kept it going and soon had down all the length of pipe, but our lights were very poor.

"As daylight began, I could detect oil on the ditch and slush pit. When Curt and Byrd came with my little bit of breakfast, the slush pit had a big showing of oil on it. We at once sent Byrd for Captain Lucas, who at that time lived within one and one-half miles of where we were drilling.

"On his arrival, he showed some excitement and asked how much of a well I thought it would make . . . I thought it would easily make fifty barrels per day.

"After Captain Lucas watched the circulating ditch for a while, he asked us to put up another joint of drill pipe in order to see how much oil formation there was. After making about thirty-five feet through the soft sand, we struck hard going. The depth at this point was about 880 feet. We spent the morning watching the oil showing and deciding what was the most logical and practical procedure to follow . . ."[7]

Galey was summoned in haste from Pittsburgh, Lucas and his crew having decided they had struck at least a profitable deposit of oil. Playing a hunch, Galey decided they should go down another three hundred feet. The crew knocked off for a week at Christmastime, then resumed drilling on January 1, 1901, the first day of a new era in the development of petroleum.

A week later they had drilled to the 1,020-foot level when the rotary stopped running. They had run into a crevice and needed a new fishtail bit. That was on January 9. The bit arrived at the Beaumont depot early the next morning and was brought out to Big Hill in a buggy.

Within moments after the new drill was lowered, the well exploded. Up geysered a shower of mud, then four tons of drill pipe, then a roaring outflow of gas, and finally, with a sound like a cannon shot, a tremendous black gush of oil. For a few moments it looked as though the whole crew might be drowned in mud and oil or killed by falling fragments of iron casings. Then came a bombardment of rocks shot out of the well. Cattle stampeded miles away. The gusher sent up a towering column of oil and debris that could be seen a dozen miles from the site.

Captain Lucas was in Beaumont when he heard the explosion. He drove his buggy out to Big Hill at a gallop. When he arrived on the scene it looked more as though a disaster had struck instead of a bonanza. No one had ever seen a gusher

74

like that before on the American continent. Lucas still couldn't believe his eyes. He grabbed Al Hamill, coated with oil and mud, hugged him and still unbelieving asked, "Al, Al, what is it?"

"Oil, captain, it's oil!"

"Thank God," were the only words Lucas could find.

The stuff was thundering out of the earth at a rate later estimated at seventy-five thousand barrels every twenty-four hours.

On foot and horseback, in buggies and spring wagons, people rushed toward Big Hill by the hundreds, stood in the lake of oil surrounding the well, and let the gusher rain down on them. The evening edition of the Beaumont paper told the story calmly enough: "At about 10 o'clock this morning while the men employed by Mr. A. F. Lucas were boring for oil, an explosion occurred that forced the tubing into the air like it was a mere plaything, and then immediately followed a stream of black petroleum. The news was the cause of great excitement, every available livery team being pressed into service to carry people to the well." The paper had been sardonically skeptical about the long, dogged effort to penetrate the wealth of Big Hill, but it was now willing to admit oil might be as important as rice to the local economy. "This discovery will no doubt induce capitalists to prospect on the lands which were not leased, and the result will be very beneficial to Beaumont."[8] It was, in fact, the start of the wildest rush since the discovery of gold in California.

Back east, in a matter of days, its deeper significance was perceived by men who had never seen a gusher but who had the money to profit from every drop of oil that spewed out of the Texas plain.

Standard's monopoly was broken.

Guffey & Galey of Pittsburgh realized they were sitting on a mountain of liquid wealth, or black gold as romantics liked to call it. But they were also confronted by a dilemma. In order to exploit their find, they needed immense amounts of new capital. They simply weren't geared for a spectacular like Big Hill — or Spindletop, as Patillo Higgins called it — which would take millions to develop. Galey hurried to Beaumont and found an emergency situation. Hundreds of men and scores of horse teams had to be hired immediately to build a dike around the well and hold in the flood of oil. Some idiot had lit a cigaret and tossed the match away, causing a fire that sent thousands of dollars worth of oil into the air as black smoke. Guards had to be hired to patrol the whole perimeter of the oil lake. Extra workers had to be engaged to cap the gusher.

Galey wired Guffey to raise all the money he could and send it to Beaumont immediately for the payroll and supplies. But Guffey knew that the firm had sunk everything into Spindletop. Where would he get the emergency funds, not to mention much more needed to build pipelines and refineries, to drive new wells?

His choice appeared to be limited to Standard — abhorrent, because Guffey was an old Pennsylvania operator who hated the "octopus" — or the local financial kingpins, the Mellon family. He chose the Mellons, but the conservative Mellons weren't, at first, enthusiastic about the sonorous colonel or his proposition.

The Mellon banking house was headed by Andrew and Richard Mellon, who had inherited it from their father Thomas. Andrew Mellon, whose pinched face soon became more familiar to Americans as the Secretary of the Treasury under Harding and Coolidge, was a wispy gentleman who, it was said, "looks like a tired double-entry bookkeeper afraid of losing his job; worn and tired, tired, tired."[9] But never too tired to drive a hard, shrewd bargain. The Mellon bank specialized in financing men who had made a business reputation for themselves but needed capital to expand. Such applicants were always exhaustively investigated. Sometimes the Mellons took shares in the venture they were reinforcing, and thus they

came to control Pittsburgh Reduction, an aluminum manufacturer and eventually to form the aluminum trust.

Oil, too, had come to their attention, though as sober Orange-
men (the Mellon family had migrated from northern Ireland)
they viewed it with considerable suspicion; too chancy, too
full of Falstaffian types like Colonel William McClurg Guffey.
An enterprising member of the clan, William Larimer Mellon,
nephew of Andrew, was permitted to venture into the West
Virginia oilfield early in the 1890's, where profits were modest
but steady. William learned the oil business from the sump
pit up, built pipelines and refineries, and proved to be a true-
blue Mellon by selling out at a nice profit to Standard Oil in
1895.

And when Colonel Guffey, the one-man vaudeville, showed
up billowing with excitement over Texas gushers and talk of
millions, Andrew Mellon sensibly called in nephew William to
winnow specifics out of the Guffey rodomontade. They pondered the situation while Guffey teetered on the verge of a
nervous breakdown. Finally, on William Mellon's advice, the
T. Mellon & Sons Bank supplied Guffey with contingency funds
to keep going, but said they would defer any major financing
until more proof of Spindletop's productive capacity could be
offered. That, certainly, was a masterpiece of banking caution,
with the one well steadily regurgitating almost a hundred
thousand barrels a day. Guffey & Galey, however, drilled two
more wells at the site and both were gushers.

The Mellons were convinced and now proceeded to demon-
strate how financial enterprise inevitably triumphs over mere
standard virtues like courage, determination, hard work and
ingenuity.

Yes, they told Guffey, they would now put up $3 million
to develop and exploit the Spindletop field. First, however,
there would have to be some corporate streamlining; too many
partners around. The Guffey Petroleum Company would be
incorporated, with Guffey as president, and both his old partner Galey, who merely had the talent for finding oil, and Cap-

tain Lucas would have to be shuffled into the discard. Their work was done and they would only be supernumeraries in the serious business of refining and marketing the fruits of their efforts. Fortunately for the Mellons, neither Lucas nor Galey was much interested in money as such.

The understanding was that Guffey would buy out Galey for $750,000, but the colonel knew how indifferent to money Galey was and pared the offer in half. Galey accepted and went his way. Captain Lucas was a little more obdurate, but finally accepted $400,000 in cash and a thousand shares of stock in the new company. Patillo Higgins, the real pioneer of Spindletop, got his tiny fraction of the payoff but only after bringing suit against Lucas and settling out of court. True to his nature, and that of most oil prospectors, he spent the money drilling into other Texas mounds and coming up with nothing but mud or dust. He lived on for another half-century without, he claimed, any bitterness over his ill-rewarded discovery of Spindletop.

What the temporarily triumphant Guffey didn't know was that he was almost as expendable as the partners whom the Mellons had used him to eliminate.

Until eastern capitalists took a firm hold on Spindletop and its adjoining hillocks, predictably anarchic conditions prevailed in the new field. If trade follows the flag, it is equally true that monopolists follow the stampeders. At first it was every man for himself, a manic period of lease-swapping, claim-jumping, and land-grabbing that quickly transformed the rice-market town into the capital of a nightmare. Forty thousand avid strangers descended on a pre-boom city of ten thousand. Six special trains daily brought not only prospectors, speculators and camp followers — including a Madame La Monte, who set up her fortune-telling business in the Cordova Hotel and promised her clients she would tell them exactly where a gusher could be located — but thousands of tourists lured by the Texas railroads' advertising: "In Beaumont, You'll See a Gusher Gushing!"

Often tourists got more than they bargained for, when the horizon flared at night from fires in the new oilfield. On March 3, 1901, one such fire was started by sparks from a passing excursion train and towering flames lit up the southern sky for days. Fire fighting was one of the contingencies for which oilmen were not prepared, mostly because Texas-type gushers, spreading lagoons of oil, had never been encountered before. The ingenious Captain Lucas, fortunately, was still on the scene when that fire started. "When we found there was no possible hope of saving the oil," he recorded, "we started a counter-fire about a mile below the oil lake. When the two conflagrations met there was a heavy explosion which threw the blazing oil high into the air while the earth trembled as if shaken by an earthquake. We were glad to know that our great well was perfectly safe having been covered with sand in view of this very contingency."[10]

Meanwhile other leaseholders were drilling as fast as they could assemble the necessary crews and rigs. In addition to Guffey & Galey (or Mellon's), there were three other wells quickly sunk into land near Spindletop. One was drilled by Scott Heywood, a former vaudeville performer and participant in the Klondike gold rush.

Within a few months the Beaumont promoters were able to boast that the six producing wells on or near Spindletop were spouting as much oil in one day as all the wells in the rest of the world, every one a 100,000-barrel gusher.

Speculators hardly needed that encouragement. There was one lucky thing about Spindletop from their viewpoint. In his necessary haste to comply with Guffey & Galey's requirement that he secure leases on fifteen thousand surrounding acres, Captain Lucas had skipped over many small tracts, bits and pieces of a few acres each. These were now feverishly bought and traded, scraps of meat tossed to the tigerish speculators.

One syndicate headed by Jim Hogg, an ex-governor of Texas, bought a fifteen-acre plot for $180,000, then profited hugely by selling one two-and-a-half-acre piece for $200,000 and the rest in parcels as small as one-thirty-secondth of an acre.

In the oil-crazed town, leasing, selling and trading went on around the clock. Nobody slept much, because latecomers could only find a chair in a hotel lobby, a pool table or a cot in the city auditorium where men slept in six-hour shifts. Tent saloons and gambling houses were mobbed day and night. With the fever of speculation running so high, nobody dared to sleep for more than a few hours for fear of losing out on a fortune. A new company was formed every hour. A new syndicate, tied together over a poker table, went into operation every day.

One professional observer, on hand for a technical journal, collected tales of some of the overnight fortunes made. A woman sold her pig pasture for $35,000. Lots previously selling for $40 an acre now brought $40,000. Another tract valued at a pre-boom $8 an acre was sold for $35,000. The land boom spread far from Beaumont. "Thousands of acres of this land 150 miles from Beaumont," he reported, "have sold for as much as $1,000 an acre. Land within the proved area has sold for nearly $1,000,000 an acre; $900,000 having recently been paid for one acre. No sales were made for less than $200,000 per acre. Spindletop today may be justly assessed at a valuation of $500,000 an acre, or $100,000,000. Two years ago it could have been bought for less than $10 an acre."[11]

The atmosphere seemed to become more demented with each passing week. Values became so scrambled that oil was selling for 3 cents a barrel, drinking water for 5 cents a cup. The Women's Christian Temperance Union's local chapter asserted itself by dispensing free boiled water when doctors warned that it was safer drinking whiskey than from the municipal water supply.

The lobby of the Crosby Hotel served as the bourse, where leases were auctioned by men standing on chairs. One plot, barely an acre, was sold for $8 in the morning and changed hands so many times during the day that the last buyer paid $35,000. The Hogg syndicate was selling bits of land so small that only a derrick could be squeezed onto them. Thousand-dollar bills could easily be changed in bars or brothels. The lease-traders carried their money around in suitcases, some of them holding a hundred thousand in cash.

And wells were being sunk almost as rapidly as leases were traded. A few months after the first gusher on Spindletop there were 214 wells bored into that mound. All around Big Hill a forest of derricks sprang up, most of them heavy producers. It was a wonder the whole section didn't collapse into a huge oil-soaked crater with all the oil and gas being suddenly removed from their pockets.[12]

The exploitation of Spindletop was, in fact, a disgraceful example of unrestrained enterprise. By the end of 1901 there were 440 wells dug into Big Hill and the mound was spouting oil so fast that much of it was wasted or destroyed in the frequent fires. And gas pressure, which boosted the oil to the derricks, was being released in one great puncture. The derricks on Spindletop were so close together that workmen laid planks from one wooden structure to the next so they could make a quick escape when an oil fire flared up. It wasn't until midsummer 1901 that a safety committee was organized and regulations were drawn up to provide stiff fines for anyone lighting a match in the field, to insure proper drainage from the wells, and to prohibit the building of saloons within one thousand feet of any oil well.

The operators were more concerned with getting their oil out of the region than protecting their workmen, and by the end of Spindletop's first year three pipelines had been built, two to Port Arthur and one to Sabine. Other pipelines to New Orleans, Houston and Galveston were in the planning stages. Meanwhile a huge tank farm had to be constructed to relieve the glut in the field, the storage facilities eventually capable of handling 5 million barrels; the railroads began running in a total of fifteen hundred tank cars, and the Guffey (Mellon) Oil Company was building five tankers, one of them with a capacity of sixty thousand barrels. Refineries were being built in Port Arthur to process crude direct from Spindletop. American industry was undergoing on-the-job training on how to cope with the truly frightening problems of an enterprise that seemed to mushroom out of the soil overnight.

It all seemed quite marvelous to the technical journal's observer. Within a year of Spindletop's discovery, he wrote, "Beaumont oil is burning in Germany, England, Cuba, Mexico, New York and Philadelphia. By its energy steamers are being propelled across the ocean, trains are hastening across the continent, electricity generated and artificial ice frozen in New York, ores ground and stamped in Mexico, Portland cement manufactured in Havana and Texas, and gas enriched in Philadelphia; and this, too, while half the world is either unaware or incredulous of the value of this fuel."[13]

Despite early reports that Spindletop crude contained too much sulfur and had a heavy base of asphalt, it was seized upon by an industry which was finding the demand outpacing the supply. Within a few months Standard Oil tankers had begun regular shipments to its refineries. The Texas discovery had also attracted the attention of Standard's leading competitor in the world market, Sir Marcus Samuel of Shell Oil in London, who cabled Colonel Guffey: "Telegraph immediately lowest price f.o.b. Port Arthur one hundred thousand tons year for five years fuel-oil." Sir Marcus' plan, according to his biographer, was to secure a huge and assured supply of fuel oil to convince the Royal Navy it must convert from coal to oil-burning warships to keep up with the Imperial German Navy. The crude would be piped to Port Arthur, then onto a fleet of Shell tankers, which would transport it to the English refineries.[14]

Sir Marcus, however, found Colonel Guffey a dodgy specimen to deal with. His agents seemed unable to corner Guffey in his Pittsburgh office. Finally they were told that Shell would have to make their arrangements through John Hay, a very minor broker doing business in London. Hay had obtained from Guffey an option on all the Texas oil diverted to the European market. "Marcus," as Samuel's biographer related, "nearly went mad at the news of Hay's option," and cabled his American agent, "Hay has no position or influence. Shell absolutely refuse associate with him."

Samuel sent his brother-in-law, Henry Neville Benjamin, steaming across the Atlantic on the first available Cunarder to make certain that Shell contracted for a goodly share of Spindletop crude the moment that Hay's option expired. Benjamin found Colonel Guffey easy enough to deal with, "a hearty nature, an example of the generally accepted type of American . . . His companions did not avoid alluding to certain of his peculiarities, either in his presence or in his absence, but all was done and received with a good temper . . ."

The colonel's Mellon-appointed associates undoubtedly were reflecting the attitude of their chiefs, the Mellon brothers and Mellon nephew, who could not have been pleased by Guffey's awarding an option to a broker so contemptuously regarded in England. Benjamin also found that transacting business with Andrew W. Mellon himself was a less genial procedure than with the "hearty" Guffey. Mellon's desire to be "absolutely secured in any event I frequently found a stumbling block during the negotiations." He soon learned that Mellon was the real power in the Guffey Oil Company, and that "as he protruded his personality and experience on all occasions, his friends, to my regret, were obliged to give very great weight to his views, and little or nothing was done without his approval." Finally, twenty-eight days after the Hay option ran out, Shell and the Mellon interests signed a contract giving Shell the privilege of marketing Guffey oil abroad. After personally inspecting the Beaumont field, Benjamin's only fear was of "over-production."

Almost everyone was pleased by the arrangement except,

perhaps, Standard Oil. There was strong anti-Rockefeller prejudice in the state. To restrain Standard Oil operations in Texas, the state legislature had passed stringent laws against "trusts, combinations and monopolies."

Standard's executives pretended not to care that not one tentacle of the octopus was allowed to encroach on Texas oil. "After the way Mr. Rockefeller has been treated by the state of Texas," H. H. Rogers proclaimed, "he'll never put another dime down there." "Never" is an easily modified adverb in the oil industry.

In 1951, at the fiftieth anniversary celebration for Spindletop, the late Everette Lee DeGolyer took the rather sentimental view that something more precious than crude oil came out of that field. "I once travelled over the countryside of Cape Breton for some weeks. It was a hard land. 'What does this country produce?' I asked. The reply was from a dour Scot. He looked me squarely in the eye and replied 'Men.' And so it was with Spindletop. It was a producer of men."[15]

Actually Spindletop was a producer of ruthless competition which only the boldest and craftiest — not necessarily the best or even the manliest — survived. It was a Darwinian forcing-bed. If a frail, remote Andrew Mellon came out ahead of a Colonel Guffey, who out-survived a Captain Lucas, a John Galey and a Patillo Higgins, it didn't prove much beyond the crushing financial power of a great banking house administered without any glow of humanity.

Spindletop as a "producer of men," in DeGolyer's view, did mark the rise of several eminent oilmen. J. S. Cullinan got his start in the Spindletop field and founded the Texas Company, which soon became a major operator in all the southwestern states. The Sun Oil Company, controlled by the four Pew brothers, had been a small Philadelphia refinery until Spindletop gave it the necessary impetus. Two young men named W. S. Farish and Lee Blaffer made their stake in the same hurly-burly and established the Humble Oil Company. But Spindletop ruined far more men, physically, morally or financially, than it made.

The fate of Colonel Guffey was instructive as a study of the corporate morality governing such events. It was evident from the recollections of the Shell negotiators that he had little actual control over the Guffey Oil Company, which could so easily have been strangled by the Mellon purse strings. At first his company was bound to a Mellon subsidiary, the Gulf Company of Morgan City, Louisiana, by a contract requiring him to deliver twenty-five hundred barrels of crude daily at 25 cents a barrel. If the market price went down, so did the amount Guffey received.[16] In 1907, Guffey was suddenly displaced as president of the company named for him and was supplanted by W. L. Mellon. The company was subsequently renamed Gulf Oil, with a half-dozen subsidiaries in the Netherlands, Mexico, and Venezuela, and became one of the giants of the industry.

"They throwed me out," Guffey explained with endearing simplicity. Furthermore they threw him out, he claimed, owing him a large sum of money. After twenty years of battling the Mellon lawyers, he was awarded a judgment of $348,695 when he was eighty-six years old. With all their hundreds of millions, the Mellons appealed once more against paying out that relative pittance to the man who had earned so much for them, and the judgment was nullified. Guffey died a poor man at the age of ninety-one.

In retrospect, it would seem that Spindletop stands now as a towering monument to human greed and fecklessness. Three years after discovery, Captain Lucas came down from Washington to look over what his successors had wrought and confessed he was saddened by the rape that had taken place. By 1904 only a hundred of the thousand wells drilled there were producing as much as ten thousand barrels a day.

"The cow was milked too hard," he said, "and moreover she was not milked intelligently."

Events were conspiring, as novelists of the period would say, to make Spindletop and other discoveries soon to follow of the greatest significance to the style and atmosphere of American life. "Spindletop's industrial significance," oil historian Carl Coke Rister has written, "can hardly be overestimated." Oil flooded the market and new ways to use it had to be found. And just then, testifying to the peculiarly dependable luck that seems to attend the industry at every critical point, the need for gasoline arose.[17]

The Spindletop production threatened for a time to swamp the refineries and storage facilities throughout the United States. Even earthen reservoirs were constructed to hold the overflow, and at the 3-cents-a-barrel price the crude still went begging.

All of a sudden the tiny sales departments became of the greatest importance, and "oil drummers" were hired by the hundreds to take to the road and persuade American industrialists to convert from coal to oil in running their factories. Even at 50 cents a barrel, they urged, it would be cheaper than coal. Two Texas industries, the American Brewing Company of Houston and the Star Flour Milling Company of Galveston, were the first to succumb to the new gospel. The oil salesmen also moved with dispatch upon the railroads. The first demonstration run with an oil-burning locomotive was held in June 1901. A locomotive of the Gulf, Colorado and Santa Fe Railroad made a test run of 450 miles, using forty-two barrels or the equivalent of twelve tons of coal. Four years later the Sante Fe alone had 227 engines with oil-burners under their boilers. The International & Great Northern experimented with two locomotives, one using oil, the other coal, and on parallel tracks between Palestine and Houston it was shown that the oil-burner operated better and cheaper. A little more than a year after Spindletop first gushed, American ships began operating on fuel oil, their conversion encouraged by the visit of Shell's oil-burning tanker *Strombus* to Port Arthur. In the spring of 1902 the United Fruit Company's steamer *Break-*

water made a record-breaking voyage from Belize to New Orleans (two days and nineteen hours) after converting to oil. Oil-burning machinery was now in great demand throughout the country.

Just then gasoline, one element in the distillation of petroleum, was also coming into its own. The electric light was beginning to supplant the gas mantle and the kerosene lamp, and the oil industry might have foundered if a new demand for gasoline and lubricants had not suddenly developed. Standard Oil had been trying to encourage people to use gasoline-burning stoves for years but they were regarded as "more dangerous than a keg of gunpowder." Now there were four thousand horseless carriages on the roads and streets of America, many more powered by steam or electricity; but soon enough they would be called motorcars or automobiles and they would run on gasoline. If steam and electricity had been promoted as vigorously . . . But that is a bootless might-have-been. The Standard Oil salesmen and promotion experts were everywhere — they even showed up with wooden barrels of gasoline and tin containers of lubricants at Kitty Hawk in 1903 when the Wright brothers were preparing to take off in their flying machine. They never missed a bet.

The next ten years would be known as the fuel age of petroleum. It was also the beginning, though not then perceivable, of the smog age. It marked the rise of Texas to a super-state, the birth of a new breed sometimes flatteringly, sometimes jeeringly called the super-American. One thing rapidly became certain: he would use up more than his share of the available oxygen.

II.

The Automobility

'Twas said by a Whig
That a man with a gig
Enjoyed a clear claim to gentility,
But a man who could now
Win a parvenu's bow
Must belong to the automobility.
    — Anonymous, *ca.* 1902

4.

Gentlemen,
Start Your Engines

"Motoring," in 1908, was a sport for the venturesome. There were only a few stretches of paved highway, and most roads ended in a farmer's barnyard. A sharp rock could blow a tire. There were no road maps. Cars were repaired, if possible, in a blacksmith's shop. In many parts of the world the natives had never seen an automobile; many didn't even know it existed. The idea of an automobile race more or less around the world was obviously harebrained.

Yet it came off, the road race of 1908 from New York to the Pacific coast to Japan to Siberia to Moscow, Berlin and Paris. Ever since, it has been regarded as the grand climax to the golden age of the automobile, when motoring was in a class with steeplechasing and tiger-hunting as a preserve of the more adventurous rich. After that, Henry Ford and the deluge of Sunday drivers. In the democratic West, the time in which the privileged can enjoy exclusive pleasures is often pitifully short.

Three hundred thousand persons were watching in Times Square, New York City, when the race started on February 12, 1908. As initially laid out, the entire race would be on wheels, crossing the American continent in the dead of winter, driving down the frozen Yukon, crunching over the ice packs of the Bering Strait to the Siberian coast, then over tundra and steppe to the more civilized portions of Europe. Six cars — three French, one American, one Italian, one German — were entered in the race for glory, fatherland, and cash prizes put up by the Czar of Russia, the *New York Times*, and others. The men involved in the race, including drivers, navigators and mechanics, acutely typified the nations they represented: Ives St. Chaffrey, the volatile Corsican representing the honor of France; Lieutenant Hans Koeppen, a thirty-three-year-old Guards officer who drove from sunup to sundown with the ramrod efficiency demanded by the Greater German General Staff, which was taking a professional interest in the race; Antonio Scarfoglio, the gay and dashing poet-son of a Naples newspaper publisher; and George Schuster, the practical and resourceful American (still alive at the age of ninety-six). One car was equipped with a sail, another with a Norwegian navigator with Arctic experience, another with cases of champagne.

The story of that magnificent adventure, along with all its comic and tragic misadventures, has been told by the participants in their various languages. Here the account is useful only as it illuminated the problems and possibilities of the oil industry as it became the supplier of motive power, and the struggle to adapt the automobile as a utility for the masses at a time when most people, particularly in America, were separated from each other by distances almost as great as the social gap between the rich and the poor. Until then people were leading separate lives, farmers isolated, immigrants trapped in the great industrial cities, all unaware of each other and the soon-realized prospect of being amalgamated into an amazingly prosperous and powerful entity.

It may seem in retrospect that the harebrained race of 1908, conceived as a grand sporting event, nothing more, was the spark that ignited our flaming affair with the automobile. The attention of every American who read a newspaper, and people throughout the literate world, was focused for months on the "auto-maniacs" who pushed on through blizzards, wolf packs, primeval swamps and international chicanery. It proved that the automobile could travel over mountain trails and bamboo bridges, go anywhere, and do anything demanded of it — but only if a plentiful and widespread supply of gasoline and lubricating oils was available. The aspect of supply was seized upon immediately by the ubiquitous promotion men of Standard Oil, who set up supply stations throughout the United States and reaped a great harvest of publicity. The monetary rewards came with amazing swiftness; three years later there were more than six hundred thousand automobiles on the American streets and roads, most of them consuming Standard Oil products.

The new mobility of the human race was illustrated in the detailed reporting of the race, its hazards and difficulties. To millions it seemed as fantastic as the space flights of a half-century later. One of the French entries dropped out after encountering the snowdrifts on the Albany Post Road, and the other cars had to switch over to the towpath of the Erie Canal. In open cars, through alternating blizzards and intense cold, the survivors battled their way across the midsection of America until another of the French drivers quit in a rage when his car got stuck in thawing snow and mud going *down* a fifteen percent grade. The German entry was penalized fifteen days for putting his car on a flatcar and traveling in speed and comfort all the way from Pocatello, Idaho, to Seattle. Scarfoglio, the mishap-prone Italian, was surrounded by a wolf pack in Death Valley and had to kill twenty of the beasts with his pistol before he could proceed; later he was harassed by cowboys who hurrahed him, firing their guns and "whooping like Comanches."

It took the American car forty days to reach San Francisco, where it was assigned to explore the hoped-for route across the Bering Strait from Alaska to Siberia. The snow was so deep at Valdez, Alaska, that the American crew and their Thomas Flyer got stuck trying to drive off the dock. Instead of taking the Alaskan route, the race officials decided that the cars would be shipped across the Pacific, resume their contest across the Japanese home islands, and take a ship to Siberia. Along the 300-mile route from Kyoto to the Sea of Japan they found Japan far from ready to enter the automotive age; the contestants had to stop and build bamboo bridges over mountain streams. The importance of a plentiful gasoline supply was highlighted in Vladivostok, when the American, Italian and German drivers found that the surviving Frenchman had cornered all the gasoline commercially available. He was forced to drop out when his backers withdrew, but the race was held up until the Russian Automobile Club scrounged around the Russian maritime provinces and located a cache which had been reserved for marine engines.

For the three remaining entries Siberia was a nightmare of mud and breakdowns which had to be surmounted on the spot. Finally they had to quit the boglike roads and drive over the unballasted right-of-way of the Trans-Siberian Railroad. The Americans dashed into a tunnel to escape a downpour and were almost wiped out by the St. Petersburg Express thundering into the tunnel from the opposite direction. Scarfoglio was held up for hours by Buryat tribesmen who had never seen an automobile and wouldn't let him proceed until they had satisfied their curiosity. He and the other entries were often held up by vast herds of cattle and sheep, by ferry crossings over the wide Siberian rivers, by the necessity of searching villages for bottles of sewing-machine oil to be used as lubricants. Scarfoglio was outdistanced by the Americans and Germans who drove from dawn to 11 P.M. through the long Siberian twilight; he was also held in a Russian jail for three days after his car struck a cart and a small boy was killed in the accident.

In the final stretch Lieutenant Koeppen, with Prussian honor (and his career) at stake, roared down the thousand-mile

94

stretch from Moscow to Berlin in two days and one night, and arrived in Paris on July 26. Four days later the Americans drove into the outskirts of Paris at dusk and were promptly arrested by a gendarme for driving without lights. They finished the race with a bicycle and its headlamp held on their running board. Thousands awaited them at the finish line in front of Le Matin's building, the greatest reception given Americans until the American Expeditionary Forces came over in 1917 and Lindbergh flew the Atlantic ten years later. The Americans were adjudged the winners of the New York-to-Paris race because of the penalties charged against the Germans for their dastardly trick of riding a flatcar from Idaho to Seattle. Scarfoglio and the Italian entry finally limped into Paris on September 17, the least successful but most gallant of all the contestants.[1]

What did it all prove, beyond the foolhardy magnificence of the human species, the peculiar adaptability of Germans and Americans to anything mechanical, the amazing durability of the Thomas Flyer (thousands of rough miles traversed without a spark plug changed or a valve ground)?

It showed that even though the world wasn't quite ready for the automobile with the necessary roads, service stations and garages, the automobile itself was chugging its way into history. "Great turnpikes and throughways now run where our Thomas Flyer struggled through mud, snow and sand," the victorious George Schuster recently pointed out. "I like to think that our race back in 1908 helped a little to bring it about." It helped a lot. A great thirst for gasoline was developing, and the greatly expanding oil industry — with another giant to rival Standard Oil now vigorously entering the competition — was ready to meet that development.

Royal Dutch Shell was the name of that rival, a coupling of the Royal Dutch Company of Holland, with its producing base in the East Indies, and Shell Oil Company, the pioneering British firm founded by Marcus Samuel, later Viscount Bear-

95

sted. It soon became Standard Oil's most formidable competitor and remains so today.

Shell, however, was only the corporate device through which the British, with the slenderest of oil resources, invaded and occupied a huge sector of the world market. Its conquest was partly accomplished through the efforts of an eccentric visionary who happened to be the kind of English admiral that even Gilbert and Sullivan could not match for sheer, ebullient idosyncrasy. He was Admiral Sir John Fisher, First Sea Lord of the Admiralty from 1904 to 1910, master builder of the scientific new Royal Navy, and prophet (after the American Alfred Thayer Mahan) of the ineffable sway of Anglo-American seapower. A short, bouncy, rubicund, monkey-faced bundle of energy, "Jackie" Fisher was a man obsessed by his visions. They were imperial sized. He was an ambitious careerist, but also a man of extraordinary perception; he had an exalted view of the importance of the British Empire to the future of civilization, but also an acute appreciation of the forces that endangered it. The world he saw presented the gravest perils to the continued domination of Britain and swarmed with enemies who might destroy it, if the Royal Navy wasn't kept at the highest possible pitch of efficiency.

First of all, Germany and the new navy she was building. It was during Fisher's term as First Sea Lord that Kaiser Wilhelm began beefing up the German High Seas Fleet, and Fisher predicted almost exactly how and when the decisive collision (at Jutland in 1915, as it turned out) would come. The only way Britain could hope to survive the coming war with Germany, he believed, was to build heavy-gunned dreadnoughts with a flank speed of twenty-five knots. And that could only be accomplished, he knew, by conversion to oil-burning ships. A secondary obsession was that unless a political and military union between Britain and the United States was achieved, both would eventually be overwhelmed by Teuton, Slav, and Asian in succession or in combination. This fear was heightened when he read *Valor of Ignorance*, the alarming treatise by Homer Lea, the American military prophet, who warned that both Britain and America awaited the "doom of the Purple Persian" unless they armed themselves for a long and ruthless struggle against internal and external forces coalescing to destroy them.

As far back as 1882, Fisher had begun riding his hobby-horse. Lord Moulton, a renowned chemist, would recall meeting Fisher at the spa of Marienbad that year and hearing him expound in his explosive style: "The use of fuel oil can add a full fifty percent to the efficiency of any fleet that uses it!"

By the time he was appointed First Sea Lord, Fisher's sermonizing had become so notorious that he was known as the Oil Maniac. With crusading fervor he kept bombarding the government with memorandums on the immediate necessity of conversion from coal to oil, all of them phrased in the blunt, forceful style he believed was essential to penetrating political skulls. A fair sample of his quarterdeck style in addressing the Cabinet: "The use of fuel oil increases the strength of the British Navy 33 percent because it can re-fuel at sea off the enemy's harbors . . . With two similar dreadnoughts oil gives three knots more speed — that is, if ships are designed to burn oil only instead of oil and coal — and speed is everything . . . It is an economic waste of good material to keep men grilling at a baking fire-hole at unnecessary labor and use 300 men when a dozen or so would suffice . . . In the oil-driven ship one man turns a tap. It is criminal folly to allow another pound of coal on board a fighting ship. Oil does not deteriorate by keeping. Coal does. You can store millions of tons of oil without fear of waste or loss of power, and England has got to store these millions of tons, though this reserve may be gradually built up. The initial cost would be substantial but the investment is gilt-edged."[2]

Fisher did succeed in turning the Royal Navy oilward, but in 1910 he was forced to resign as the result of a bureaucratic squabble. However, that did not end his interest in the problem. A few months after retirement he wrote Marcus Samuel of Shell Oil, "I have put my bottom dollar in 'Shell.'" He also informed Samuel of the dynastic considerations plaguing the English-born Rajah of Sarawak, an oil-soaked fief of the Brooke family in the East Indies, and of a trip to the United States which convinced him that an Anglo-American union would save civilization for the stately old homes of England. "I had wonderful 'tête-à-têtes' with many great men and the universal deep desire to draw closer to England struck me greatly. Neither Politicians or newspapers seem to understand this, *but it is there*! . . . Have you read the *Valour of Ignorance* by the American General [*sic*] Homer Lea? It is read as Gospel in the United States. All this is drawing them to England and we are damned fools if we don't exploit it for the peace of the world and the dominance of our race! A great English-speaking Federation! They are 100 millions of people now and they will be 250 millions and they are only 25 to the square mile . . . Their language English, their literature English, their traditions English and unknown to themselves their aspirations are English . . . About 70 millionaires gave me a private lunch — (they all seemed to know me far better than in my own land!) — and you should have heard them cheer when I told them it was a fine old hen that hatched the American Eagle!"[3]

Oil, of which the United States had deep reserves, would be the tie that bound her to Britain, which had none in the home islands and little in her possessions. To Fisher it was plain that the two navies, plus an assured oil supply, would guarantee and expand the world hegemony of the Anglo-Saxon race. That concept was eagerly taken up by Winston Churchill when he became First Lord (political) of the Admiralty shortly after Fisher resigned. Adapting Fisher's ideas, he went a step farther and decided that the Royal Navy must not only fuel itself with oil but must *itself* own or control an assured supply of petroleum. The source of that supply had not yet been seized upon, but in 1912 Churchill and Prime Minister Herbert Asquith called upon Fisher in Naples and urged him to accept the chairmanship of the Royal Oil Commission charged with looking into "Oil Fuel and Oil Engines for the Navy." Fisher did accept after being reminded of his dictum that "Oil is the very soul of future sea fighting." Several years later, of course, he was summoned back to active duty in the Admiralty and was intimately involved in the oil-tinged decision to send a British expeditionary force to the Dardanelles.

He had served as the indispensable godfather to the British oil industry when its prospects were dim, but the corporate paternity of Royal Dutch Shell could be traced directly to Marcus Samuel and to Henri Deterding.

Samuel was the descendant of Dutch and Bavarian Jews who had migrated to England and become dealers in antiques and curios. By one account, possibly legendary, the Shell insignia, almost as familiar now throughout the world as the Coca-Cola sign, stemmed directly from the Samuel family trade in bric-a-brac. Their London shop specialized in "shell boxes" labeled "A Gift from Brighton," which were decorated with seashells. Marcus Samuel, born in 1853, got his start as a businessman while still a boy by going to a nearby dock on the Thames and buying rare shells brought back from the Orient by merchant seamen. He was brought up in the mean streets near the Tower of London and its adjacent docks, which thirty years later became an unofficial ghetto with the influx of eastern European Jews. English Jews then were allowed only a measure of their civil liberties. A Jew could be elected to office but could not hold that office unless he took the Christian oath, which his religion forbade. (Disraeli had been baptized a Christian and therefore had no difficulties.) It wasn't until five years after Marcus' birth that the Jewish oath was permitted in Parliament. No such strictures as those then obtaining in Germany prevented English Jews from engaging in any form of commerce they chose.

The opening of trade with the Chinese treaty ports and with hitherto isolated Japan provided the Samuels with the opportunity to expand their business from curios to general merchandise. They moved to more respectable quarters in Finsbury Square with its graceful Georgian houses, and the family began acquiring a sizable foothold on the import-export trade with the Orient. Marcus and his younger brother were sent to a good Jewish community school in Edmonton. A handsome, black-haired youth with a high forehead, and venturesome in the bargain, Marcus Samuel went out East himself at the age of twenty and eventually established himself, and the family trading post, in Hong Kong. In 1880, at the age of twenty-seven, he returned home to marry Fanny Benjamin. In partnership with his brother Sam, he prospered modestly in the Far Eastern trade, particularly with Japan, to which they exported machinery and from which they imported lacquer, china, carvings and bric-a-brac. In the 1890's the Samuel brothers began importing coal from Japanese mines — coals to Cardiff — and that led them into the lamp-oil business. As oil became more important, Marcus Samuel started acquiring tank ships and distributing oil from the American and Russian fields.

With the collaboration of the Paris Rothschilds — but not the London Rothschilds, who did not accept him until he successfully invaded their own province of merchant banking — Marcus Samuel became heavily involved in the distribution of Baku oil. The essence of his scheme was to build up a fleet of tankers which would carry Russian oil to the Orient on terms which would undercut the Standard Oil monopoly on that trade. He managed this trick by persuading the governing body of the Suez Canal to permit Shell tankers to use that waterway, which was forbidden to Standard Oil tankers. Standard's ships were kept out of the canal on the grounds that they were not fitted with the "expansion tanks" which eliminated explosive gases and other safety devices. Samuel made his ships "safe" by canal standards and thus was able to ship oil to the Far East much cheaper than Standard could.

For six years Samuel's firm contented itself with shipping Rothschild-produced oil from Baku to the Orient, then in 1897 announced that he was forming the Shell Transport and Trading Company which would undertake the production and refining of petroleum as well as its transportation.[4]

That meant he had to find producing wells somewhere, the same step Rockefeller had been forced to take in the United States. His agents scouted everywhere for an opportune location, particularly his energetic nephew Mark Abrahams, who was managing the family's tank storage facilities in the Dutch East Indies. Despite his ability, Mark Abrahams and his saturnine Uncle Marcus, who was only ten years older, often found themselves in violent disagreement. Mark, according to Samuel's biographer, "was entrusted with immense responsibilities, yet violently condemned for showing the least initiative without authority from home. Mark was perhaps the only man—apart from Deterding at a much later period — who could really enrage his uncle Marcus. Yet Mark stood up to him and, as often as not, had his way."

While his agents scouted for production sources, Marcus Samuel pondered the consequences which would probably ruin Shell if he didn't undertake expansion into allied fields. "First," wrote Sir Robert Henriques, his biographer, who married a Samuel granddaughter, "any oil they got from the Orient for the Oriental markets could be sold at a lower price, or at a greater profit, or both, than oil from Baku. Secondly, the Bnito [Paris Rothschild] contract was already half-run, and in less than five years time would be due for renewal unless, by then, he could find an alternative source of oil, a source both large enough and dependable enough to keep his great fleet busy and his extensive marketing organization supplied. Failing this, he would have to accept a new contract for Russian oil on whatever terms the Rothschilds and their allies chose to dictate. Thirdly, he grew ever more dissatisfied with the way the Bnito contract was working: the Rothschilds, operating from within the shelter of their alliance with Standard Oil and other Russian producers, were able to demand a price which, in view of Archbold's price war, left a very small margin of profit . . . Fourthly, for reasons beyond the control of the Rothschilds, the prices of Russian oil were fluctuating wildly and unpredictably; Russian oil was not a reliable commodity; Russia was not a reliable country."[5]

Marcus Samuel "hated" Russia, as his biographer notes, mainly because of the pogroms which had driven so many Russian Jews into exile. At the same time Count Witte, the mainspring of the Czar's government, was adopting a tax policy disastrous to the foreign oil interests exploiting Caucasian oil. "Everything that could possibly be called a luxury was heavily taxed, not only to raise revenue, but especially to discourage consumption at home and encourage production for export. And one of the first 'luxuries' Witte attacked was kerosene. Illuminating oil, by which a peasant could read in the evenings, and thus become more difficult to govern, was plainly a luxury that the peasant was better without." Count Witte also juggled the tariffs on the state-controlled railway from Baku to Batum, a lesson he learned from Standard Oil practices in the United States, to bring the foreign producers more closely under his regulation.

Oil history is liberal with fortuitous entrances and exits, Just about the time Samuel was looking everywhere for a producing oilfield, possibly at the suggestion of his nephew Mark Abrahams, a Dutchman named Jacobus Hubertus Menten appeared in Samuel's London offices. Menten was a middle-aged mining engineer recently retired from the service of the colonial government of the Dutch East Indies. He had acquired a concession in the Kutei district of eastern Borneo which gave some indication of being a big oil-producer. His only lack was capital with which to develop the field. Menten had already approached Royal Dutch, an Indies-based firm with which Samuel's future partner Henri Deterding was connected, but Royal Dutch had no money available for new investments.

Menten was one of those prickly tempered enthusiasts often found in the vanguard of oil exploration, with "all-but-maniacal dreams of becoming a millionaire and a magnate, a Rockefeller of the Dutch East Indies."[6] Under close questioning by Samuel and his associates, it developed that Menten's main proof of oil on his concession was the oily substance found floating on a stream that flowed through it to the Strait of Malacca. Few professionals would have been willing to gamble on that kind of evidence, but Samuel was so eager for his own field that he signed an agreement with Menten to drive a test well in the concession. He also appointed Mark Abrahams to take over management of the hoped-for field after spending a short period at Baku studying production methods. Abrahams, after completing that short course, proceeded immediately to the eighteen-acre clearing in the eastern Borneo jungle which was the site of the first well. Laborious months passed before the necessary equipment was shipped out. Finally a test well was bored — and oil came spouting up at the 150-foot level. Shell was now in the production business.

Developing a field in the jungle proved more difficult, however, than Marcus Samuel or his bustling nephew had imagined. London kept urging haste; the field headquarters at Balikpapan could only reply with a list of grievances. Marcus Samuel became so exasperated that he cabled his agent in Singapore to find out whether his nephew had become a drunkard.

Mark Abrahams to London: "People in London are cramming you with the idea of putting down your wells close together. What a mistake in this porous ground, like boring a lot of holes in the bottom of the same bucket . . . You show an utter lack of confidence in anybody on the spot and one of your Seniors has telegraphed to Singapore asking — *Does Abrahams Drink?* Therefore I am leaving . . . The whole European staff is working under difficulties which you have no idea of. The Panama Canal is the only near approach to anything like what we have to put up with . . ." Abrahams pointed out that the home office had instructed him not to hire unskilled Chinese labor, but that several of the white men sent to him from Singapore were incapacitated or incompetent, one arriving with an advanced case of beri-beri from having been on the beach too long, another with only one finger on one hand and the other hand paralyzed. Since people in the home office believed that the operation could be run from Singapore and London, he concluded his cable, they were to send out his replacement immediately.[7]

The trouble between Mark Abrahams and his superiors was smoothed over, and shortly thereafter a tremendous gusher was struck at Balikpapan. There was no doubt that Shell was now assured of a plentiful supply of crude oil. Even so, Marcus Samuel had to keep an eye on another problem: all-out competition with Standard Oil which would arise as soon as Shell became powerful enough to worry the Rockefeller interests. It seemed likely that in order to survive such a struggle he would need still greater supplies of crude so he could respond in kind to the favorite Standard tactic of price-cutting. Whether Samuel was aware of it or not, Standard, through what amounted to an espionage network, was keeping a close watch on the output of the Balikpapan wells. It was ready to pounce, but only after it became clear whether Shell or Royal Dutch was the more dangerous to its trade in the Orient.

Marcus Samuel, meanwhile, was clearing up the details necessary for him to operate in a Dutch colony. Holland's laws required that any oil company operating in the East Indies had to be registered either in Holland or the Indies. Samuel therefore organized Nederlandische Indische Industrie en Handelsmaatschappy as the official owner of the eastern Borneo concession, then sold its stock to Shell. Dutch officials were undeceived by the legalism, but did not object. Most Dutchmen were anti-British on principle — the English had succeeded the Netherlands and France as the leading colonial power, and the Dutch Boers were about to rebel against English rule in South Africa — but they feared the encroachments of Standard Oil. Another consideration was that Royal Dutch and Shell might amalgamate, and confront Standard on something like potentially equal terms. The Dutch out East were making it so difficult for Standard's men to conduct their business on Dutch territory that one of them, John H. Fertig, who operated the agency and listening post in Batavia, wrote John D. Archbold, his superior, "It would be a very good idea if the American fleet could come to Sumatra, and surely the war which the Dutch have been waging against the Achinese, should be sufficient excuse in the cause of humanity. If this cannot be done, then please send none but Diplomats here, if you wish to accomplish anything, and warn them never to hurry . . ."[8]

At the turn of the century events continued to propel all interested parties — Samuel, the Rothschilds, the men who ran Royal Dutch — toward the whispered idea of combining Shell and Royal Dutch. There was the heat of competition from Standard Oil, which was detected in the act of trying to engineer a ruinous panic on the Amsterdam Bourse which would have affected the financial stability of both Royal Dutch and Shell. It was apparent to the directors of both companies that with Standard they were confronted not only by a competitor but a sworn enemy. In addition, there was the appetizing prospect of combining Royal Dutch's greater production with Shell's worldwide transportation and distribution network. And the British Admiralty, after years of prodding from Admiral Fisher, was developing a mighty thirst for fuel oil for its various fleets. Amalgamation made sense; it was a natural, provided there wasn't a clash of Anglo-Dutch temperaments. There was one barrier to combining, but a death at sea, in 1900, finally cleared the obstruction.

Marcus Samuel's opposite number at Royal Dutch (after the fortuitous death) was Henri Deterding, a character of directly opposite tendencies. Samuel was a gentlemanly fellow, so well regarded by the British establishment that he was elected Lord Mayor of London in 1902 and was admitted to the fox-hunting gentry. No one ever thought of gentlemanli-

105

ness as a leading characteristic of Henri Deterding, not even after he had been knighted. One thought of boldness, power-hunger, domination, and a prehensile grasp on the main chance.

Deterding was thirteen years younger than Samuel, born in 1866 in Amsterdam. He was six years old, one of five children, when his father died of a fever in the Far East. From his earliest years, evidently, young Henri yearned to follow his father's career as a seafaring trader in the Orient. He was imbued with the nationalistic fervor that had made the Netherlands, eternally menaced by the sea, the possessor of a mighty empire overseas. That empire now mainly consisted of the Dutch East Indies, which required a brutally efficient colonial army to keep the people of Java and Sumatra under control.

Early, too, he realized that any hopes he had of making a real career lay in the Indies as a soldier-administrator, a ship's captain, or a trader. He studied hard and learned English, French and German in the Higher Citizens School which he attended until he was sixteen, because he knew that eventually he would be speaking those languages as much as his native Dutch. At sixteen his hard-pressed widowed mother informed him that he would have to go to work while two of his brothers, according to the plan laid out by his father, continued their education and went into professions. Later he said that he had "begun to think like a man" at that age and understood the necessity for him to quit school, even to sacrifice himself for his brothers.

At that age he was employed as a clerk by the Twentsche Bank of Amsterdam. The work bored him, but he stuck at the job for six years to learn as much as he could of the mechanics of trading and financing. At twenty-two he placed first in an examination given for candidates for overseas posts with the Netherlands Trading Society, which functioned much as the British East India Company had; it was a colonial enterprise, mainly concerned with financing ventures in the Indies which would provide revenue for the government, its shareholders, and the royal family.

He went out East, a stalwart, energetic, square-jawed youth, with that extra gland of ambition working overtime for him. Eight years of bending over the ledgers for the Netherlands Trading Society, in such outback Sumatra towns as Deli and Medan, eventually convinced him that he needed greater opportunities and sterner challenges than those afforded by a long-established organization. But he was learning all the time how the world — the business world, the only one that mattered — operated, how important columns of figures could be: the difference between success and failure. In that ability to find something like romance and adventure in ledgers and cash balances, which does require a high order of imagination, he was something like Rockefeller. On his first job he found the books at the organization's branch at Deli in a deplorable state. Instead of going along with the local system, he tackled the job of straightening them out, a task which required weeks and months of overtime, unpaid effort. And that, he later said, made all the difference in how his career turned out. The way he explained it also revealed much about the man and the reason he became one of the richest and most powerful men in the world.

"Had I let that tough bookkeeping job at Deli master me, instead of mastering it," he related in his autobiography, "my whole life would have been different. A minor bookkeeper I was then, and a minor bookkeeper I should probably still be, if I had not grappled with and finally throttled that hydra-headed monster in the shape of the jumbled, confused mass of figures I had then to unravel. The supreme advantage to me of unraveling those figures was that it gave me the unraveling habit."[9]

It took him four months of "unraveling," but the effort paid off in a raise in salary, in a promotion to the larger branch in Medan, and in the fact that his superiors had marked him as managerial material. In Medan he was charged with investigating the possibilities of various enterprises which called upon the Netherlands Trading Society for financial backing — rubber, tea, and tobacco plantations — and more importantly learning to size up the character of the applicants and weeding out the adventurers from the worthy businessmen. He also had to learn how to make quick decisions, how to increase the Medan branch's turnover without taking disastrous risks. Subsequently he was promoted to the Penang branch, where he could study such esoteric matters as the fluctuating in discount rates and how they could be taken advantage of. He made money for the Society by juggling long-term and short-term drafts between London and Penang by cable.

Even then, in his late twenties, there were visible to his associates certain traits which became even more marked as he grew older, wealthier and more powerful. He was not overly concerned by fine points of scruple; he was obsessed by results and profits, and casual about the means he used to achieve a desired result. He had the embryo magnate's fixation on achievement, and damn the methods necessary. Young as he was compared to most of his colleagues, he had a high-handed tendency, rather un-Dutch in a way, that conflicted with the usual Dutchman's respect (testifying to Teutonic origins) for seniority, higher authority, the chain of command. A lack of respect bordering on arrogance — and soon to be arrogance to a supreme degree — was noted in his communications to the Society's headquarters. But he also had charm, a twinkle in his eye that worked with men out East and later with women, when he could afford them, all over the map. Deterding was a lusty fellow, with a sensuality few in his profession could contain without tapping the till, and possibly his strongest drive was to obtain the money to satisfy his appetites.

He kept badgering headquarters for a share in the profits he was making through his cleverness with the discount rates, and that, too, annoyed his superiors. It was unheard of for a junior executive to demand a share of the profits — almost sacrilegious. He was coldly rebuffed.

While still rankling over that rejection, he received an offer from J. B. A. Kessler, the managing director of Royal Dutch, the oil company with concessions throughout the Dutch East Indies, but decided to think about it. About that time he was given two months leave to recover from overwork and a minor illness. He had hardly begun relaxing at the resort of Magelang when he was summoned back to Penang because a Chinese cashier had been caught falsifying his accounts.

Deterding returned to Penang in a foul temper. Shortly after his arrival he sat down and wrote a letter to the Society's directors reminding them that he had warned them against keeping on the embezzler and that he had been unjustly treated in having his profit-sharing proposal summarily rejected. He concluded: "I would rather not work for the Netherlands Trading Society if I am never to share in the profits of Penang but am called back, notwithstanding, when something goes wrong in my absence." His second letter went to Kessler of Royal Dutch. In the spring of 1896, at the age of thirty, he became an oilman.

At that time the Dutch East Indian oil industry was sixteen years old. The first field had been discovered in northern Sumatra in 1880. Ten years later a royal charter was granted the Royal Dutch Petroleum Company to undertake a concentration of all the available resources, from oil wells to pipelines to refineries, and make them a paying proposition. J. B. A. Kessler, a Dutch businessman with no experience in the industry, was sent out to the Indies to make a survey of the possibilities and to determine why the Indonesian wells weren't showing a decent profit. His recommendations so impressed the Royal Dutch board that he was appointed managing director of all the production facilities.

Kessler solved some of his problems by piping oil through the jungle to a huge new refinery at Pankelan Brandon. Then he found that he could not sell all the refined oil he produced. He needed new capital, a new approach to marketing. During one low-water period, Kessler could not even come up with the payroll at the Sumatran refinery and all the white employees, mostly Dutch and American, voluntarily passed up paydays so that the native workers could be paid. About the same time the Dutch stockholders in the company back home were so annoyed by skipped dividends that they rioted outside Kessler's home in The Hague and smashed its windows.

Kessler saw that what he needed was a hard-driving young man with brains, ingenuity and a high degree of enterprise, someone who could find a market for Royal Dutch oil; someone, in fact, who could stand up to Standard Oil and battle for Holland's share of the Far Eastern trade.

Kessler nominated young Deterding, whom he met in Penang, for that tough and possibly hopeless assignment. Deterding accepted only after studying Royal Dutch's problems on the spot, then undertook, with brash self-confidence, the role of super-salesman. First, however, he helped Kessler beat back a takeover bid by Standard Oil. Citing the old Dutch proverb, "Cooperation gives power," he persuaded Royal Dutch's producing rivals to join in resisting all foreign encroachments. Standard Oil was trying to buy control of Royal Dutch by purchasing large blocks of its stock. The takeover attempt was blocked, however, when the matter was presented to The Hague and the company was allowed to create new special shares, which were to be held only by Dutchmen and which gave them control over the company's affairs.[10]

Standard retaliated by declaring a price war in India and Malaya, the only markets Royal Dutch had thus far managed to penetrate.

Deterding's riposte was to enlarge his own sector of the market and compete tooth and nail, fang and claw with the Standard Oil distributors throughout the Far East. He saw that it would be necessary to cut the time between sale and delivery, and with Kessler raising the new capital needed, they managed to build a small fleet of tankers and establish storage facilities in trading centers, hitherto monopolized by Standard, such as Madras, Bombay, Calcutta, Hong Kong, Shanghai and Bangkok. It took about two years for this modest expansion to be accomplished, part of Deterding's larger dream of having the huge, brightly painted storage tanks of Royal Dutch oil standing ready to service clients in every port from Aden on the Red Sea to Vladivostok on the north Pacific.

In that period the oil industry seemed to stagger from crisis to crisis, price wars with Standard, trouble with native workers, shortage of capital, sabotaged pipelines, oilfield fires — the list seemed endless. Oil was the most volatile of commodities in every respect. In August 1898, Kessler, Deterding, and their staff were just celebrating the arrival of a big new tanker at Pankelan Brandon from its European shipyard when bad news arrived almost simultaneously. From the other end of their jungle pipeline came the report that their most productive Sumatran field at Telega-Said had started spewing up salt water. Deterding was temporarily rocked on his heels; he had just secured a number of large contracts for immediate delivery. If a shortage of crude forced Royal Dutch to renege, it might never be able to win back those customers. He had to obtain a large supply of crude immediately, but where? Not from Standard Oil, certainly. It happened that Kessler was a member of the board of a company operating at Baku. The two men made the cables hum for a few days, and the Baku company agreed to ship a large supply "not too profitlessly," as Deterding later recorded, to fufill the contracts. Actually, through Kessler's connections, they got the Russian oil at a bargain rate of 7 cents a barrel less than Shell and the Rothschilds were paying. The day was saved.

That experience taught Deterding, at least, a lesson. You had to make alliances. You had to make sure of supply and transport. Consolidate or perish became his religion. You also had to be more scientific or risk such unpleasant surprises as the saltwater foaming out of the Telega-Said wells. Gone were the days of the bowler-hatted old-timers who claimed they'd "smelled" oil all over the world, worked by guess and by God, and expressed contempt for "educated fools." Deterding began hiring a small army of geologists, engineers, analysts and chemists.

Deterding would ally himself with Standard, Shell, or the Devil himself if oil were a proven resource of hell. And there he differed with Kessler, much as he liked and respected the older man. Kessler was an old-fashioned Dutch nationalist, determined to keep his company one hundred percent Dutch. As Deterding's rather unsympathetic biographer Glyn Roberts explained that discrepancy of opinion, "Deterding was all for coming to terms with the Shell group and the other Rothschild interests operating in the East." Actually Shell and Royal Dutch were operating on a parallel course, one with wells on Sumatra, the other with wells on Borneo, and were also selling in the same market. Amalgamation would make for greater efficiency, stable prices and higher profits. "But there is every indication," Roberts wrote, "that Kessler was against it. Kessler aimed at expansion, aimed at growth and greater power, but he envisaged all these things as the attributes of a purely Dutch enterprise. He was a nationalist in commerce, and a purist. The day of the great international combine had hardly dawned, and he could not see his Royal Dutch becoming the germ of a great world-embracing trust covering dozens of countries and controlling nearly two hundred companies. That was not what Kessler wanted . . ."[11]

Deterding's manner was as imperious as his vision was imperial. Perhaps there would have been a head-on collision between his international outlook and Kessler's parochial view, but again the element of fortune incalculably made its appearance. In March 1900 Kessler, aging and work-worn, decided to return to his home at The Hague. Kessler died while his ship was still at sea, off Naples. A few weeks later Deterding took his place as managing director of Royal Dutch.

During the next five years, through a series of delicately balanced and intricately structured deals, Deterding and his collaborators brought about a revolutionary change in the international oil industry. Simply put, they succeeded in contriving a balance of power for the first time and made it certain that Standard Oil could never establish a worldwide monopoly. Involved in those long negotiations were several disparate personalities: Deterding, Samuel, and perhaps the most important of all, Frederick Lane. The latter was a shipbuilding magnate whose skill at negotiation had made him the Paris Rothschilds' leading collaborator in London. He represented their interests in Shell, but also acted as the matchmaker between Deterding and Samuel. And that marriage of convenience, with dower rights involving millions of pounds, was a complicated affair it would have taken a Balzac to recount in all its human and corporate variety.

From the available evidence — Shell archivists claim that many of the key documents are missing — it appears that Samuel was the wooed, Deterding the wooer, and Lane the marriage-broker. Probably it would not have come off if negotiations had been left to the principals, face to face, without the tactful interventions of Frederick Lane. Toward the end of 1901, in fact, Samuel was incensed because Royal Dutch had just signed a more favorable contract with the Paris Rothschilds for Baku oil than Shell had been given despite its longer association. Samuel at first had been cordial to the idea of a Shell–Royal Dutch merger, Lane wrote Deterding on November 1, but recently Sir Marcus "told me in plain English that the basis of my scheme was, in his opinion, ridiculous. He pointed out that the expenditure of the Shell Company in steamers and installations amounted to something like three millions-and-a-quarter to three millions-and-a-half sterling, whereas, he estimated, that your expenditure was not more than a tenth of this, and under my proposed scheme the Shell Company would have to make a present of something like one-and-a-half million sterling to the Royal Dutch . . ."[12]

But Deterding was undismayed and Lane was, as Deterding said, "the cleverest man I ever knew." To strengthen his own position, Deterding proceeded to buy control of a number of smaller Dutch oil firms operating in the Far East. Now in his mid-thirties, he endlessly preached to Lane (and through Lane to Samuel and the Paris Rothschilds) that they and all their competitors would eventually wither and die in the heat of competition with Standard if they didn't amalgamate. If Samuel was shy about an outright merger, Deterding was willing to make the first step a working agreement.

The details are vague, but Sir Marcus had come to see that "ruinous competition" must be eliminated. He and Deterding were finally brought face to face in Shell's London headquarters in April 1902. They were not fated to like or trust each other; Samuel regarded Deterding as a bumptious young man, Deterding considered Samuel admirably suited to the pompous role of Lord Mayor of London. During the years of their uneasy relationship, as Sir Robert Henriques has written, they alternated between "something quite like affection" and "bouts of almost frenzied irritation." A typical exchange during that first meeting:

Samuel pointed out that Shell had storage facilities at more than thirty Asiatic ports while Royal Dutch had only four outside the East Indies.

"Do you want us then to start selling in competition with you in another ten or twenty ports?" Deterding brashly retorted.

In the next twelve months, however, an agreement was reached to create a new company in which Shell, Royal Dutch, and the Paris Rothschilds would participate. Titled the Asiatic Petroleum Company, it would market oil products throughout the Far East. Marcus Samuel undoubtedly was prodded along by the sea trials of H. M. S. *Hannibal* conducted by the Admiralty to test liquid fuel supplied by Shell, the need to secure for the Royal Navy a large and dependable oil supply, and the urgings of his friend Admiral Sir John Fisher.

Sir Marcus was appointed chairman of Asiatic, Deterding the managing director, Frederick Lane the deputy managing director, a ranking which suggested the relative assets each group was contributing. Of the £900,000 capitalization, each party held an equal share. The inequality of the arrangement was perhaps not as apparent to Samuel as to Deterding and Lane. Deterding's driving ambition and youthful dynamism were certain to bring him out on top. Samuel was satisfied by the working agreement afforded by Asiatic, but to Deterding it was only a step in bringing about a complete merger of Royal Dutch and Shell. Increasingly, too, Samuel was bored by the mere acquisition of money and more engrossed in his life as a country gentleman. Meanwhile, Deterding was operating at full blast. He managed to outmaneuver the Germans, who had no petroleum resources in their own country, and through a front formed by the Deutsche Bank hoped to control the important new Rumanian fields, which was the logical source for German industry (and the German navy).

Neither Deterding nor the national interests behind him wanted to see Germany become self-sufficient in that respect; they were determined to control her oil supply and therefore her ambitions to expand beyond the German borders. Deterding, in one of his more masterful operations, quickly bought up a number of small Dutch and Rumanian firms operating around Ploesti, then absorbed the principal Rumanian oil-producer, the Astra Romana, and Germany was frozen out.

One result of that maneuver, however, was to accelerate Germany's drive to the East — her scheme for building a railroad from Berlin to Baghdad and thereby capture the immense oil deposits of the Ottoman Empire in what is now Iraq — and to help bring on the First World War.

At the same time Samuel was suffering disastrous losses

through a European price war with Standard Oil and in order to pay a dividend to rebellious stockholders he was forced to dispose of six of his best tankers to German buyers. This brought him to the humbling moment when he had to amalgamate with Royal Dutch or possibly go under. And this time Samuel went to Deterding, instead of vice versa, and proposed consolidation.

"On what basis?" Deterding is said to have asked.

"Fifty-fifty," Samuel was quoted as replying, "with no party to have any advantage over the other."

Deterding shook his head. He cited the fact that his management had made a thundering success of Asiatic; that Shell had recently eked out a five percent dividend while Royal Dutch's last dividend was a startling sixty-five percent. In the past several years Royal Dutch had simply overtaken and sped past Shell in earnings and acquisitions. Deterding proposed that a sixty-forty ratio in favor of Royal Dutch be established on amalgamation, and Samuel had to give in. It was just one more defeat; the worst was to see the pride of the Shell tanker fleet flying a German flag. Not that Deterding was particularly gracious about his triumph. He told Samuel that he would have to accept or turn down the sixty-forty proposition before he left Royal Dutch headquarters or the whole deal was off.

The new setup provided that one company would be established at The Hague to handle all production, another (Anglo-Saxon Petroleum) in London to control storage and transport. Asiatic would continue to handle all the marketing operations.

At the general meeting of the Shell Company Sir Marcus himself took the blame for what he called a "painful occasion." It was a "great calamity to British prestige" that "supplies of liquid fuel sufficient to meet the Naval requirements of this country have passed from British hands . . ." He had tried before the Dutch takeover bid to restore Shell's position by obtaining a concession in Burma (to replace crude oil, for which he had contracts, formerly obtained from Texas), but the government had refused. He had also tried to wangle a fuel-oil contract from the Royal Navy, but the government had decided that it would buy only from concerns wholly British owned. (This presumably was an argument his friend Admiral Fisher lost.) The result, according to Samuel, was that "never in the annals of British trade has so gross a wrong been done to any company . . . in classifying the Shell as a foreign corporation . . ." when he sought the Burmese concession. A further result was that Henri Deterding, basing himself in Britain, now enjoyed the protection of British imperialism and had the financial power and the corporate muscle to take on Standard Oil.

5.

A Chinese Interlude

Gasoline was obviously the coming thing in the oil industry, with consumption rapidly rising in both the United States and Great Britain, and western Europe not far behind. Another use for one of the fractions in the petroleum-distilling process seemed likely to be found through the experiments of a German engineer named Diesel. It would have seemed that kerosene was a minor item by now, but in most parts of the underdeveloped world, where electricity was used only in the larger cities, the lamp still lighted peasant huts. Particularly in China, which was one of Standard Oil's most lucrative markets.

"Oil for the lamps of China" had taken on the ringing tones of a holy crusade. Rockefeller-supported missions dotted the vast Chinese countryside while Standard Oil agencies worked the Chinese kerosene market for all it was worth. It was a question for cynics whether Standard's ubiquitous salesmen were more successful converting the Chinese masses from peanut oil to kerosene than the missionaries in swaying the people from their amiable domestic gods to the Christian faith.

The cheap little tin *Mei Foo* (good luck) lamp was the key to Standard's merchandising success in China. After breaking the power of the mandarin merchants, who objected to kerosene on commercial grounds, and the village priests, who claimed there was something evil about it, Standard's Far Eastern executives were still confronted by another problem. Their prospective customers had nothing in which to burn the kerosene. So, to introduce their product, they gave away 8 million *Mei Foo* lamps, then 2 million more each year. It was understood, of course, that *Mei Foo* lamps were designed to bring good luck only if they burned Standard's kerosene.

The outlay for the lamps was inconsequential compared to the millions of dollars raked in from the little stores which sold kerosene a half-pint at a time to impoverished villagers and farmers. Standard sent its best and brightest young men out to China, its proving ground for the executive offices at 26 Broadway, New York. The recruiting and forwarding process for those young salesmen was described by Alice Tisdale Hobart, who went out to China to visit her sister, stayed on, and married an American oilman, whose experiences were described in her *Oil for the Lamps of China*, a novel vastly popular during the pro-Chinese 1930's in the United States: "He was in New York, sitting in the classroom high up in the Oil Company's great building. It was the morning the appointments were made. The instructor of the class in foreign trade stood at the blackboard, drawing a rough map of the world. Stephen could feel the old tightening of his heart. Would he stand the last test? Three months before there had been one hundred men in this class. Now there were but twenty. Then his name and station were read out . . . After the assignments had been made, a director of the Company had spoken to them of what the corporation wanted. Cooperation, emphasis on the whole and not the individual, hard work and loyalty . . ."[1]

Mrs. Hobart's hero, Stephen Chase, looked upon his kerosene proselytizing in China with that curious mixture of idealism and practicality which often baffles the rest of the world. "In Europe and America, the lamp which burned coal-oil, as it was then called, had been the forerunner of the machine

119

age. Might it not be so out here?" In her fictional version it is Stephen Chase, with his vision of what lamp light could mean in peasant villages otherwise dark from sundown to sunup, who invents the little *Mei Foo* lamp which enriched Standard Oil. "Gradually," as Mrs. Hobart described her hero's moment of inspiration, "the fluttering light took on familiar shape, the tiny lamp of his childhood, the night-lamp that stood by his bed. Suddenly he felt the electric shock of inspiration. Why had no one thought of such a lamp — to be exported with the oil? A tiny chimney, tiny bowl that would hold a few coppers' worth of oil! A lamp that peasants and coolies could afford to buy! Stephen smiled to himself, seeing their childish delight, remembering the pleasure they took in examining his watch, his flashlight . . . His dream expanded. In time the Company could put a lamp in every inn, every hut in Manchuria, in China! Four hundred million people, millions of lamps."

Stephen Chase's dream took shape, but not always in ways he had envisioned, when he superintended the long caravans of carts loaded with tin cases of kerosene down the dusty byroads to the scattered markets of the interior. By then Stephen had become a company man, completely dedicated to his career and to the higher echelon, and the Chinese world receded from his consciousness. The Chinese themselves were only faceless consumers — actors in a corporate drama. All his thoughts were centered on outwitting the Chinese merchants and increasing his company's profits. Diluting the kerosene, which the merchants did, was to be overlooked. Chase's only object was to increase sales and thereby climb the corporate ladder.[2]

No doubt Mrs. Hobart's portrait of an American oilman based in China was accurate. It mirrored the attitude of the executives in Standard headquarters at 26 Broadway, to whom China was merely a fief, a set of balance sheets. But their hegemony over the Chinese market, long taken for granted, suddenly became a matter of piercing anxiety. The growing competitive menace of Henri Deterding and his Anglo-Dutch combine was looming over it.

Before the balloon went up, however, Deterding, with his aversion to "ruinous" competition and price wars, did make an effort to arrive at an understanding with Standard, did try to arrange an unwritten agreement. It was his credo that big business could continue prospering only if it avoided the temptation to corner markets; eliminating smaller rivals, of course, was intelligent and progressive, but the giants should never battle and tear down their own temples of profit.

As he saw it, Standard with its huge reserves of American oil simply flooded the market whenever it chose to drown out irksome competition. It could afford to do so by keeping prices high on the American market and making American consumers pay for price-cutting competitive tactics abroad. "Today," he told an interviewer for a trade journal, "the world's oil markets are dominated by the Americans, who possess the greatest stocks which they can throw into any part of the world, in order to impose their will. Their system is to crush competition in order to be able to dictate prices. As for us, we do not yet possess as much oil as do the Americans, but we will arrive at that yet. That is why we work intensively in our oilfields, and why we endeavor to prove the largest number of oilfields possible.

"When we possess the necessary quantity we can realize our ideal, which is: at all points of the globe the same reasonable price for all the products of oil, so that the consumer, the manufacturer, and the merchant may find it worthwhile. Today, with the strangling system of the Americans, certain people pay much too dearly for oil, whilst in other countries oil is thrown into the water. Because of this, many producers are at a standstill, many refineries are ruined, while subsidiary industries cannot make progress. Everywhere we come we bring our experience, our work and our capital, and we are happy when we are received as sincere and faithful allies, who succeed in finding a satisfactory profit for ourselves, as well as assuring prosperity and progress for our neighbors, thanks to the natural riches of the country, the work of the population side by side with us, and a community of interests and reciprocal good feeling."[3]

Glowing with this hope of being received as a "sincere and faithful ally," Deterding had made friends with Walter Clark Teagle, a youthful Standard Oil executive then stationed in London, and preached the Deterding gospel of price stability and gentle competition to him. Young Teagle was so impressed that he suggested that Deterding accompany him to New York and give the same sermon to his superiors.

"Come over with me to 26 Broadway," Teagle urged, "and tell them on the fourteenth floor all you've just told me."

"I'll tell them all right," Deterding replied.

They took the next ship over, and one day early in 1907 the two young men with their scheme for industrial cooperation went up to the policy-making fourteenth-floor offices at 26 Broadway. There they confronted John D. Archbold, the hard-bitten veteran from the earliest days of Standard's successful war on its domestic rivals. He listened with a faint smile as Deterding trotted out all the arguments which had prevailed when Royal Dutch was swallowing up its East Indies competitors and later engorged, in effect, Shell Oil, something like a rabbit ingesting a boa constrictor. Archbold knew this much about Deterding's persuasiveness: the persuader invariably took over the persuaded. Deterding, of course, even with his consummate gall, couldn't be hoping to swallow up Standard Oil, but there was likely to be an advantage for Royal Dutch Shell in any cooperative scheme that wouldn't necessarily accrue to Standard Oil. Standard didn't have to make deals with its largest competitor.

"There may be something in what you say," Archbold said grudgingly when Deterding had finished his plea.

Deterding was affronted by the coolness of Archbold's reception, his obvious skepticism, when he had expected so much more of the meeting. Teagle, after all, had arranged the meeting. Now Archbold was treating him as a supplicant.

"I venture to tell you, Mr. Archbold, that there is a very great deal in what I say," he retorted. "You have the idea that the best way you can do good business is by cutting prices, but although I am much younger than you are, I have been watching every move in the oil game very closely, and I must tell you respectfully that I know you are wrong. Believe me, your customers all over the world will give you many more orders, and you will do an even better business than you do, if you will only agree to keep prices level. At present, because of price fluctuations, the average retailer keeps his stocks at a minimum."[4]

Archbold was politer than usual in turning aside Deterding's arguments, perhaps sensing that the Dutchman would make a most formidable enemy. Standard, he said, saw hard competition in exactly the opposite way. It was good for business and good for Standard. In effect, he told Deterding, he was free to try changing Standard's mind.

To Deterding that was as good as a declaration of war. In an all-out, no-quarter war, he saw that Standard would suffer from one irremediable handicap. It had all the oil it needed to inundate a rival, but almost all of it was produced in the United States. That meant Standard was burdened, particularly in a long-drawn struggle, with the price of transportation from American ports to the scene of competition. The more distant the battle, the more costly to Standard Oil in transportation costs. Its whole structure maintained an internal stability through sharp fluctuations of price, huge profits in one area financing a price war in another. There were two ways to get at Standard, Deterding saw, and bring it within clawing distance. One was to fight it in a distant market. The other was to invade the American market — something no one else had dared to think about — and threaten Standard's home base. A pincer attack. Like every industrial carbon-copy of Napoleon Bonaparte, Deterding was inclined to think in military terms.

Before taking on Standard, he streamlined Royal Dutch Shell and made certain it was ready for war on all fronts. After the merger it had available, he estimated, a combined capital of £21,369,000. He weeded out those Shell operations which weren't paying off, explaining in his memoirs, "I knew just where Shell was losing money and I preferred to leave these activities alone. Not unnaturally Marcus Samuel referred to this reproachfully: 'I notice that you have deleted from our inventory certain sections of our business although I put them in at very little and I think you should take them over.' I replied: 'I am sorry to disagree with you, but those particular sections are not making money. A thing which has no earning power is no good to me.' In slower-moving days it may have been possible to run business on the old-fashioned averaging-out principle, but today you endanger profits if you remain tied to the fetish known as 'running the good with the bad.' "[5]

For the next several years Royal Dutch Shell and Standard Oil were clutched in an all-out struggle for supremacy throughout the world. The war started in Europe, where Deterding relentlessly kept cutting prices. Until then Standard, in alliance with the Rothschilds and Nobels, had dominated the European kerosene market, where it kept prices high to finance its campaigns elsewhere. His close-at-hand source, the Royal Dutch–controlled Rumanian oilfields, with adjacent refineries, allowed him to undersell without hurting him as much as Standard's price-cutting hurt his enemy.

Standard responded by acquiring concessions in the Dutch East Indies and canceling an agreement with Asiatic, in force since 1905, to buy all its surplus gasoline produced in the refineries of the Indies.

Deterding then lured Standard into fighting for the Chinese market. He could bring kerosene from his Sumatran refineries to the Chinese ports much cheaper than Standard could haul its product from the United States, and in the long run Standard would be exhausted by the effort. The Chinese were not so sentimental about their Rockefeller-donated *Mei Foo* lamps that they wouldn't burn Shell kerosene in them if it was cheaper. Though he may have been still smarting over his own defeat at Deterding's hands, Marcus Samuel joined in the fray and proved a valuable ally. He took over the paraffin-wax sector, because that commodity was sold in vast quantities for making candles in the Orient. "Very much regret we have gone to war with the Standard Oil Co.," he wrote a Far Eastern representative, "and we shall need all our weapons if we are to fight them successfully. Can you let me know at what you estimate approximately the cost of our wax, both at Kutei and Sumatra? . . . It will be of a great importance to work all our plants to maximum capacity as part of our plan of campaign must consist of selling wax in markets where hitherto the Standard have had a monopoly."[6]

The effort of endlessly cutting prices to meet the constant challenges from Royal Dutch Shell was ruinous to Standard. It admitted defeat, allowed Deterding to share the Chinese market, and agreed to quit joggling the price structure.

Deterding later admitted the war against Standard had cost him at least $4 million but maintained it would have been worth many times that to bring Rockefeller to heel. "The American interests," he later wrote a little smugly, "discovered too late that they had let competitors grow whom they could no longer smash and immediately their policy was changed into making understandings, instead of high-handed competition."

Another lesson in humility was to follow.

6.

An Ailing Octopus

We had no other alternative but to expand, expand, expand.
— Henri Deterding

In the fourteen years from his retirement in 1896 to 1910, it was estimated that the personal fortune of John D. Rockefeller, Sr., more than quadrupled (to close to a billion dollars) because of the rising profits from gasoline and the thousands of automobiles being produced annually in the plants around Detroit. From all appearances, Standard Oil was as sound as the 1907 dollar. Rockefeller Senior had left the day-to-day operation of the company to his carefully selected brigade of vice-presidents, who combined bold enterprise with discretion; to his brother William, who was in charge of finances, and to his son, John D. Jr. He returned to the offices at 26 Broadway from his estates and golf courses only at long intervals.

What was known as the Rockefeller crowd had come into existence. Financially and socially, it was much more sportive than during the days of John D. Sr.'s direct control of Standard Oil. Wall Street's unofficial historian, Henry Clews, kept a close watch on the Rockefeller crowd and its venturesome activities from the beginning. With huge amounts of Standard capital at its disposal, the clique introduced into their stock-market operations "the same quiet, unostentatious and resist-less measures that they had always employed theretofore in the conduct of their corporate affairs." It struck with force and precision. It had command of such resources that its manipulations of the market took on the character of a general offensive rather than the "raids" and "corners" engineered by lesser and more vulnerable operators like Thomas Fortune Ryan and Jesse Livermore. "Their sources are so vast," Clews remarked, "that they need only concentrate on any given property in order to do with it what they please. They are the greatest operators the world has ever seen, and the beauty of their method is the quiet and lack of ostentation . . . With them the process is gradual, thorough and steady, with never a waver or break."[1]

A number of Rockefeller's top men lived double lives in their careers. While rendering unto Rockefeller the time and effort required to keep Standard running smoothly, they managed to enrich themselves by combining their enormous earnings from the corporation and throwing their weight around in the market. Thus at various times they captured large Mesabi iron-ore properties, Amalgamated Copper, various railroads, and public utility companies.

With individual fortunes piling up year after year, they had no reason to maneuver against each other or indulge in executive-suite power plays. If they were not exactly a band of brothers, they did work together without friction apparent to the outside world. The top men were roughly equal, but Henry D. Flagler was perhaps a little more equal than any of the others, who included Henry H. Rogers, John D. Archbold and William Rockefeller. It was noted that, particularly after the pious presence of John D. Sr. removed itself from the scene, his satraps behaved with more individuality and less inhibition; they were no longer the faceless men who executed the senior Rockefeller's orders to the letter.

The energetic Archbold was probably the most directly concerned with day-to-day command of the company's affairs. As the notorious affair of the Archbold letters showed, he was in charge of the lobbyists, of keeping Congress, state legislatures, and the judiciary in their place. And that was all-important, particularly the high tariff wall behind which Standard could keep out foreign competitors while maintaining high price levels for all oil products in the home markets.

William Rockefeller may have been more than slightly relieved when his brother withdrew from active direction of the company. He was John D.'s opposite, known as a "regular fella" at least among his peers. He drank his share of liquor, smoked cigars, told racy stories, and developed an affinity for racehorses. Through his friendship, James Stillman, president of the National City Bank of New York since 1891, became a member of the Rockefeller crowd. He and Stillman formed a close friendship after serving on a railroad's board of directors; the result was that Standard money poured into the National City Bank and increased its deposits from $12 million to $100 million. Both of Stillman's daughters married Rockefeller sons.

Of all his brother's hand-picked minions, William Rockefeller was closest to Henry H. Rogers, perhaps because of shared tastes in the clubman style and a mutual fascination with stock-market manipulation. Rogers was undoubtedly the most interesting of all of those human money-making machines because of his open enjoyment of his millions and his candor, as well as his moments of great generosity. "I am a gambler," he once said. "Every now and then John W. Gates will come to me and say, 'Henry, don't you think it's time we had a little fun in the market?' We made lots of killings and had plenty of fun. I must have action."[2] A handsome man with a love of story-telling, he made no secret of the fact that in his business life he was an unabashed freebooter who left ruined competitors and depleted fortunes in his wake. ("We are not in business for our health but are out for dollars.") In his

128

private life, he was remarkably sensitive, considering his public proclivities, to other people's misfortunes. Though many insisted that his initials stood for "Hell Hound" and that he suffered from a "cannibalistic money-hunger," he could be generous with his time and money in causes he respected. He paid for Helen Keller's education, helped support the Cooper Union, patronized the arts, and donated schools and other buildings to his hometown of Fairhaven, Massachusetts.

Rogers claimed at least a footnote in literary history by befriending Mark Twain when the writer had lost everything and went heavily into debt over his bullheaded determination to develop a typesetting machine and enter the ranks of those he claimed to despise, the plutocrats of the Gilded Age. After becoming Rogers' protégé, financially at least, Twain said of his benefactor, "He's a pirate all right, but he owns up to it and enjoys being a pirate." Rogers took over the personal management of Twain's financial affairs until the royalties on his books paid off his debts and Twain was in the clear again.

Since he was personally beholden to one of the Rockefeller crowd, the experience blunted Twain's tendency to decry great wealth. He was saved from financial ruin by a plutocrat and it would have been base ingratitude to continue attacking or satirizing the plutocracy. There was also an element of self-interest in Twain's mellowed attitude toward those who were buying up or stealing the country; he paid "the price of his becoming a provisional member of the plutocracy," as a recent biographer has noted, through a "demoralizing of purpose." As Twain himself once wrote, "You tell me whar a man gits his corn pone and I'll tell you what his opinions are." It should be added that Rogers helped Twain simply out of his admiration for the writer and out of compassion for his predicament, not as a deliberate means of disarming a critic. One writer, no matter how popular or influential, could do little more than stick barbs in the corporate hide of Standard Oil.[3]

The oldest of the senior Rockefeller's partners, Henry Flagler, was increasingly diverted from Standard Oil's problems by his subsidiary career as the patron secular saint of Florida. In addition to emulating Ponce de León, evidently discovering the Spanish explorer's fountain of youth, Flagler found time for sexual adventures that must have caused John D. Rockefeller, Sr., to shake his head sadly over the graham crackers and milk at his Pocantico Hills estate. Flagler went south on a vacation about the time John D. retired, and he fell in love with Florida's climate and scenery but was appalled by its lack of luxury hotels and dependable transportation. He immediately launched projects to convert Florida into another Riviera; built the Florida East Coast Railway and extended it over the swamps from Miami to Key West, put up hotels along the route, constructed schools, hospitals and churches (an approving nod from his senior partner), and sank $40 million into making Florida a vast winter resort.

His vitality undiminished by these projects, he decided that he needed a new wife to enhance his newly regained youth. His activities in the social world became so interesting that Colonel William D'Alton Mann — whose earlier and more scandalous connection with the oil industry has been related — stationed a special correspondent of his society scandal weekly, *Town Topics*, in Miami to keep an eye on Flagler's activities. Not surprisingly, Flagler's name was among those listed as contributing funds to Colonel Mann's enterprise, which was one way — the only way — to avoid being smeared in the *Town Topics* gossip columns. In 1901, however, Flagler could not escape widespread publicity when it was charged that through his influence the Florida legislature passed a law making insanity a cause for divorce. Flagler lent credence to the charges when he divorced his wife ten days after the legislation was enacted and promptly married a much younger woman. Some years later, an evidently still-virile seventy-one-year-old, Flagler was named corespondent in a divorce suit.

Thus, while it may have seemed that the Standard Oil machine was functioning smoothly, that it was still an unshakable monolith of American industry, it was equally evident that the higher echelon — Rogers and William Rockefeller with their outside interests, Flagler rejuvenating himself in Florida — was not entirely occupied in minding the store.

Just then Standard was under almost constant attack from one quarter or another. Having accumulated so much power, it would always be bound to defend itself from certain democratic processes with which it came into conflict and from the demagoguery of politicians looking for a handy outsize target. Standard's high command may have been confident that it could deal with such matters in the time-honored fashion, but on the judicial front at least, as a trust in everything but terminology, it was being seriously and repeatedly threatened. By mid-1907 the federal government was pushing seven different actions against Standard, the most serious being pressed in the U.S. Circuit Court of eastern Missouri, where it was demanded that the Standard group of companies be disbanded despite the legal fiction they already had been.

Bulldozer methods simply weren't working as well as they had in the glorious days of Pithole.

In Kansas, they came a head-over-heels cropper. It was a bad place for an industrial giant to shoulder aside would-be competitors, in the first place, because the state was aflame with populist sentiment and the curious corn-fed prairie brand of radicalism. Home-grown agitators were stomping up and down the state and telling farmers to "quit raising corn and start raising hell" about the railroads and other oppressive monopolies; the mere mention of Wall Street caused Kansans to brandish their pitchforks.

In 1903, wildcatters struck oil — part of the great mid-continent field which included Oklahoma — and Kansas was swarming with opportunists. Four thousand wells were drilled and production quadrupled in one year from a million barrels in 1903 to 4,250,000 barrels in 1904. Standard, the octopus of old, made its appearance as soon as the field showed great

131

promise. Its pipelines snaked along the prairie to its refineries, and competition was barred.

Standard behaved as though nothing had happened since 1859. Because of the tremendous production in Kansas, it ordained that daily output be limited to ten thousand even while the producers were pumping out thirty-five thousand barrels daily. The latter rejected all pleas to keep to a reasonable quota, and Standard responded by cutting the price from $1.30 a barrel for crude to 80 cents. A few interlopers tried to break the impasse. An independent refiner boldly set up shop in Humboldt, Kansas, but was frozen out when Standard let it be known that they wouldn't buy crude from anyone who sold to an independent. Across the line in Oklahoma Territory, Mike Benedum had begun developing another field even more promising than Kansas. There the Standard Oil Company disconnected its pipelines from producers who sold to an independent.

The Governor of Kansas, E. W. Hoch, was an oilman himself and helped to whip up the easily inflamed sentiment against Standard's monopolistic practices. At an indignation meeting held at Independence, a "new Declaration of Independence" was passed after Governor Hoch declared war on the "methods and business policies" of Standard Oil, thundering at the crowd, "In this contest we will put every dollar of our resources, every bit of our manhood and womanhood and every particle of governmental power and we will fight it out until victory shall finally crown our efforts. The eyes of the civilized world are on Kansas and I have been flooded with letters and congratulations. The heart of the Union is with us and President Roosevelt is with us heart and soul."[4]

Daniel O'Day, who was entering the first rank of Standard executives, countered with the observation that Kansas protests were "the old, old story" of a sudden glut in oil production. "As they get too much oil, they must expect the price to decline as in the case of an over-crop of corn or cotton, or any other commodity. When the prices decline, they naturally kick very hard."

Ida Tarbell came to address the Kansas oilmen as the Joan of Arc of the anti-Standard movement and to annihilate O'Day's explanation of how a free-market economy operated. "Stop sizzling," she advised the Kansans, recalling how little good "sizzling" had done in the Pennsylvania uprising against Standard Oil. "Play the game as well as Standard Oil plays it. Your problem is to get in touch with the world market. You cannot do this by cursing Standard Oil. Play the game with the energy with which Kansas men can play a game, but play it like gentlemen, that is with due regard for the rights of men, something the Standard has never done. Get down to business. The time you spend in talking in Independence, the Standard Oil Company spends in putting up one or more fifty-thousand-barrel tanks and laying ready for use ten or twenty miles of pipeline and refining tens of thousands of barrels of oil. It is keeping quiet and doing business."

One of the men who listened to Miss Tarbell expound, and who used her words as a primer to guide his own success as an independent, was a young oilman named Harry Sinclair, who had started out in the Kansas field. He grasped the reason why Standard reared back in alarm at overproduction. A glut was the worst thing that could happen to a monopoly.

The second worst thing — as had been proven elsewhere — was an enraged citizenry. The Kansas legislature apparently was not one of those in John D. Archbold's pocket; it began churning out laws to curb the Standard monopoly with a fervor that eastern newspapers regarded as near-socialistic. Laws were passed during its 1905 session declaring pipelines to be common carriers, placing them under the jurisdiction of the state railroad commission, and establishing equitable freight rates on refined oil transported out of the state by railroad. The refinery at Humboldt was enabled to reopen and compete on equal terms with Standard. In its enthusiasm for booting

Standard wherever it hurt the most, the state legislature, advised by the state's attorney general that it could not go into the refining business itself, decided to build a new $100,000 penitentiary — with a kerosene refining plant attached. Convict labor would operate the plant. Before the project could be started, however, the courts ruled it was unconstitutional. In any case, it was unnecessary. In 1906 Congress passed the Hepburn bill controlling the rate schedules of the pipelines. The bill was stalled in the Senate, which was packed with Rockefeller sympathizers, until President Theodore Roosevelt released a Corporation Bureau report along with his own hard-bitten summary: "Standard Oil has benefited almost up to the present moment by secret rates, many of these secret rates being clearly unlawful."

Standard was being harried in courts throughout the country for various violations of state and federal laws. In Indiana it was indicted on charges of accepting freight rebates. In Texas a local oil firm was "unmasked" as a dummy for Standard and criminal indictments were handed down against Rockefeller and his associates. There were suits against Standard in a half-dozen other states.

John D. personally was made aware of the rising legal pressure against his complex of companies when he and members of his family, accompanied by a physician, sailed for Europe to see one of his daughters. She had suffered a mental or nervous breakdown. The daughter of the world's richest man, with an irony no dramatist would dare to invent, was afflicted by the delusion that she would die in poverty. The newspapers, however, reported he was fleeing the country to avoid testifying before the Interstate Commerce Commission. Shortly after he reached Compiègne, France, he was indicted along with several directors of Standard Oil of Ohio, for violating the state's antitrust act. He was forced to return to the United States after a few days with his ailing daughter to answer the summons from Ohio. "I never despair," he told a newspaperman, though he was close to seventy and the peace of mind he sought in retirement was more elusive than ever. "Sometimes things that are said of me are cruel and they hurt, but I am never a pessimist. I believe in man and the brotherhood of man . . ." He had to spend the winter in Cleveland while the legal maneuvers proceeded, and returned east in the spring with the case still pending, not without memory of how whenever he made an appearance in public ugly crowds gathered in the city where he had started making his fortune.[5]

The whole country seemed to be rising up against Standard Oil. President Roosevelt, in one of his big-stick moods, had made it clear that he hated trusts and Standard Oil more than any of the others. One legal action brought against Standard by the U.S. Attorney General, which the railroad magnate R. H. Harriman later claimed was the cause of the depression of 1907 because it shook the confidence of business, resulted in the most spectacular penalty thus far levied against a corporation in legal history.

It seemed a rather minor matter to the Standard executives at 26 Broadway when it first came to their attention. The case involved rebates which the government charged that the Chicago & Alton Railroad made to Standard.

Perhaps it would have gone on and on, endlessly delayed by Standard's high-priced lawyers, until the government gave up in disgust or a federal court administered the usual slap on the wrist. This case, however, had come under the purview of a man of restless ambition, of a theatrical personality. He was Federal Judge Kenesaw Mountain Landis, named for the Civil War battlefield, a christening he aimed to live up to. Judge Landis made himself famous for presiding over the case, and his lean features, his thin pursed mouth, and piercing eyes, giving him the appearance of a Torquemada, became the delight of photographers and sketch artists. The reputation he won in the Chicago courtroom was responsible some years later, after the Chicago Black Sox scandal, for his appointment as the first commissioner of baseball.

President William Howard Taft, Roosevelt's successor, was

so distressed by Landis' weakness for dramatic gestures that he remarked that "he is too much of an actor and too much occupied with how he appears in public to be a good judge." There was little doubt that Landis determinedly played to the gallery, mindful of how much anti-Rockefeller sentiment had been aroused in the country. The government prosecutor asked that John D. Rockefeller, Sr., not be summoned as a witness because his testimony might give him immunity in the federal antitrust action (under the Sherman Act) being pursued in other courts. Judge Landis demurred. On July 7, 1907, the senior Rockefeller was summoned to the witness stand. His testimony was so vague that it was of little value to either side. When the prosecution asked him for details of Standard Oil of New Jersey's operation, he faltered: "They have a refinery and they refine oil. That was the . . . yes . . . it would be impossible for me to give . . . to make an answer to that question intelligently without a study of the case."

Actually the government had a rather weak case against Standard on this occasion. It rested on the claim that the railroad charged Standard less on 1,462 separate shipments from Whiting, near Chicago, to East St. Louis, Illinois, than it reported to the Interstate Commerce Commission. Judge Landis excluded any evidence offered by the defense that no competitor was injured by the rebate.

After laborious weeks of testimony, the jury brought in a guilty verdict, to the visible satisfaction of the presiding judge. He then tore into Standard Oil with a tigerish but injudicious fury, and demanded that counsel for the defendant produce a statement of its net profits for 1903, 1904 and 1905. On August 13, 1907, after raking Standard Oil fore and aft, he announced his verdict: the company would be fined $20,000 for each of 1,462 instances in which it was charged with having received a rebate. The total, hitherto unheard-of fine was $29,240,000.[6]

Even more infuriating to Standard Oil was Judge Landis' statement that the company was no better than counterfeiters or people who stole from the U.S. mails. For the moment, however, Judge Landis could bask in the general approbation of the newspapers, although the Brooklyn *Eagle* dissented in an editorial declaring that "No theory of law or justice sustains such a thumping penalty."

Standard was convinced that it had been the victim of a publicity-minded judge and was determined to fight back with every weapon at its disposal. "Landis," Rockefeller was quoted as saying, "will be dead a long time before the fine is paid."

The octopus obviously was ailing when anyone dared to attack it so openly and with so much general approval. For the first time, in an effort to reverse an unfavorable public opinion, Standard decided it needed the services of a public relations expert. It was a new field of endeavor; Madison Avenue had not yet erected its glassbox temples to the new priesthood, and the only corporation with a publicity man was the Pennsylvania Railroad, which had engaged Ivy Lee for that purpose only the year before.

Standard hired itself a colorful Irishman named Joseph I. C. Clarke to change the public's mind about the corporation and its activities. On entering 26 Broadway the first time, Clarke found that the only indication the company was aware of public opinion was a tiny office in which a boy pasted clippings into scrapbooks. Clarke set about his task of opinion-molding with vigor. He had learned how to handle the vagaries of the rich and powerful as a reporter and editor on the New York *Herald*, which was published by the lordly and irascible James Gordon Bennett, Jr. His first assignment on the *Herald* was covering an outing given for the Grand Duke Alexis of Russia on Governor's Island. With a Celtic imp apparently sitting on his shoulder, Clarke wrote an irreverent account of how only the Duke and the wealthier guests were provided with carriages, ending with the couplet:

> *Them that's rich can ride in chaises;*
> *But them that's poor must walk, be Jasus.*[7]

137

After living that down, Clarke became an editorial writer and managing editor of the *Herald*. He secretly nourished literary ambitions, however, which conflicted with Bennett's dictum that his employees must devote every ounce of creative energy to their work for the newspaper. Clarke defied him, wrote a play titled *Prince of India*, and was greatly offended when the publisher ordered the drama editor to ignore it when it was produced on Broadway. Clarke quit the *Herald* and went over to Standard with his considerable talents.

Shortly after he took over from the office boy, huge packing cases of publicity releases written by Clarke in defense of the company's position in the Chicago & Alton case, as well as other adverse legal proceedings, were sent out from the headquarters at 26 Broadway, not only to newspapers throughout the country but to schools and Standard agents everywhere for general distribution. Clarke had made many friends on Park Row during his years with the *Herald* and soon articles friendly to Rockefeller and Standard — including such Sunday magazine spreads as "How the World's Richest Man Spends Christmas" — began to appear even in the formerly hostile columns of Pulitzer's *World* and Hearst's *American* and *Journal*. A few thousand dollars listed on Clarke's expense accounts as having been spent over the Park Row bars did wonders for the journalistic portrayal of his employers.

The fact that the stock market suffered a disastrous decline just one week after the Landis decision, with a consequent spell of unemployment, shook the prevailing faith that trust-busting was the answer to all the nation's problems. One who was unshaken was President Roosevelt, who blamed the panic of 1907 on "malefactors of great wealth," but many believed it was time to go easy on the great corporations. Eventually the U.S. Circuit Court of Appeals dealt with what many considered a "confiscatory" fine against Standard. The appellate court not only reversed the previous decision but severely criticized Judge Landis for fining Standard on the basis of each rebated shipment and labeled the size of the fine "an abuse of judicial discretion."

Just about the time Rockefeller and his associates were jubilating over the appellate court's reversal (in August 1908), a far more serious matter than a $29,240,000 fine was about to arise with effects that even the genial and skillful Joe Clarke couldn't contain. This was the affair of the Archbold letters. If anyone thought that the American capitalist system was a gigantic conspiracy, they could ponder the fact that the nation's leading newspaper magnate, William Randolph Hearst, whose family fortune had been made in gold mining, was gleefully taking on the nation's most powerful industrial combine. A multimillionaire with a muckrake was a picture to confound the most ardent Marxist.

And the gilded muckraker, William Randolph Hearst, had found himself a rich compost pile of corporate and political scandal to expose. Though largely forgotten now, it was actually a riper bit of infamy than either the Credit Mobilier which preceded it or the Teapot Dome case which followed it.

The affair was uncovered largely as a result of Archbold's astonishing carelessness in handling company documents. Standard's vice-president employed a Negro butler, James Wilkins, at his Tarrytown mansion. Wilkins had served him faithfully for twenty years. At Wilkins' request Archbold found a messenger job downtown for the butler's twenty-four-year-old stepson Willie Winkfield, who unknown to his stepfather or his employer had a weakness for betting on losing horses. In 1904, Winkfield found himself heavily indebted to the bookies. In desperation, he conceived a money-raising idea. As a trusted employee, in and out of Archbold's office all the time, he noticed that his employer kept important-looking letters and cables on his desk and in unlocked filing cabinets. The information contained in those messages might be valuable to Archbold's enemies, particularly at a time when

Standard was under attack from all quarters. Willie Winkfield decided to go into business for himself, but decided he would need the cooperation of a white youth named Charles Stump, nineteen years old, who was employed as a night porter in the building and who admitted he could use a supplemental income.

As a sample of what they could provide the circulation-hungry newspapers on Park Row, Winkfield and Stump filched a telegram and two letters from Archbold's desk one day and took them to the New York *World*, an editor of which said he wasn't interested in stolen property, and then over to Hearst's *American*, where the managing editor, Fred Eldredge, was not so finicky. Eldredge gave the two young men a list of two hundred men whose correspondence with Archbold might be of interest to the Hearst papers.

For three months Archbold's files were systematically looted for damaging information. Almost every night Winkfield and Stump took a batch of letters and telegrams from 26 Broadway to the *American* offices, where they were photographed, then immediately returned to the files. The night work paid off handsomely, about $20,000, with which the two culprits opened a saloon at Seventh Avenue and 134th Street. Hearst was even more pleased with the transaction. He had acquired explosive evidence of how Standard, with Archbold as wire-puller and paymaster, had arranged much legislation favorable to the oil trust. Standard checks for years had been paid to U.S. senators and representatives, state and other public officials, as the correspondence clearly showed.

Hearst decided to sit on his photographed evidence until what he judged to be an opportune time. Archbold meanwhile had somehow learned that his files had been tampered with, and waited with ulcerous anxiety for the fire storm of revelation. Several years went by, with Hearst sitting on his nest of dynamite, until the presidential campaign of 1908 in which he had decided to foist his own man on the electorate. William Jennings Bryan, as usual, would run as the Democratic candidate. The Republican nomination was contested by William Howard Taft, Roosevelt's choice for his successor, and Senator Joseph B. Foraker of Ohio. The nomination went to Taft. Then Hearst announced that his Independence League would field its own third-party candidate, one Thomas Hisgen of Massachusetts, whose axle-grease firm had barely survived a price-cutting war with Standard that followed his refusal to sell the company to Standard.

Hearst campaigned more vigorously for Hisgen than Hisgen did for himself, possibly because he thought a respectable showing in the 1908 campaign would give the Independence League candidate four years hence (just maybe Hearst himself) a fair chance of winning. During his tour of the Midwest in mid-September, Hearst was enraged by charges from both the major parties that he was a "traitor" who had jumped from one to the other, and finally into his own bandwagon, to further his personal ambitions.

On the night of September 17, 1908, in Columbus, Ohio, Hearst decided to open his Pandora's box of photographs and call down a plague on both the other parties. With a brief preamble that he was going to read a series of letters connecting this "giant of corruption, Standard Oil" with corruption of both Democratic and Republican leaders, he let fly with a segment of the Archbold letters. In a hushed Memorial Hall, he read letters from Archbold to Senator Foraker and Mark Hanna, the Republican boss of Ohio, directing them to work for certain legislation and against other proposed laws. Several notes referred to the enclosure of $15,000 certificates of deposit to Senator Foraker; in the first four months of 1900 alone that leading member of the U.S. Senate's "gentleman's club" received $30,000 from Standard Oil. Another letter Hearst read was from Republican Congressman Joseph C. Sibley of Pennsylvania to Archbold, which ended "For the first time I told the President [Roosevelt] some plain if unpalatable truths as to the situation politically, and that no man should win who depended upon the rabble rather than upon the conservative men of affairs . . . Anything you may desire here in my power please advise . . ."

Next morning the Archbold letters were headlined throughout the country, and that was only the beginning of the Hearst revelations. Panic at 26 Broadway. Archbold, unwisely, denied everything. Senator Foraker, more sensibly, admitted to corresponding with Standard officials but maintained all references to legislation and payment dated back to his pre-senatorial law practice. "That I was employed as counsel for the Standard Oil Company at the time and presumably compensated for my services was common knowledge." Hearst shot down that alibi in his next speech at St. Louis when he read two letters from Archbold to Foraker. One specifically referred to Foraker's opposition to an amendment to the Sherman Antitrust Act which Standard wanted to be killed in the Senate. Another mentioned the fact that Archbold had sent Foraker $50,000 "in accordance with our understanding." And just when the Democrats began to gloat over the mud which had spattered the Republicans, Hearst continued his public readings in Memphis, Denver, El Paso, Los Angeles, New York, and linked Senator Joseph Bailey of Texas, a Democrat, to the Standard clique in Congress. Governor C. N. Haskell of Oklahoma, treasurer of the Democratic National Committee, was similarly smeared and forced to resign. Other eminent political names were revealed to have been on the Rockefeller payroll during Hearst's stumping for his all-but-forgotten candidate and for several years afterward when his papers' circulation needed a boost. They included Mark Hanna, who had made McKinley President in 1898; Senators Platt and Depew of New York, Senators Penrose and Quay of Pennsylvania. Some senators did not have to be seduced, but had applied directly for their welfare checks. Senator John L. McLaurin of South Carolina to John D. Archbold, in May 1902: "I can beat Tillman if properly and generously supplied. There is no time to lose, however."[8]

Thus the national campaign of 1908 was heavily tainted by

oil money. Theodore Roosevelt was furious with Rockefeller for announcing near the end of the campaign that he was backing Taft. "It is a perfectly palpable and obvious trick," declared the President, "to damage Taft. It is a cheap trick intended to aid Bryan." Taft, however, was elected despite Rockefeller's support. Senators Foraker and Bailey and Representative Sibley were driven from public life. Hearst's Independence League, despite all his efforts, never got off the ground. Archbold's career prospered despite his carelessness with delicate correspondence and he was promoted to president of Standard Oil of New Jersey. The greatest damage was done not to any of the culpable parties involved, but to the confidence of the electorate in the honesty of their representatives. There was a fascinating footnote to the affair in the fact that one of Senator Foraker's few defenders in Ohio was the publisher of a small-town newspaper, Warren G. Harding, who a dozen years later would preside over a notably oil-smeared administration.

There were larger cracks in the foundation at 26 Broadway than the publication of Archbold's correspondence indicated. One was the continuing campaign of the federal government to break up its New Jersey–based trust arrangement. This campaign had started midway through the Roosevelt Administration when the U.S. Attorney General filed a bill of equity in the federal court at St. Louis asking that Standard Oil be broken up under the provisions of the Sherman Act. As special counsel the government engaged an able and aggressive lawyer named Frank B. Kellogg, who would serve as Secretary of State under Coolidge, to build its case for dissolution. Against him Standard arrayed so many high-priced lawyers that cynics observed that the legal profession itself had struck oil at last.

All through 1908, Kellogg stuck doggedly to his task of proving that Standard hadn't been dissolved under the terms of the Sherman Act but had reconstituted itself, through legal artifice, under the shelter of the New Jersey laws. Four hundred witnesses were called and their testimony filled twelve volumes totaling twenty thousand pages. There was nothing startlingly new developed in all that testimony, but a mountain of facts was constructed to show that Standard Oil of New Jersey, the holding company, controlled sixty-five corporations; that it exercised a virtual monopoly over the petroleum industry; that it indulged in "rebates, preferences, and other discriminatory practices"; and that its tactics against competitors constituted restraint of trade.

The senior Rockefeller himself was summoned as a witness. Under examination by his chief counsel, John G. Milburn, his testimony was crisp and well ordered. The impression he gave regarding rebates, which were still the most effective of monopolistic devices because they crippled the competition, was that they were foisted on Standard Oil by the railroads. The New York *World*, commenting on that revelation, said the Rockefeller definition of a rebate was "a voluntary compensation paid by the railroads for ample services rendered at a great disadvantage to the beneficiary of the rebate."[9]

Under cross-examination by Kellogg, Rockefeller seemed to suffer extensive lapses of memory but he did produce one moment of humor in the droning proceedings. Kellogg asked him what dividends Standard had paid the previous year, and Rockefeller replied that they totaled $40 million. No, Kellogg corrected him, the total was $39 million. "One less million for poor old Standard," said Rockefeller wryly.

The court handed down its decision November 20, 1909, ruling against Standard, finding it in violation of the antitrust act as a "combination in restraint of trade," and ordering the dissolution of New Jersey Standard as a holding company.

Standard appealed to the U.S. Supreme Court, still confident it would prevail. The White House, however, was still an enemy citadel. The new President, William Howard Taft, ordered Attorney General George Wickersham to press the government's case with all possible vigor.

On May 15, 1911, after delays occasioned by the death of

an associate justice and the necessity of rearguing the case, the Supreme Court handed down its verdict. It upheld the lower court. Standard was given thirty days to dissolve.

The majority opinion written by Chief Justice Edward D. White was a definitive, if cumbersomely worded summation of the American people's case against Rockefeller and his works. "We think no disinterested mind can survey the period in question without being irresistibly driven to the conclusion that the very genius for commercial development and organization which it would seem was manifested from the begining soon begot an intent and purpose to exclude others which was frequently manifested by acts and dealings wholly inconsistent with the theory that they were made with the single conception of advancing the developing of business power by usual methods, but which, on the contrary, necessarily involved the intent to drive others from the field and to exclude them from their right to trade, and thus accomplish the mastery which was the end in view . . .

"The exercise of the power which resulted from that organization fortifies the foregoing conclusions, since the development which came, the acquisition here and there which ensued of every efficient means by which competition could have been asserted, the slow but resistless methods which followed by which means of transportation were absorbed and brought under control, the system of marketing which was adopted by which the country was divided into districts and the trade in each district in oil was turned over to a designated corporation within the combination, and all others were excluded, all lead the mind up to a conviction of a purpose and intent which we think is so certain as practically to cause the subject not to be within the domain of reasonable contention . . ."

There was one eloquent dissent to the verdict, which raised the question of "judicial legislation," an interpretation of the high court's powers which echoes even more loudly today. The aging Justice Harlan of Kentucky believed that the Supreme

Court was exceeding its constitutional powers. He had championed the Sherman Act from the beginning, but asserted that there was danger in the majority opinion that there must be evidence of "an undue restraint," an "unreasonable restraint." In its ruling on the Standard Oil appeal, Justice Harlan declared, the court's majority was inserting "words in the antitrust act which Congress did not put there." That crevice of "undue" and "unreasonable" restraint of trade, in fact, proved most helpful to U.S. Steel and other giant corporations — but it could not benefit Standard Oil in its present difficulties.

Standard was broken up into its component parts, though no one can say that it collectively or separately endured much financial suffering. Standard Oil of New Jersey, or Esso, is still the largest oil company in the world; Mobil, formerly Standard Oil of New York, is third largest; Standard of California, Standard of Indiana, and Continental are all in the top ten.

Just as it was suffering these setbacks, Standard was confronted by foreign competition in the domestic market for gasoline. Until a few years before, gasoline had been burned off in the distillation process as a waste product; now it was all-important. Henry Ford was turning out thousands of Model T's; by 1909 the annual gasoline consumption in the British Isles was 40 million gallons, and by 1912 there were more than a million cars on the American roads. The greatest opportunity for expansion had arrived with Standard, an octopus with severed tentacles, in poor shape to meet the competition with its formerly all-conquering methods.

The competition was lustily embodied by Henri Deterding, who was proving himself more than a match for the aging high command at 26 Broadway. He was not to be underestimated merely because his personality had some of the overtones of "those *bon viveurs* whose glorious mistresses were painted by Rubens," because he was not one of those somber

146

burghers whom Rockefeller himself more closely resembled. "Certainly," an oil historian has written, "he shared that artist's [Rubens] enthusiasm for beautiful and voluptuous women. His amours were famous throughout the capitals of Europe, and he sometimes rewarded his favourites with an impetuosity and generosity that outran even his ample financial resources."[10]

Deterding in pursuit of a woman was a man obsessed. He gave Lydia Pavlovna, then the wife of a Russian general but later his own for a time, a $1.5 million emerald-encrusted trinket from Cartier's only to learn that he didn't have enough money to pay for it. The jewelers waited a few months for payment until he received his director's fees from Royal Dutch Shell. His tastes were sybaritic, but he was no Edwardian playboy. His working day began with a plunge into the cold water of a swimming pool before breakfast and often continued until midnight; one of his collaborators once heard him say, "If I were a dictator I would shoot every idle man." The search for and disposal of oil was "more a recreation than a business" to him; "it is a kind of sport," which was equally as engrossing as chasing a woman or buying a new country house.

If gasoline was a best-selling product in America and Britain, he would go after those markets with a ruthless and ingenious determination to come out on top.

During his Chinese rate war with Standard, he had already served notice that he would not hesitate to invade the American market. His ploy on that occasion was so deft and sure-handed that it left Standard's executives with their mouths hanging open. Deterding had sent several tankers loaded with gasoline to Germany, where the market price suddenly dropped. He ordered them to turn around and head across the Atlantic. With the collaboration of the Dutch Minister of the Colonies, he had succeeded in having the import duty on gasoline shipped into the Dutch East Indies abolished; under the terms of the McKinley tariff that meant a Dutch company, reciprocally, could send its products to the United States duty free. His tankers thus sailed past the Statue of Liberty and dumped their gasoline on the American market at a competitive price.

The Standard high command recovered itself eventually and viewed with alarm the implications of Deterding's cheeky invasion of the domestic market. More serious inroads might be made in the future. Standard's London representative was instructed to call upon Deterding and demand to know what his intentions were.

"I intend to ship oil wherever it pays me best to do so," he bluntly replied, adding with a sardonic smile, "Now surely *you* won't blame me for that."[11]

He waited for several years before battering his way further into Standard's home territory. By then he had devised a way of offsetting Standard's natural advantages and long successful strategy. Standard had been so unassailable because of its huge American reserves, the refined products of which it could ship anywhere in the world. Deterding decided to counter with a strategy of encirclement. Shell had no oil at its home bases, London and The Hague, so it became his policy to develop oilfields as close as possible to his potential markets, thus cutting the costs of transportation and giving him more flexibility in operating against the fixed position of Standard Oil.

Between 1911 and 1913, Deterding not only invaded the American market with Shell products, particularly gasoline, but bought up his own sources of supply in the United States. Deterding's biographer speculates that his cause may have been aided by the banking house of J. Pierpont Morgan, who was hostile to the Rockefellers. "The House of Morgan, then as now, was closely allied with England and her policy." A few years hence Britain's war effort would have foundered without the huge loans floated by the Morgan bank in the United States. "Personal ties bound John Pierpont Morgan the Elder with England, just as his even more influential son is today [1938] friendly with everyone of the highest standing in England — the King himself, the Archbishop of Canterbury, the Prime Minister and the Governor of the Bank of England. Did the mechanism of Morgan assist 'British' oil interests in their penetration of the territory of their outstanding commercial rival? It is not easy to say whether such assistance was given as far back as 1911–1912, but there is no doubt that it has been given since."[12] Even without the secret help of the Morgan bank, Deterding was powerfully financed and politically protected by his Anglo-Dutch combination and had the collaboration of the Paris branch of the Rothschild family.

His policy in regard to Standard combined the aggressive with the conciliatory, and had been successfully tested elsewhere. He would use the tactics of a battering ram, if necessary, to obtain his share of the desired market; but once in he would work for cooperation rather than cutthroat competition with his rivals. His philosophy was that in oil there was enough loot for everyone — almost everyone — and the game would be ruined only if someone got too greedy. Looking back in his sere and memoir-writing days on the American invasion, he wrote, "To compete successfully in price, a big trader in oil must obviously have the right entry into all the world's markets. This fact is now freely recognized by most American traders, whatever may have been their attitude toward overseas competitors in bygone years. At the same time, it must be remembered that if too many try to do this, regardless of competitors, there is created an enormous duplication of facilities and terrible overheads . . . there *must* be cooperation."[13] Cooperation, that is, against newcomers. It is probably significant that Deterding always referred to himself as a "trader" in the old Dutch sense, suggesting a flexible and quick-moving style, rather than adopting the attitude and outlook of a magnate, a tycoon, a captain of industry.

The success of his technique is visible on thousands of American street corners where the Shell emblem is as familiar and equally acceptable as any American brand of gasoline. But it wasn't proven out without a struggle. Deterding had to enter through the back door — California — first by shipping gasoline from the Dutch East Indies in his group's tanker fleet. Standard reacted by cutting its price from 18 to 10 cents a gallon in California. Shell obviously couldn't survive such resistance with gasoline refined in the distant Indies and shipped all the way across the Pacific. Producing fields would have to be secured close to the market.

The cloak, if not the dagger, was Deterding's next resort. In the summer of 1913, his California agents learned that the Coalinga field, largely unproven, was up for sale. Standard would naturally try to buy it, to keep it out of Shell's clutches, if Deterding didn't move fast. He got a week's option on the property. Meanwhile, from Holland, he had dispatched a mining engineer named B. H. van der Linden to California to scout for oil-bearing land. Using the alias of G. Warner in hopes that no one would suspect him of being a Dutchman and therefore a Shell operative, van der Linden hastened to Coalinga even as the Standard manager of a nearby oilfield was asking the manager of the Coalinga field, "Have you seen some Dutch fellow who is supposed to be snooping around here?"

Van der Linden had only a few days to determine whether Coalinga's potential was worth millions. There was no geological survey to guide him. He had to make his own two-day appraisal on the spot, concluding, more as a guess than a scientific estimate, that the field would produce 4 million barrels a year for at least ten years. The engineer's five-page report was cabled to Deterding in London. He didn't have time to consult his board of directors and decided to gamble on the accuracy of van der Linden's report. Just before the option expired — all of this done in six days — he bought the highly productive Coalinga field for $3 million in cash and $10 million in Royal Dutch Shell stock. Quickly adding a pipeline and a refinery at Martinez to his California property, Deterding soon was producing his own gasoline. In the next year or two a Shell subsidiary also bought up oilfields in Oklahoma and Illinois. It was here to stay.[14]

Shell obviously had succeeded in its venture at the strategic moment when Standard was off guard, preoccupied with its internal difficulties. It would be almost sixty years before another foreign invader, wholly British this time, ventured to make the same move. In 1968 British Petroleum, after a decade of plotting and planning and maneuvering, entered the American market. Once known as Anglo-Persian, British Petroleum hopes to sell gasoline in the United States through a complicated deal by which (with Justice Department approval) it would acquire a Sinclair refinery in Pennsylvania, an Atlantic Richfield refinery in Texas, and a chain of fifty-six hundred Sinclair filling stations in the eleven eastern states. The deal would involve $300 million — an indication of how big and complex the oil industry has become since Deterding, with only $3 million, accomplished the same maneuver in less than a week's time.[15]

7.

Oil as the Aztecs' Revenge

It's got the Klondike faded . . . we're taking out $90,000 a day in gold from a mere eight-inch hole in the ground.
— Oilman quoted by Jack London

Just how acutely the quest for oil could affect, and warp, international relations was strikingly demonstrated early in 1914 at the Mexican oil port of Tampico. Within the year the First World War would break out, and the survival of the British Empire would depend on the moral, financial and eventually the military support of the United States. It did not take a seer to foresee that war was coming or that American participation might tip the balance; every great European nation had been preparing for the showdown for years. Yet oil had a way of distorting values, whether viewed from Whitehall or Pennsylvania Avenue, and of twisting national interests out of shape.

The incident that illuminated this curious distortion occurred when revolutionary mobs, enraged by a turn of events that favored the American policy of the moment, besieged the resident Americans, mostly oilmen, in their hotels. It looked for hours as though the hotels would be stormed and the Americans lynched, the forces which had been in control of Tampico having been driven out by another revolutionary army. The American flag was torn down and spat upon. Out in the oil-streaked harbor there were a number of warships, English, Dutch and German, but no American naval presence. The captain of the German warship called a conference with the Dutch and English captains and proposed that they all send shore parties in to protect American citizens. His suggestion was refused. Undoubtedly acting on instructions from their capitals, the British and Dutch were prepared to let the Americans be mobbed. They were pawns in a war that had been going on for years, and the British and Dutch destroyers, in effect, were flying the house flags of their oil companies. The war for Tampico oil superseded all other considerations.

A mild-mannered little Irish-American, whose vague and gentle demeanor concealed a chromium-plated will to succeed, was largely responsible for turning that section of fever swamp around Tampico, in the southern part of the Mexican state of Tamaulipas, into a forest of derricks and eventually a battle ground.

Edward L. Doheny was a product of the western frontier from his rundown boot heels to the tin star he had once worn as chief vigilante of Kingston, New Mexico. Born in Wisconsin, he had drifted out west like so many of his post–Civil War generation. Mostly he was a prospector, first for gold in the Black Hills, then for silver in New Mexico, and finally for oil in California and Mexico. It was a long dusty road that Doheny traveled. When he went broke looking for silver or gold, he would take a town job, as a surveyor in Atchison, Kansas, as a horse-buyer in the Indian Territory. His luck began to turn when he teamed up with a Minnesotan named Charlie Canfield, also in his middle or late twenties, and they began working a silver claim near Kingston.

First, however, Doheny made a name for himself as the

153

local upholder of law and order. He was teaching school in the New Mexican mining camp while he and Canfield saved up for a grubstake. Kingston then was ruled by gunmen, rustlers and outlaws. A vigilance committee was formed, and the meek-looking little Doheny was appointed its head. The local riffraff soon learned that he had the guts of a mountain lion. They warned him to get out of town or he would be killed. Doheny stayed. One afternoon a rustler celebrated for his marksmanship opened fire on Doheny, who did not even bother to draw his gun but sauntered across the street and arrested his would-be assassin. Not that Doheny had any qualms about shooting a man. A short time later a drunk blazed away at him with a revolver. Doheny drew and shot the tippler in the leg with one carefully aimed bullet. That display of cold nerve was witnessed by a miner named Albert B. Fall, and was the beginning of a long friendship between the two men. Again the freakish element intrudes: many years later Fall was Secretary of the Interior in the Harding Administration and with Doheny was a principal figure in the Teapot Dome scandal.

After turning in his chief vigilante's badge, Doheny with his partner Canfield began working a claim Doheny had staked near Kingston. They struck a profitable vein of silver, sold the claim for about $100,000 each, then parted company for a time, Canfield returning to his family in California and prospecting for gold in the Mojave Desert while Doheny spent his share looking for another silver mine.[1]

Years later, both broke, they got together again in Los Angeles shortly after Lyman Stewart brought up a gusher in Ventura County just north of the city. That was the beginning of the Union Oil Company. Doheny was driving a barrel cart for an oil company to keep himself alive, and some of the product he was transporting must have seeped into his consciousness. Maybe black gold was more profitable than the yellow variety. He noticed wagons hauling chunks of tar on the streets of Los Angeles and decided to investigate. The tar was dug from the La Brea pits, a black reeking bog full of the bones of prehistoric mammals. The Indians had used it to waterproof their baskets, the Spanish to build the roofs of their adobe huts. Now ice companies were digging the tar and burning it as fuel in their plants.

Tar . . . oil . . . was there a connection? It seemed to Doheny those tar pits must be feeding from a subterranean pool. The oil thickened and became tar. On fire with his idea, Doheny looked up Canfield at his Mojave diggings and persuaded him to resume the old partnership. They had only enough money between them to buy a small lot out at the tar pits. Neither had ever seen an oil well. So they became oil miners. With pick and shovel they began sinking a shaft on the perpendicular, four by six feet, instead of driving a well. At the 165-foot level they poked their way through a layer of rock and struck a pocket of oil. Their first well produced seven barrels a day. It wasn't much but it financed other Doheny-Canfield ventures; they now had enough money to buy a drilling rig.

While Doheny kept production flowing at their La Brea wells — a mere trickle compared to that in the eastern oilfields in 1887 — Canfield ventured northward and began drilling in the Coalinga foothills 120 miles north of Los Angeles. One well produced three hundred barrels a day. He and Doheny then began scouting various locations throughout the state, using a state geological survey as their guide. Wherever "seepages" had been noted they investigated and sometimes drove wells. Thus they developed the Brea-Olinda field in Brea Canyon; eventually it yielded more than 300 million barrels. Enthusiastic as they were about the state's oil prospects, even Doheny and Canfield didn't realize that below the shallow wells they drilled were deeper "mother" pools worth billions of dollars.

By 1900 they were respected, if not top-drawer, businessmen who had increased California's oil production a thousand percent in the past dozen years. Their greatest problem was marketing the oil. California crude was heavy, and asphalt-laden, with only a small kerosene content. Doheny and Canfield had to develop their own market. They persuaded sugar refineries and other industries to use it for fuel, and the southern California cities to pave their streets with asphalt. The Santa Fe Railroad also became a good customer when Lyman Stewart, their fellow pioneer, invented an oil-burning engine for its locomotives. A contract was signed with the railroad for all the oil they could produce at $1 a barrel. They produced so much the Santa Fe was swamped and had to settle the contract by buying some of the Doheny-Canfield oil properties.

The amiability of their relations with Santa Fe indirectly resulted in their greatest venture, the long and arduous exploration for Mexican oil. A. A. Robinson, a Santa Fe executive, assumed the presidency of the Mexican Central Railroad. From his Santa Fe experience, Robinson knew how much cheaper and more convenient it would be to run his Mexican engines on fuel oil. Late in 1900 he invited Doheny and Canfield to explore southern Mexico, though only a few years before Cecil Rhodes, the South African empire-builder, had spent half a million dollars in southern Tamaulipas looking for oil; so had a successor British company, which abandoned the effort after an eminent geologist made a survey and reported that oil would never be found in quantity in Mexico.

Doheny and Canfield had their own misgivings as they rolled down toward the port of Tampico in the private car arranged by Robinson. From the central mesa the railroad plunged down steep grades through the tropical rain forests near the Gulf Coast. It was a jungle, beautiful to the sightseer with its waterfalls and other spectacular views, disheartening to an oil prospector who had to think in terms of labor, equipment, pipelines, refineries. As literate men, they may have pondered the judgment of the German geographer Humboldt a century earlier: "Mexico is a beggar sitting on a bag of gold." Gold had already brought conquerers to Mexico — but oil would be the Aztecs' revenge.

156

From Tampico Doheny and Canfield, unlikely successors to Cortez, set out with guides and a burro train into the swampy lowlands. For days they slashed through the jungle growth, swinging their machetes in the damp heat and followed by swarms of insects. It was the worst place in the world to look for oil, they assured each other. Finally one day they came to a hillock in a clearing and found oil bubbling out of a spring. Hardships were instantly forgotten. "The sight," Doheny wrote later, "caused us to forget all about the dreaded climate, its hot humid atmosphere, its apparently incessant rains, those jungle pests the *garrapatas* [sheep ticks], the dense forest jungle which seems to grow up as fast as cut down, its great distance from any center that we could call civilization and still greater distance from a source of supplies of oil-well materials — all were forgotten in the joy of discovery with which we contemplated this little hill from whose base flowed oil in various directions. We felt that we knew and we did know that we were in an oil region which would produce in unlimited quantities that for which the world had the greatest need — oil fuel."[2]

They stood on the brink of a fortune that day. With all the financial resources at their disposal, with the backing of the Mexican Central, they could set about developing this section of rain forest in the most methodical way. They'd sew up everything in sight before the majors — Standard and Shell — got a whiff of their discovery. For the next several months they went on a land-buying spree. At the end of it they were the master of 450,000 acres. As one hostile historian described the process by which foreigners could make those enormous land-grabs in pre-revolutionary Mexico, it was not a very heart-warming spectacle. Corruption, the *mordita* (bite) system, ruled the countryside from the haciendas to the presidential palace where old Porfirio Díaz had been ruling as a dictator for forty years. "In every village a traitor can be found who through bribery of drink or women will sign a bill of sale. In

157

every district venal judges can be persuaded to uphold such documents and void old titles dating from the Toltecs as they may. Indians mulcted of their property go to work at the derricks for a few pesos a day, slowly achieve a dim idea of the economic world of the foreigner, and, if the work does not kill them, move restlessly to other sectors when the derricks begin to pump salt water. The oil has spoiled the land . . . But the foreigners have no time to contemplate the misery they have wrought. They are absorbed with the struggle of their drills against the earth, and with the struggle among themselves."[3]

Such considerations did not, of course, concern Doheny and Canfield. They were obsessed men confronted with the enormous task of developing an oilfield in the coastal lowland against all the obstacles of a hostile environment. They were able to work without attracting too much attention at first because the Spindletop boom was on — and in any case they were longer than they believed possible from tapping the riches of Tampico. In May 1901 they began drilling into the hillock where they had spotted the oil spring. After two weeks of drilling they reached the 545-foot level. One morning they were awakened in their tent nearby by the boss of their crew, who reported, "There's so much oil coming into the hole that it's lifting the tools off the bottom and I can't drill any more."

True enough, they'd struck oil — but not very much. About ten barrels a day oozed up to the surface. But that was a sure indication of oil deposits, even though their first hole struck a shallow pool. For the next several years they kept sinking one hole after another, striking shallow pools and bringing up small amounts of a heavy asphaltic oil which their friends at Mexican Central rejected as unsuitable for their locomotives.

Doheny and his partner spent more than $3 million in the continued exploration, expending their funds as fast as their California wells could pump them up. Few oilmen would have stuck to their faith in Tampico after all the discouragements they received. But Doheny and Canfield were certain that oil would be produced in commercial quantities in that section. In 1905 they had persuaded the Mexican authorities to use asphalt for paving roads and streets, and had also arranged a contract with the Mexican Central to buy six thousand barrels a day.

They were so certain they were onto something that they built a sixty-five-mile pipeline to the port of Tampico. One of their many wells was producing fifteen hundred barrels a day. Slowly but surely they were proving out their belief in the Mexican field. And their modest measure of success had attracted the attention of a British engineer named Weetman Pearson (later Lord Cowdray), who had just finished construction on the Tehuantepec Railway across the Mexican isthmus. Pearson was intrigued by his workers' reports of oil seepages along the right-of-way. He staked out a concession south of Tampico, right up against the Doheny-Canfield properties.

Pearson brought in a tremendous gusher at Dos Bocas, starting a fire that burned for forty days and could be seen by ships miles out on the Gulf of Mexico. The Britisher then hastened back to England to obtain financial and governmental backing for his enterprise. The British government was always more intimately connected with such enterprises than the American; once an opportunity like Pearson's was spotted it was exploited with the full resources of the diplomatic corps and the Secret Service. Pearson organized the Mexican Eagle Oil Company with some very highly placed people in the background. Several years later Winston Churchill charged in the House of Commons that funds of the Liberal Party, then dominant, had gone into the financing of Mexican Eagle.

A short time later, in 1910, Canfield and Doheny finally brought in their first gusher at Cerro Azul. Oil literally exploded out of an underground "ocean," as Doheny called it. It blew in uncontrolled. Even when it steadied down, it produced seventy thousand barrels a day. Cerro Azul broke the world record for daily production and before it started choking up salt water it had pumped 80 million barrels.

159

Cerro Azul started the great Tampico rush, with Mexican Eagle already on the ground, Standard Oil and Gulf Oil not far behind. After lengthy negotiations Doheny arranged to sell all his oil to Standard at 39 cents a barrel. Gusher after gusher blew in along the Mexican Gulf Coast, which soon became known as the Golden Lane.

Thus began the saturnalia of oil competition in Mexico in the last years of Porfirio Díaz's regime. Tampico and the surrounding countryside swarmed with adventurers, bandits, hard-bitten gringo drillers and riggers, spies (for Díaz, the oil companies, and the various governments involved), political fixers, lawyers specializing in leasing and buying, and all their camp followers. It was the new Klondike. Many participants in that gold rush, in fact, had turned to the search for oil bonanzas. Jack London, who had tapped a literary mother-lode in the Klondike, came down on a magazine assignment and found the atmosphere — though hotter and damper — quite similar to the frozen north. He talked to a sourdough he had known seventeen years before in the Klondike, who told him, "It's got the Klondike faded . . . we're taking $90,000 a day in gold from an eight-inch hole in the ground . . ."[4]

Pipelines and railroads snaked through the jungle and Tampico was Americanized almost overnight. The hero of Joseph Hergesheimer's *Tampico*, solidly researched on the scene, muses that in the year since he arrived it had become "a city without color . . . There were almost no Indians on the street and no serapes; the places for dairy lunches had multiplied, and the open cantinas were disappearing." Tampico was a "peculiarly dangerous, treacherous city, a place of bitterness and greed and desperation and implacable powers. Nothing was what, at first, it had appeared to be; practically nothing said there could be counted on; speech was ulterior and covered the cost of murder. It was the field of private wars and of attacks planned in London and Holland and New York and executed surreptitiously in Tampico, by writs at law and gunmen and bribery . . . there was the infinite multiplication of individual struggle for success, for oil — the lying vendors of fabricated leases and worthless ground; old drillers from Texas hoping for capital, certain of ultimate success; Mexicans with properties black, they said, with seepages; men from outlying camps, Tuxpam, Chiapas and Toteco, with secrets — for sale — the reports of great masked wells, wells capable of flowing a hundred thousand barrels and pinched to nothing . . . Those were wild times, with no check on what might happen, what did happen; nights when no one wanted to be safe or sober . . . Life then seemed to have no future, the nights no following morning. The Palais Royal, while it had lasted, was always in an uproar, with empty beer bottles hurled from any of the three galleried storeys into what had been a courtyard below. There had been practically continuous fighting, fringes of shots on the outskirts of the city, endless rumours of occupation, wanton bullets on the streets . . ."[5]

National loyalties yielded to company loyalties. You worked for and fought for the company that paid you, with no regard for whether its headquarters was in New York, in Los Angeles, or in London. Everette Lee DeGolyer, who was the son of a mining prospector, got his start with an English-owned operation, the Mexican Eagle Oil Company. He joined Weetman Pearson in the Mexican jungle shortly after taking leave from the University of Oklahoma. In his first year as a professional oil-finder, DeGolyer met with astounding success. He brought in what became known as Petrero del Llano No. 4, south of Tampico, which eventually produced 130 million barrels. It came in wild, spewing 110,000 barrels a day over the jungle. Cattle died by the thousands as a vast carpet of oil spread over their grazing lands. When the uncontrolled outflow reached the sea, it contaminated the shores of the Gulf of Mexico for a stretch of three hundred miles — a premonition of what the new technology would bring. DeGolyer quit Mexican Eagle to return to the University of Oklahoma and obtain his degree, but only after promising Pearson he would come back as the British company's chief geologist, a post

THE AUTOMOBILITY

he held until Mexican Eagle was sold to Royal Dutch Shell and DeGolyer started his own spectacularly successful oil exploration firm.

Fortunes were made overnight, but Tampico was sitting not only on an ocean of oil but a political volcano. Revolution would have come in any case; "Díaz and Death," as rebellious peons called the dictator's party, had outlived its usefulness even to the plutocracy, but the process was speeded by the involvement of oil competition.

Mildly disposed, devoutly religious as he had always been, Doheny's character was tempered like Damascus steel by his years of struggle in the coastal jungle. He had "bought" Díaz — so he thought — and believed that he was entitled to the majority interest in Mexican oil. He could retain the upper hand, however, only if he could stay in Díaz's favor and obtain still more concessions. The political and financial muscle that required probably convinced him that the tie-up with Standard Oil was necessary. Even with Standard as his ally, though, he soon ran into trouble in Mexico City. Díaz and his clique had decided that Doheny had become too powerful, and they listened attentively to the whispered warning of British diplomacy that the Doheny-Standard combination would soon control the whole country if it wasn't checked.

Dictator Díaz then decided to tip the balance of power in favor of Weetman Pearson, Mexican Eagle, and their unseen allies in Whitehall. New concessions went to Mexican Eagle, none to Doheny. The latter suddenly awakened to the fact that Pearson was winning out; that his British rival — all the more galling to an Irish-American — had obtained fifty-eight percent of the Mexican production. A period of intense intrigue followed, first Doheny and his allies against the British, then against Díaz himself. From the British viewpoint Pearson was saving Mexico from becoming an American vassal: "It was Mr. Pearson who, in spite of all difficulties and all Standard Oil's intrigues — the Americans even hired bands of Mexican brigands, who destroyed Pearson's oil-pipes and set his wells on fire — held on in Mexico, and thus prevented that country from altogether turning into an economic province of the United States."⁶

A visionary turned statesman, an intellectual who made himself into the political messiah of the Mexican masses, was the instrument by which Doheny and Standard avenged themselves on Díaz, and by the way opened a decade of political turmoil, revolution, counterrevolution, U.S. intervention, and incidentally the death of thousands.

It was not, of course, a sudden attack of idealism that caused the American oilmen to take up the Madero cause. They hoped that if they subsidized him, Francisco I. Madero would favor their interests over the British. The testimony of several witnesses before the U.S. Senate Foreign Relations Committee in 1913, two years after the uprisings throughout Mexico which sent Díaz and his friends scurrying to Parisian exile, directly linked Standard Oil money to the Madero cause.

Lawrence F. Converse, who served as an officer in Madero's revolutionary army, told the senators: "Mr. Madero himself told me that as soon as the rebels made a good showing of strength several leading bankers in El Paso stood ready to advance him — I believe the sum of $100,000." He added that Governor Gonzales and Secretary of State Hernandez of the state of Chihuahua told him that "the Standard Oil interests had bought bonds of the provisional [Madero] government of Mexico . . . They said that the Standard Oil interests were backing them in their revolution . . . Standard Oil was to have a high rate of interest and there was a tentative agreement as to an oil concession in the southern states of Mexico."⁷

The tender-minded Madero took his place as president in the National Palace, once the halls of Montezuma (and Emperor Maximilian, Juárez, and Díaz), and tried to cope with a revolution that would not stop spinning. For a time he felt secure enough in the knowledge that Standard Oil supported him and so, therefore, did Washington. His promise of social and political reforms satisfied neither the masses nor the lean and hungry leaders who had put him in power: Orozco, Zapata and Villa, who were being efficiently organized into a counter-revolutionary movement. Arrayed against Madero were not only the British, but certain American interests. Madero was the member of a family which had enriched itself on copper mining and smelting. They were the chief business rivals of the American mining and smelting combine of the Guggenheims. And President Taft's ambassador to Mexico, Henry Lane Wilson, was a friend of the Guggenheims. While official Washington policy favored Madero — as did American public opinion — the American ambassador worked to overthrow him. Capitalism, in its Mexican interlude, turned to cannibalism.

Now it came the turn of General Victoriano Huerto, who was an able schemer despite his addiction to brandy and cocaine, to take center-stage. Secretly backed by the British, Ambassador Wilson, and the copper interests, he offered to take charge of the necessary military campaigning against the peasant armies of Orozco, Zapata, and Villa, which were attacking federal posts and threatening a march on Mexico City. Huerta, soon to be known as the bloody usurper, showed he had the right kind of stuff as the tool of competing imperialisms. He arrested Madero "for his own protection." A few days later, while Madero was being transferred from the National Palace to a prison, despite the appeals of Señora Madero to Ambassador Wilson, he was shot to death by his guards, in the classic Latin tradition, "while attempting to escape." Now Mexican Eagle, the British, and the Guggenheims were in the ascendancy. Lord Cowdray, ex-Pearson, later confessed that he had made a substantial loan to General Huerta.

Woodrow Wilson, on assuming the presidency, refused to believe the assurances of Ambassador Wilson that Huerta represented the will of the Mexican people. The late Madero, after all, was a sort of Mexican Woodrow Wilson. The new President not only recalled Ambassador Wilson but refused to recognize the Huerta regime.

164

The British Foreign Office, believing the time had come to relax Anglo-American tensions, sent Sir William Tyrrell over to smooth down ruffled feathers in the State Department. There he was confronted by Secretary of State William Jennings Bryan and Walter Hines Page, the new American ambassador to London. There was a briskly undiplomatic exchange between Bryan and Sir William:

BRYAN: The Foreign Office has simply handed over its Mexican policy to the oil barons for predatory purposes.

SIR WILLIAM: Mr. Secretary, you are talking just like a Standard Oil man . . . you are pursuing the policy which they have decided on.

PAGE (who related the conversation and made more sense than either of the principals): What the devil does the oil or commerce of Mexico or the investments there amount to in comparison with the close friendship between the United States and Great Britain? The two countries should agree upon this primary principle — to leave their oil interests to fight their own battles, legal and financial.[8]

Ambassador Page's excellent advice went unheeded; there was too much at stake. The overt and covert interference of the U.S. and British governments, originally on behalf of their oil companies, involved their separate national prestige. If it now seems incredibly crass and brutal — particularly when viewed against the incalculable suffering of the Mexican people, who paid in blood and sorrow for every barrel of oil shipped out of their country — such recent examples as the Anglo-American rearrangement of the government of Iran in the early 1950's, though less bloody, come to mind.

In the U.S. Senate, Doheny's old friend Albert B. Fall of New Mexico was thundering that American troops must be sent to Mexico to "lend their assistance to the restoration of order and the maintenance of peace in that unhappy country." Doheny himself appeared before the Senate Foreign Relations Commitee and provided more pragmatic reasons for intervention: "Inasmuch as both Germany and Great Britain are seeking and acquiring sources of supply for large quantities of petroleum, it seems to me that there can be no question but that the United States must avail itself of the enterprise and ability and pioneer spirit of its citizens to acquire and to have and to hold a reasonable portion of the world's petroleum supplies. If it does not, it will find that the supplies of petroleum not within the boundaries of United States territory will be rapidly acquired by citizens and governments of other nations." The Mexican fields, he added, were necessary to building an American merchant marine "that can compete for cost of operation with any other fleet which the great nations of the world may have or construct."[9]

Doheny thus presented the two themes of oil propaganda which have been sounded consistently ever since: the appeal to nationalism, the threat of depletion of American reserves, both constantly used to justify the industry's claim on government cooperation in foreign relations and in tax policy.

The Wilson Administration needed little encouragement to take up all available weapons against the Huerta regime. President Wilson, like the guerrilla leaders who now canonized Madero, viewed Huerta simply as a "bloody usurper," and instructed his Mexican embassy that if Huerta did not surrender power "it will become the duty of the United States to use less peaceful means to put him out." An embargo was placed on the shipment of munitions to Huerta and his federal army but customs inspectors along the border looked the other way when arms in quantity passed through their stations to Huerta's rivals. The latter now included General Venustiano Carranza, who seemed more respectable than the peon leaders Zapata and Villa and whose aspirations for the presidency Wilson supported.

Now the problem was to force Huerta out, despite the fact that Lord Cowdray and the British had bought his bonds, as Standard Oil apparently had bought Madero's. A pretext for intervention cropped up when the Vera Cruz incident erupted in March 1914, by which time Carranza's ambitions had been refueled by a $100,000 cash advance, plus $685,000 in credits, from Doheny.[10] At Vera Cruz an American naval officer and several of his men were arrested when they went ashore to buy supplies. The U.S. government demanded that Huerta release the men and apologize by tendering a thirteen-gun salute to the American flag. When he refused, hoping to unite Mexico behind him against Yankee arrogance, President Wilson applied the ultimate force to unseat Huerta and replace him with Carranza. Four naval landing parties seized the Vera Cruz customs house. They were immediately followed into the port by four U.S. army regiments which had been mobilized for the first available opportunity. Two days later the regular army was mobilized to invade Mexico from the Texas border.

A war fever, its temperature considerably boosted by "On to Mexico City" headlines in the Hearst papers (whose proprietor was enraged because his mines and ranches in northern Mexico had been confiscated), gripped the United States. It even infected Jack London, who had formerly urged on the Mexican revolution but who now appeared in Vera Cruz as a "war" correspondent. London was a great disappointment to his socialist comrades; he not only believed that the United States should take over the country, but maintained that the rebelling peons were nothing but bandits. "What peon with any spunk in him would elect to slave on a hacienda for a slave's reward when, in the ranks of Zapata, Carranza or Villa, he can travel, see the country, ride a horse, carry a rifle, get a peso or so a day, loot when fortune favors, and, if lucky, on occasions kill a fellow creature — this last a particularly delightful event to a people who delight in the bloody spectacle of the bull ring."[11]

Huerta was forced out of the National Palace, scurrying well heeled to Spanish exile, and Carranza was slipped in. The British found that they had ignored all those "Monroe Doctrine — No Trespassing" signs to their own disadvantage. Yet

Carranza, once in power, was no great comfort to the victorious American oilmen. Those watchful gentlemen noted symptoms of ingratitude when he announced that he would "vindicate" the 1911 revolution. The new constitution he produced was even more disillusioning to those who had financed his successful takeover bid. It contained Article 27, which was to bedevil them henceforth and raise that most dreaded specter: expropriation.

Article 27 provided that "The ownership of lands and waters comprised within the limits of the national territory is vested originally in the Nation which has had, and has, the right to transmit the title thereof to private persons, thereby constituting private property . . . In the Nation is vested the legal ownership of all minerals, petroleum, and all hydrocarbons — solid, liquid or gaseous. Legal capacity to acquire ownership of lands and waters of the Nation shall be governed by the following provisions: Only Mexicans by birth or naturalization and Mexican companies have the right to acquire ownership in lands, waters and their appurtenances, or to obtain concessions to develop mines, waters, or mineral fuels, in the Republic of Mexico. The Nation may grant the same right to foreigners, provided they agree before the Department of Foreign Affairs to be considered Mexicans in respect to such property, and accordingly not to invoke the protection of their governments . . . Within a zone of 100 kilometers from the frontiers and of 50 kilometers from the seacoast, no foreigner shall under any conditions acquire direct ownership of lands and waters."

Thus both American and British oilmen were barred from further concessions except under the most galling controls. They proceeded to extract every barrel they could, in the shortest possible time, from their wells around Tampico. The Americans pressed Indian labor into the dangerous work of hastily sinking wells in the fever swamps, heedless of the lives lost by their reckless methods. According to one description,

"The Americans were playing the dangerous game with all the zest of football. They drove five or six drills at the same time. Their drillers were like matadors; they received several thousand dollars in bonuses for quick jobs and they paid their *cuadrillas* out of this . . . Hardly a day passed without its toll of dead men. In the offices at the refineries, local managers read telegrams from the drilling camps: 'Four dead this week, five last week.' But if one expressed concern over such mortality, they laughed. The dead they spoke of were not men. In the argot of oil, a dry hole, a drilling that did not produce oil, was a 'dead man.' . . . Fifty dollars to the family of a poor Indian, or to labor agitators, and the matter was forgotten. Where 'dead men' cost thousands, the cost of dead Indians was negligible."[12]

By early 1916 it appeared that the oilman's hopes that the ingrate Carranza might be turned out of office had acquired some substance. Through the activities of the untamed guerrilla chieftain of Chihuahua, Pancho Villa, whose depredations Carranza had been unable to check, another American intervention might be arranged. A journalistic outcry went up when Villa's forces, ranging into Sonora, took twenty-three American mining engineers off a train and shot them to death. A short time later Villa raided across the border, attacked a U.S. cavalry post at Columbus, New Mexico, and shot up the place. Villa then withdrew into the mountains of Chihuahua, while liberal newspapers in the United States, opposed to any more military adventures in Mexico, charged that "Wall Street money" had paid for Villa's raid on Columbus in order to provoke an American retaliation.

Following the raid, wrote one of Villa's biographers, "Curious rags of information appear that, at first, had been overlooked. Questions, doomed never to be answered, are asked — Why to this wretched desert hamlet forty miles from the nearest city of size should there come brisk gentlemen in smart New York clothes but a week before the raid? What was their business? How did it happen that the raid was made immediately after a part of the garrison had been withdrawn, and while but one officer, a lieutenant, remained on duty in the camp southeast of the town? Why did the attackers, apparently some four hundred strong, and easily in force to perpetrate a massacre, persistently fire their rifles in the air, and, in the course of a three-hour occupation of the hamlet, confine their attention chiefly to looting, inflicting only such casualties as, in the madness of such a moment, would seem inevitable *even if their instructions had been merely to make a gesture?* Why, when it is the invariable custom of Mexican troops to charge with a battle-cry, and then save their breath for the business in hand, did the attackers monotonously chant for three hours, 'Viva Villa! Viva Villa!' "?[13]

If its purpose was provocation, President Wilson and his advisers fell neatly into the trap. Deciding Carranza's army wasn't up to the job of capturing Villa and rounding up his forces, Washington mounted a 10,000-man "punitive" expedition under Brigadier General John J. Pershing and sent him after the guerrilla. The result, aside from warming up the U.S. army for the expeditionary force to Europe a year later, was a cautionary lesson in the stickiness of partisan warfare. Wherever Pershing's laboring columns lumbered on the scene, the Villistas simply faded into the arroyos and mountains. Villa was not captured. The expedition was a costly ($132 million) failure; Pershing's columns returned to their own soil, and Carranza's oil-conservation program stayed in effect. Mexico was just about washed up as an oilman's hunting preserve.

Deterding and Royal Dutch Shell had been caught flat-footed, for once, in the race for Mexican oil. He entered the competition at the end of World War I by buying out Lord Cowdray's Mexican Eagle Oil Company. Elsewhere in the southern hemisphere he was quicker to seize upon the possibilities of exploiting oil resources through an understanding with the local tyrant. Deterding's chosen field of endeavor was Venezuela, where the long, iron-handed dictatorship of General Juan Vicente Gómez guaranteed stability. Gómez came to power in 1908, Deterding to Venezuela shortly thereafter. The general, renowned as the "father of his country" for having fathered an estimated one hundred illegitimate children, soon became the richest man in South America and ruled from a 200-room palace at Maracay surrounded by six army barracks.

The presence of oil had long been established in Venezuela, and furthermore its presence close to the Panama Canal provided a shortcut to the Far Eastern markets. But there were many technical problems involved, which only large amounts of money and expertise could solve. The oil-bearing land was located in the Lake Maracaibo basin, where sandbars at the outlet to the sea prevented tankers from entering. Previous attempts to tap the basin had all failed. The concession now was owned by the General Asphalt Company of Philadelphia, which didn't have the resources to build lake tankers and pipelines through swampland to get the oil out. Five million dollars so far had gone down the drain. Deterding, however, sent a corps of experts to look over the concession and decided on what he called "the most speculative venture of my life." He then devoloped the Venezuela field into one of the world's largest. An arrangement with dictator Gómez provided cheap, unagitated labor (his motto was "Peace, Union and Labor," which his enemies translated to "Peace in the cemeteries, union in the prisons and labor on the roads") for which Deterding paid an estimated $4 million annually in "royalties" to Gómez.[14] A salubrious deal all around, except for the Venezuelan people, who have been yoked ever since to the international oil industry.

The race for oil resources was entering its most hectic period in the years just before World War I, when gasoline powered the fledgling air forces, the truck convoys, and the first tank battalions. It was the essential ingredient of victory. Mexico and Venezuela and the competition between Standard and Royal Dutch Shell were merely sideshows to the strategic penetration of the Middle East.

III.

The Wilhelmine Dream

In October, 1913, when England launched the *Queen Elizabeth*, first of the cruisers to burn crude oil, I knew then that it was up to me to concern myself with the supply of oil for my country and not with archeology.

— T. E. Lawrence to Gertrude Bell

8.

The Man from Mount Morgan

In oilmanship there were many styles, the roughneck American, the stolid bowler-hatted Dutchman, the gentleman-trader
Englishman, the bull-necked German with a string of university degrees, the raffish Rumanian. None of these set the style
for the Middle East. There, around pioneering Baku, and later
in the blast-furnace heat of the Persian, Mesopotamian and
Arabian deserts, the aspect was crowded with exotic symbols:
mountaineers with crossed bandoliers, effete pashas, sly vi-
ziers, mad-eyed dervishes and bearded mullahs, oil princelings
accompanied by armed retinues.

Baku was the fashion plate. There oil derricks first sprang
up among domes and minarets, and Western technology made
its juncture with Tolstoy's Russia and the Arabian Nights.
Geographically Baku was a southern appendix of Mother Russia but ethnically it was part of the Caucasus, its blood feuds
and religious differences. The population was composed of
warring Georgians, Circassians, Armenians, Tartars, Cossacks
and Jews. It was a city of overnight millionaires and a brutally
oppressed labor force. One writer declared that Baku produced
more rich men than the whole U.S. oil industry, though none

of them acquired the super-fortunes of the Rockefellers and Mellons.

They took Kublai Khan as their model. Tartar millionaires like Tagiev and Armenian oil magnates like Mantachoff, Gukassod and Adamoff erected enormous palaces, always taking care to build underground vaults behind steel doors to which they could escape when communal riots swept the oil-soaked peninsula. In the streets surrounding their mansions murder, robbery, racial and religious rioting were almost daily occurrences. There was a chanciness about life in Baku, even for the two hundred millionaires, that impelled them to enjoy their wealth — and be damned to the workers who lived in wooden barracks, worked sixteen hours a day for little more than their keep, and were fired if they married, because no oilfield worker could hope to support a family.

One magnate, in a moment of self-fulfilling prophecy, built his mansion to resemble a house of cards. Another, Mantachoff, the richest of them all, distilled his kerosene in platinum cisterns. Another lived in a villa gold plated from cellar to roof. Essad Bey, the son of one of the Moslem oilmen, recalled in his memoir a boyhood surrounded by ten servants for every member of the family, in addition to his father's *kotschis*, a bodyguard of thuggish Georgian retainers armed to the teeth, which every magnate recruited as soon as he made his first million.

Moslem, Tartar and Armenian alike, they imported unofficial harems of beautiful young women from all over Asiatic Russia. Italian architects were called in to convert oil-reeking Baku into Xanadu on the Caspian, to decorate the hundred-room palaces with gilt statuary; but inside plumbing was considered uncivilized and privies were built in ornamental gardens.[1]

The huge and boisterous Mantachoff, who had operated a small vineyard until oil was struck on his property, set the pace for all the Baku magnates. The son of one of his fellow Armenian producers has recalled that Mantachoff was an extrovert who gloried in spending his revenue as quickly as his oil was pumped to a Nobel refinery. "He would delight in going personally to the reservoirs where the oil owners sold their supplies for gold rubles. Then he would drive back in state, with wonderful horses, and hold Arabian Nights parties in his palace. There would be retinues of the most beautiful women from all over eastern Europe and Asiatic Russia, troupes of Oriental dancers and acrobats, vast meals and unlimited wine and spirits. Sometimes there would be fights, but Mantachoff could hold his own. Attempts were made to murder him by all manner of means, poison, daggers and rival bands of *kotschis*. But he was a match for anybody, so strong he could lift two grown men off the ground by the shoulders with his outstretched arms."[2]

While Baku oil flooded the European market and the boom roared on, that enormous pool could support all sorts of extravagance and eccentricity. The slackness of business methods appalled a representative of the London Chamber of Commerce sent to investigate the investment possibilities: "If any trade in the world were conducted on the system, or rather, utter want of system, that prevails at Baku, bankruptcy would speedily follow. Hardly any of the heads of firms are men of business, or could tell you whether they were doing a profitable trade or not, if they were at Baku, but they are generally absentees, leaving the duties to be performed by a manager who is not looked after so long as he remits funds to headquarters. I know that one of the largest firms changed its business manager seven times in about two years. Offices are only open daily from about 8:30 A.M. to 12 noon, and then again for about two hours in the evening, while much time is spent in card playing. Scandalous waste, not to say speculation, goes on everywhere . . ."[3]

As in Mexico, however, the oil boomers were sitting on a revolutionary volcano. The hectic extravagance of the profitmakers may have been induced by premonition. Long before the Bolshevik Revolution Baku's oppressed labor force was being stirred by imported troublemakers. One was a native son of the Caucasus, Zogo Dzhugashvili, the son of a Georgian cobbler and a lapsed student for the priesthood, whom Essad Bey remembered as the editor of an underground Bolshevik newspaper (*The Proletarian of Baku*). Later he was arrested and deported to Siberia; later still he adopted another name, Stalin.

The underground turmoil broke the surface early in 1905 as part of the uprisings widespread in Russia that year. In Baku the abortive revolution assumed a Caucasian coloration, with racial and religious fanaticism overriding political considerations. Moslems and their Orthodox enemies slaughtered each other in the streets and ran up a death toll of several thousand. The oilfields were set on fire and millions of pounds sterling worth of oil went up in black smoke. Then came what one observer called "a state of most unnatural peace." Long-standing feuds had not yet been resolved, and tension grew through the hot sullen months. In September the communal rioting was resumed. An English correspondent wrote, "The accounts given of the massacres, though incomplete, are full and lengthy enough to prove that in revolting cruelty what has taken place is without a parallel in the annals of Caucasian warfare and revolution."[4]

The Russian central government awoke to the fact that their oil revenues came from the most restive province in the Czarist empire, but the Cossacks they dispatched to restore order merely delighted in the spectacle of old ethnic rivals slaughtering each other. Essad Bey and his family spent weeks in their underground shelter with more than a hundred co-religionists, also a number of Jews and Armenians with whom they had established personal friendships, until the fury spent itself and they ventured outdoors to find the streets littered with the maimed and butchered. The Armenian millionaire Adamoff was surrounded in his mansion by a Tartar mob, which finally broke in and killed him and his family but not before Adamoff had picked off forty Tartars with his rifle.

Foreign investors insisted that a Russian military force be stationed at Baku to keep the quarreling Caucasians from each other's throats and the oilfields safe from sabotage. European industry now depended on Baku oil for its continued prosperity; so did the Rothschild, Nobel and Deterding cartels.

An uneasy peace was reestablished among the Italianate palaces and ramshackle workers' barracks of Baku, but the troubles there were only a reflection of the rush of rival powers into the Middle Eastern vacuum created by the deterioration of the Ottoman Empire. The great nations of Europe were playing for the highest stakes. Britain was bent on extending its domination from the Ganges to the Euphrates. German empire-builders were flooding through the Balkans and into the eastern provinces of Turkey, pushing the Kaiser's dream railway, Berlin to Baghdad, through the Anatolian plains. "It would mean," wrote an Englishman, "half a million men hopping on trains in Berlin and going right through to the gates of India. It would mean goodbye to the British Empire."[5]

Fevered by the search for oil, the Anglo-German-French-Russian rivalry was being fought out over the underground sea of petroleum that extended southward from Baku through Persia (Iran) and Mesopotamia (Iraq) to the Arabian peninsula. The winners of that race would be the victors of World War I; oil was the essential ingredient of that victory. Now geopolitics was modified by geology as well as geography.

The key, as it turned out, was an Australian mining engineer named William Knox D'Arcy, who was cut from a now familiar pattern. Men who possessed the determination to find oil in the most inaccessible, uncomfortable and dangerous parts of the world were likely to resemble each other (the lone prospectors of the American West were a similar type) in their taste for solitude, their obsession with the search, their adaptability to repeated failures, and their ability to survive in the wastelands. Like Edward L. Doheny, D'Arcy was a devout Catholic and made his stake as a mining prospector. He had prospected in Queensland and struck a fortune in the Mount Morgan gold mines.

Money in itself was not the object, though spending it could be a pleasurable occupation for a time. D'Arcy moved to England, married Nina Boucicault of the English theatrical family and for a time was one of the more lavish hosts of Edwardian London. He owned the only private box at Epsom Downs, aside from the royal family's, established himself and his wife at a country seat, and presided over a town house in Grosvenor Square which was the scene of some memorable soirees. (At one both Caruso and Melba sang for his guests.) He attained additional celebrity by never tipping a waiter or a cabbie less than a gold sovereign.

Luxurious living palled eventually, and D'Arcy felt the urge to go looking for another fortune. Perhaps from reading the Bible he became interested in the possibility of oil exploration in Persia. He knew all about the Persian temples which had been lighted for centuries by naphtha flares, and about the supposedly divine fires worshiped by the followers of Zoroaster. The prevalence of "fire temples" indicated to D'Arcy the proximity of oil deposits. The same thought had occurred almost three decades earlier to Baron Paul Julius von Reuter, founder of the British news agency bearing his name, and probably D'Arcy's research had uncovered Reuter's series of failures in that field. The technology of oil exploration had, of course, advanced considerably since 1872 when Reuter obtained a concession to exploit Persia's mineral and oil resources in its northern provinces. The Russians, regarding northern Persia as the pathway for expansion to the Persian Gulf, persuaded the Persian government to cancel the concession. Seventeen years later the persistent Reuter obtained a concession south of the "Russian" provinces, drilled three wells, including one eight hundred feet deep, and came up with nothing but dust.

In 1900, assisted by a geological consultant, D'Arcy began his long search for Persian oil. Years of searching the desert wastes of Persia followed. Initially he was financed by what remained of his gold fortune and was encouraged by the British government and the London bankers, particularly those influenced by Disraelian imperialism and impressed by the necessity of a land bridge from the eastern Mediterranean to India. Persia then was the focus of British and Russian rivalry, a long struggle, epitomized in Kipling's works, for the strategic tier of states that bounded on the southern frontier of Russia.

Persia then was even more decrepit than its ancient rival Turkey, with the Persian northern provinces a Russian sphere of influence, the southern coming under British hegemony. To Sir Arthur Hardinge, British minister to Teheran, Persia (as he wrote in *A Diplomatist in the Middle East*), was comparable to "a long mismanaged estate, ready to be knocked down at once to whatever foreign power bid the highest or threatened the most loudly its defenceless and degenerate rulers." Shah Mazaffar-ed-Din regarded the privy purse and the national treasury as his private property, and the country was deeply in debt to both Britain and Russia, an almost inevitable precondition for such exploitation as was to follow for decades.

For two years the D'Arcy exploration team pottered around Persia looking for a likely place to drill. It got 110° in the shade before seven o'clock out in the desert, up to 130° in the heat of the day. Smallpox and various fevers were endemic even in the few garden spots, the rose-covered valleys and the cypress forests. Many of the natives were hostile to all foreigners. But D'Arcy kept looking until, late in 1902, he decided that the remote Qasr-i-Shirin district was the place to sink his test wells.

Before importing the necessary equipment and technicians, he decided it was time to obtain a *firman*, concession, from the Persian government. Much of the preliminary negotiation was conducted by Alfred Marriott, who was the youthful cousin of D'Arcy's private secretary and confidential adviser back in London. Marriott found the Shah's officials eagerly receptive. They were willing to sell anything in the country south of the

Russian zone of influence. The concession was finally arranged in personal negotiations between D'Arcy and the Shah. It was so sweepingly inclusive in its terms that it would always be regarded with awe by the rest of the oil industry. Rockefeller himself never walked away with so great a prize.

D'Arcy was to pay £20,000 (then $100,000) in cash to the royal treasury, another £20,000 in stock, and a sixteen percent royalty on any oil obtained through the concession.

In return, D'Arcy received the absolutely exclusive right to drill for oil in Persia for the next sixty years. He could exploit the oil resources of all except the five northern provinces of Azerbaijan, Ghilan, Mazanderan, Astrabad, and Khorasan, which were part of Russia's sphere of influence. That left him almost five hundred thousand square miles of territory. He was exempted from paying any taxes.

It was probably the costliest document ever signed by a sovereign government. Neither party, it should be added, had any idea what the concession would be worth.

Obtaining the concession, however, was only the beginning of D'Arcy's struggle. Year after year went by, with D'Arcy pictured by some historians as living in a tent out on the desert, with his office in a leather trunk, and spiritually sustained by his Bible and a small gold ikon of Christ. (The official history of British Petroleum, *Adventure in Oil*, by Henry Longhurst, which tends to downplay D'Arcy's role in the company's early history, maintains that D'Arcy left all the donkey work out on the desert to Marriott.)

Immediately after obtaining the Shah's *firman*, D'Arcy brought in G. B. Reynolds, a former official in the Indian Public Works Department, who had once engaged in oil exploration in the Dutch East Indies, to take charge of operations out at the Qasr-i-Shirin site where the first well was sunk. Drilling equipment had to be brought by ship, rail and camelback via Basra and Baghdad. The drillers included an American, two Canadians, and a number of Poles who downed tools so often for supposed religious holidays that Reynolds had to send for a Roman Catholic calendar of saints' days to check up on their claims.

D'Arcy's men were plagued incessantly by various miseries indigenous to the climate and country. The oil camp was struck by clouds of locusts, which died and created a frightful stench. The nearest settlement, where food and water supplies were obtained after much haggling, was swept by a smallpox epidemic. D'Arcy had to keep paying out protection money to the sheikhs of the neighboring tribes or they fired fusillades into his camp at night. The obstacles seemed insuperable; the heat and swarming flies alone would have driven off less determined men. Finally, in January 1904, one of his test wells brought up oil. Not in great quantities but enough to indicate D'Arcy was on the right track.

Four months later the well went dry, and D'Arcy was back where he started, only now he was broke.

His only recourse was to make a hurried trip back to London and raise more capital. The city bankers, who had encouraged his venture when it cost them nothing, now stared in embarrassment at the shabby, leached-out little man who had once entertained them on Grosvenor Square. Some could hardly be convinced he was really William Knox D'Arcy. In every office he was turned away empty handed. The city's decision, though it was cloaked in denser verbiage, was to the effect that the financiers would back him only when he could supply absolute proof that there were large quantities of oil in the D'Arcy concession.

Then the Admiralty, with Fisher as First Sea Lord, heard of his dilemma. The admiral had formed an Oil Committee under the Civil Lord of the Admiralty, E. G. Pretyman, to concern itself with fuel-oil sources for the Royal Navy. Preference was to be given wholly British enterprises, and since D'Arcy was Devonshire-born though Australian-raised he qualified. The admirals, of course, looked upon Persia with a strategic eye. If reliable deposits could be found there, in an area dominated by Britain, located between Europe and India, so much the better. The Indian army, the principal arm of British might east of Suez, as well as the Royal Navy would be benefited. Pretyman assumed the role of financial scout for D'Arcy. He introduced D'Arcy to the heads of the Burmah Oil Company, which was lavishly financed but needed more oil than its Burmese wells could produce. The Burmah people agreed in May 1905 to provide the funds for further exploration of the Persian concession. Six hundred thousand pounds sterling would be dispensed, under the vigilant eye of Burmah representatives on the scene, through the newly formed First Exploitation Company.

D'Arcy returned to Persia and began boring new test holes, this time in the Bakhtiari province north of the Persian Gulf. He had studied reports of seepages near Shushtar and decided he would concentrate on that region. Well after well was bored while the Burmah executives in London despaired and D'Arcy kept faith with his vision of that lion-skinned, treeless, airless country forested with derricks. It must have taken an incredible persistence to endure.

The Bakhtiari tribesmen refused to be governed by the Shah's writ and kept harassing D'Arcy's drilling crews. Finally, when the Bakhtiaris threatened to wipe out the foreigners' encampments, the British consul in Teheran was consulted. "Send a gunboat" was then the prescription for all such problems, and the Admiralty of course was taking a paternal, even a proprietary interest in D'Arcy's project. It dispatched H. M. S. *Comet* up the Karun River from the Persian Gulf, but even British imperialism in full flower could not thrust its way past mudbanks. *Comet* went aground; the unfriendly tribesmen were spared a lesson from six-inch naval guns. Finally D'Arcy negotiated a settlement in the traditional, Middle Eastern manner, with the Bakhtiari khans accepting a three percent interest in whatever D'Arcy might extract from their soil.

Test borings were made for the next two years and coughed up nothing but dust, and in 1907 the disappointed natives watched from the hills as D'Arcy's crews began moving to a new location in the Zagros Mountains about a hundred miles north of the Persian Gulf. Time was running out for D'Arcy, as cables from London kept warning him. Burmah Oil's £600,000 had followed D'Arcy's £225,000 into dry holes from which not a half-crown of revenue had been realized.

Early in 1908 D'Arcy's drillers began operating at a place called Masjid-i-Salaman, the Mosque of Solomon. It was their last chance. They pushed the work at a relentless speed. In May they had drilled to a depth of eleven hundred feet without bringing up any oil. Then cabled instructions from Burmah headquarters informed D'Arcy that the money had run out and he was to discontinue drilling.

D'Arcy figured, however, that he had a month's grace, that he was entitled to continue drilling until a confirming letter arrived from London, which would take four weeks.

They worked around the clock at the Mosque of Solomon, knowing that if this boring didn't prove out D'Arcy's long search would end in failure and D'Arcy himself would be confronted by an impoverished old age. Only two weeks after the cable arrived, at 4:30 A.M. on May 26, 1908, by the light of false dawn, there was a rumbling underground. Oil spouted from the top of the derrick and showered the whole camp.[6]

D'Arcy's long and solitary quest on the Persian deserts had been crowned by a success that changed the oil picture of the world, that opened up the greatest reserves on earth.

Back in London, in the hitherto skeptical and unhelpful city, the news caused great excitement. The Anglo-Persian Oil Company was organized to exploit the Persian concession, with Burmah putting up a million pounds for development costs and the public allowed to buy "preference" shares. Even in cautious Glasgow there was a block-long queue of investors clamoring to buy shares. Field Marshal Lord Kitchener, a firm believer in any kind of imperialist activity, demanded to be given priority in obtaining a block of Anglo-Persian stock.

(There was no delicacy then about what would later be called conflict of interest; Admiral Fisher, as earlier noted, was an enthusiastic investor in Shell.)

D'Arcy, who was repaid the £225,000 of his own money he had spent in exploring Persia and £900,000 worth of Burmah stock as a bonus (meager in retrospect), found that his task in developing his Persian find was just beginning. Getting the oil out would be a problem. A 130-mile pipeline had to be laid from the mountains to the head of the Persian Gulf, then a refinery had to be built because it would be more economical than shipping out crude oil. All that took four years. And just when his long labors ended, the company organized through his efforts somehow, in a transaction concealed by official secrecy and blurred by controversy, became the property of the British Admiralty.

Just as D'Arcy's efforts to get oil out of Persia in usable quantities were coming to splendid fruition, the campaign to convert the Royal Navy to oil-burning boilers was reaching its climax. Lord Fisher, the original "oil maniac," had been forced to resign as First Sea Lord in 1910. A year later Winston Churchill became the chief civil representative on the naval board (First Lord, his professional counterpart being the First Sea Lord) and took up Fisher's cause. Churchill insisted that a new "fast squadron" of dreadnoughts must be built to meet the German challenge on the high seas. The new battleships could achieve the necessary speed with coal-fired boilers but because of their greater weight one heavy-gun turret would have to be sacrificed. With oil-fired boilers the new battleships would be able to carry the extra turret and achieve the same speed.

To work up enthusiasm for his project, Churchill formed a Royal Oil Commission to investigate how the navy could be switched to oil-burning warships on a large scale (only a few destroyers and submarines were then using liquid fuel). In *The World Crisis* he later explained the urgency of his mission: "The advantages conferred by liquid fuel were inestimable. First speed. In equal ships oil gave a large excess of speed over coal. It enabled that speed to be attained with far greater rapidity. It gave 40 percent greater radius of action for the same weight of coal. It enabled a fleet to re-fuel at sea with great facility. An oil-burning fleet can, if need be, and in calm weather, keep its station at sea, nourishing itself from tankers without having to send a quarter of its strength continually into harbour to coal, wasting fuel on the homeward and outward journey. The ordeal of coaling ships exhausted the whole ship's company. In wartime it robbed them of their brief period of rest; it subjected everyone to extreme discomfort. With oil a few pipes were connected with a tanker or the shore and the ship sucked in its fuel with hardly a man having to lift his finger . . . The use of oil made it possible in every type of vessel to have more gun power and more speed for less size and cost. It alone made it possible to realize the high speeds in certain types which were vital to their tactical purpose."

At the same time Churchill — who disliked and distrusted Deterding and his Anglo-Dutch combination — was determined that the navy would depend on reserves wholly British owned or better yet government owned. It distressed him that the navy would be dependent upon Shell and Standard for its supplies, not only because they were foreign interests but because he suspected them of overcharging.

In May 1912 he and Prime Minister Asquith journeyed to Naples to persuade Lord Fisher to take over the chairmanship of the Royal Oil Commission. Fisher felt he had been unjustly forced into retirement over a petty administrative foul-up, but yielded to their persuasions because of what he called "my consuming passion for oil and the oil engine." Churchill, knowing that Fisher's ego matched his own, was careful to define the limits of the admiral's responsibility, quoting himself later as bluntly instructing Fisher: "You have got to find the oil; to show how it can be stored cheaply; how it can be purchased regularly and cheaply in peace and with absolute certainty in war . . . But your Royal Commission will be advisory and not executive. It cannot touch policy or action."

The result of Fisher's investigation was a memorandum titled "Oil and Its Fighting Attributes," which was presented to the government on March 3, 1913. It was a lively document bearing the stamp of Fisher's eupeptic personality. The admiral did not conceal his opinion that the Royal Navy should lean heavily on Royal Dutch Shell and the "Napoleonic audacity" of its managing director, Henri Deterding. "Let us therefore listen with deep attention to the words of a man who has the sole executive control of the most powerful organization on earth for the production of a source of power which almost doubles the power of our Navy whilst our potential enemies remain normal in strength of their fleets."

Churchill had different ideas about how the navy's oil should be obtained, and they didn't include letting a Dutchman obtain a stranglehold on supplying it in peace or war. While Fisher was performing as Deterding's passionate advocate, Churchill was sending another royal commission, this one headed by Professor John Cadman, the petroleum adviser to the Colonial Office, out to the Middle East to investigate the potentialities of the Anglo-Persian Oil Company. Cadman's report indicated that the Persian reserves alone could meet the navy's requirements. But he added, "The company cannot adequately develop this extensive concession without additional capital, and we understand that the question of H. M. Government affording financial support is under consideration. Should such a course be decided on, we are of the opinion that it should be made a condition that the Government should have a voice in the direction of the Company's general policy."[7]

In July 1913 Churchill rose in the House of Commons to announce that the government had just gone into the oil business by acquiring a majority interest in Anglo-Persian. For $11 million the Admiralty had acquired control of a concession worth untold billions of dollars (fifty-six percent of Anglo-Persian's shares, it was later disclosed). Two directors were to be appointed to Anglo-Persian's board, representing the Admiralty and given the right of veto over all strategic issues.

"It is a twofold policy," as Churchill informed Parliament of his *fait accompli*. "There is an ultimate policy and there is an interim policy. Our ultimate policy is that the Admiralty should become the independent owner and producer of its own supplies of liquid fuel, first, by building up an oil reserve in this country sufficient to make us safe in war and able to override price fluctuations in peace; secondly, by acquiring the power to deal in crude oils as they come cheaply into the market . . . The second aspect of our ultimate policy involves the Admiralty being able to refine, retort or distill crude oil of various kinds, until it reaches the qualities required for naval use . . . I see no reason, nor do my advisers, why we should shrink from making this further extension of the vast and various businesses of the Admiralty." As one of the facets of his interim policy, Churchill cited the fact that government control of Anglo-Persian would permit it to "draw our oil supply, so far as possible, from sources under British control or British influence, and along those sea or ocean routes which the Navy can most easily and most surely protect."

Churchill's deal was quickly ratified, but the questions as to how it was arranged were the subject of a long period of speculation and controversy. Naturally the major oil-producers were alarmed by a government's simply taking over a huge and immensely valuable oil concession — a nasty precedent indeed. What if the U.S. navy decided to take over Tampico?

The big question, left unanswered, was just how the Admiralty managed to acquire Anglo-Persian as a controlled subsidiary. Why did William Knox D'Arcy tamely bow out of Anglo-Persian immediately after spending more than a dozen years of the most grueling effort to find oil in a desert wilderness, then to pipe it out and refine it where it could be easily transported to the European market? Was he that much of an English patriot — a man proud of being an Australian and with a colonial's resentment of the mother country? Or was it true, as later whispered, then published, that D'Arcy had been led down the garden path by an operative of the British Secret Service?

One has a choice of "truths" about the circumstances of D'Arcy's retirement from Anglo-Persian, leaving its tremendous potential to the British Admiralty and, to a lesser extent, the Burmah Oil Company.

There is one version sponsored by the French Secret Service, which leaked it at a time when the French and British were embroiled almost to the point of war over dividing the Middle Eastern spoils of World War I. This was retailed in Antoine Zischka's *La Guerre Secrète pour le Pétrole* (*The Secret War for Oil*), published in Paris in 1933, and a year later in Frank C. Hanighen's *The Secret War*, published in this country. The documentation for these accounts was impressively stated: "File No. 28779/1925, French Secret Service — Second Bureau." In England, Mr. Hanighen's book was announced for publication, then hastily withdrawn when the British oil industry engaged counsel and threatened suit on the grounds that it was libelous. Years later Deterding's biographer wrote, "Publishers and editors are scared stiff of touching the subject . . . *The Secret War* fiasco was the last straw . . ."[8]

According to the French Secret Service's report, D'Arcy was simply swindled out of his holdings in Anglo-Persian through an elaborate and brilliantly managed confidence game rigged by the British Secret Service on behalf of the Admiralty.

This version, as related by Hanighen in *The Secret War*, claims that when D'Arcy finally returned to England from Persia he had kept to himself the fact that his concession covered all of Persia except the northern provinces, that the Burmah Oil Company had financed him — it would appear — without having a look at the *firman* signed by the Shah of Persia. By this account Burmah executives believed the company they had formed with D'Arcy, the First Exploitation Company, forerunner of Anglo-Persian, owned the mineral rights to only the section around the Mosque of Solomon in the Zagros Mountains. The Hanighen-Zischka–French Secret Service account continues:

On route from Persia, D'Arcy stopped off at Alexandria, Egypt, where he met several businessmen. For some undisclosed reason he showed them the *firman*. They offered him £6 million for the concession but he refused to sell. Spies ransacked the apartment in Cairo in which D'Arcy was staying after journeying there from Alexandria. "He would like to destroy the fatal document," Hanighen's account continues, meaning the *firman*. "He no longer desires those infinite riches which lure adventurers to fighting and destruction. He is old, and in his last interview with the Shah he makes no reference to oil or railways. He talks about God, and he expresses the intention of importing not engineers but missionaries into Persia."

Then he left Cairo, shaking off the "spies and concession hunters," and boarded a liner bound for the United States. On the voyage D'Arcy closeted himself in his cabin, praying and reading missionary periodicals. Another passenger who kept to himself was a man clad in priestly vestments, who was said to be returning home from an African mission. D'Arcy sought him out and confided his plans to convert Persia to Christianity. The missionary came up with an idea to further those plans: Why not turn D'Arcy's concession over to the Church? The Shah of Shahs had forbidden Christian missionaries to enter Persia but might change his mind if they owned the concession. The concession agreement with the Shah, after all, had mentioned "heirs and assigns and friends."

Just before the ship docked, according to Hanighen and the French Secret Service, D'Arcy handed over all his rights to the subsoil riches of Persia. But the Church was not the recipient, as D'Arcy believed. Actually he had donated his concession to the British Secret Service. The priest was a fake, a British secret agent who called himself Sidney Reilly but had been born Rosenblum and who has been credited with some of the greatest coups in espionage history. Later he directed British espionage in Russia during the Allied intervention following the Russian Revolution. In 1925 he was captured in Moscow by the Soviet counterespionage and supposedly was executed.

According to Hanighen's account, Reilly forwarded the document granting D'Arcy the Persian concession to his chiefs in London. A mysterious shake-up then occurred in the British oil situation. The Anglo-Persian Oil Company, with capital of £2 million, was formed, with the names of its shareholders kept secret. D'Arcy, by this account, died before World War I in the belief that he had greatly advanced the Church's good work among the heathen. In 1914, Anglo-Persian unmasked; the British Admiralty emerged as the controlling owner in one of the world's largest oil companies.[9]

It was a wildly melodramatic tale, hardly a credit to the literary talents of the French Secret Service, even as part of the lurid history of the oil industry. Stealing a lease or even an oilfield was not unknown. But a concession covering most of a sizable nation? There were several sizable discrepancies in that concoction, of course. It seems incredible that the Burmah Oil Company could have put £600,000 into D'Arcy's venture, as the French claimed, without insisting on reading — if not taking possession of — the document which enabled the First Exploitation Company to operate in Persia. Also, D'Arcy did not die before 1914, as that account stated, but in 1917 in London. Nor can any evidence be found to indicate that D'Arcy traveled to the United States on a liner from Alexandria. He did return to London from Persia, and it would have been strange if so determined a man did not make a public protest when Anglo-Persian wound up under control of the Admiralty, when he had supposedly donated his concession to the missionary purposes of the Catholic Church; no one claims that D'Arcy died a doped prisoner of the Secret Service.

Nor has there ever been a satisfactory explanation of how the Admiralty got hold of Anglo-Persian, or why D'Arcy was content to walk away from the company — now British Petroleum, with assets of almost $5 billion — with only his original investment of £225,000 plus £900,000 worth of stock. No one could have known better than D'Arcy that the Persian concession was worth a lot more.

Reilly's own rather boastful memoir (*Britain's Master Spy*), published six years after his presumed death in a Soviet prison, does not even mention his connection with D'Arcy and Anglo-Persian.[10] But apparently such a connection did exist. A quasi-official account of Reilly's career was published by Robin Bruce Lockhart, the son of Colonel R. H. Bruce Lockhart, who had worked with Reilly in Russia to bring about the downfall of the Soviet government. This version is not only more credible but equally fascinating as an insight into the interaction of governments and the oil industry.

In Lockhart's biography, Reilly also impersonates a priest to gain the devout D'Arcy's confidence but under different circumstances. Reilly, according to Lockhart, first was connected with the Persian concession in 1904 when the Secret Service sent him to Teheran to determine just how the sensitive relations between Russia and Britain might be affected if the British found oil in the country, also to investigate the possibilities of D'Arcy's striking sizable deposits. This would indicate that Whitehall had begun taking a proprietary interest in D'Arcy long before he showed up in London to raise fresh capital for his enterprise. Reilly reported back to London that there was a good chance of D'Arcy's striking it rich, and that the Russians wouldn't object if he stayed out of the northern provinces.

When D'Arcy showed up in London, by Lockhart's account, he was disgusted by the city's refusal to provide him with enough money to continue his explorations. Suddenly D'Arcy disappeared from London, and the Secret Service picked up a rumor that he had been approached by agents of the French Rothschilds. The Rothschilds could put up the money needed. Further, it was said that D'Arcy and the Rothschilds were negotiating right then somewhere in the south of France.

Reilly was assigned to track down the Australian and bring him back to England before he could be lured into the Rothschild camp. He traced D'Arcy to Nice. There he decided it would be best to disguise himself by wearing the long black cloak of a *curé*. The Rothschild security was tight. Reilly then learned that the meetings between D'Arcy and the Rothschilds were taking place on a yacht anchored off Cannes.

For several days Reilly occupied himself by photographing all persons who went out to or came back from the Rothschild yacht, clicking away from a concealed location on the quays. One of the visitors to the yacht was positively identified as William Knox D'Arcy.

Still clad in his priestly vestments, Reilly had himself rowed out to the yacht and was admitted aboard when he announced that he was soliciting funds for a religious charity. It was easy enough for him to attract the attention of D'Arcy, who was always ready to drop business affairs for those of the Mother Church. Reilly, taking him aside, admitted that he was an imposter, that he was an agent of the British government. Word had reached high officials, Reilly told D'Arcy, that he had been unfeelingly treated by the London bankers. The British government was willing to double anything the Rothschilds offered for the Persian concession.

They agreed to meet secretly at the Grand Hotel in Cannes when D'Arcy left the Rothschild yacht later that day. At their second meeting D'Arcy indicated that he might reject the Rothschilds' offer if Reilly could bring him written confirmation of the offer from the Admiralty. He agreed to keep stalling on his negotiations with the Rothschilds for several days.

By train and Channel boat Reilly hurried back to London. The most he could get out of the Admiralty was a letter signed by the Civil Lord, E. G. Pretyman, asking D'Arcy to confer immediately with the Admiralty's oil committee.[11] (Pretyman himself partly confirmed this account. Sometime later he was quoted as saying the oil committee of the Admiralty heard that D'Arcy was "in Cannes trying to sell" the Persian concession "to the French Rothschilds." Without mentioning Reilly as the intermediary, he added that the committee "wrote asking D'Arcy to hold his hand, and D'Arcy came home post haste from the Riviera . . ."[12])

It wasn't quite the definitive offer which D'Arcy had demanded, but at his third clandestine meeting with Reilly he promised to break off negotiations with the Rothschilds and return to London.

If Reilly hadn't turned the trick, Anglo-Persian would have become Franco-Persian, the French would have had their own oil resources (like Germany, France had none to speak of), and there would have been incalculable alterations in the European balance of power. There would have been less rivalry between Britain and France when they came to the infinitely deleterious partitioning of the Middle East after World War I, perhaps, and a juster settlement might have avoided creating the tensions which afflict the area today.

Reilly's role in the exploitation of the Persian concession is more plausibly described in the Lockhart version. But that still doesn't explain why D'Arcy withdrew with a relative pittance just when Anglo-Persian's immense success was assured. One possible explanation was his self-effacing nature. It was his wife who wrote Anglo-Persian's solicitors protesting that D'Arcy's name wasn't even mentioned in the prospectus. "He will not do anything, of course," she wrote in exasperation. "I have talked to him for months but quite uselessly, so I am making a last bid for fame to you . . ." Her plea on behalf of her husband was ignored.[13]

There is another explanation, buttressed by no facts whatsoever. D'Arcy had been accepted as a member of the establishment after coming to London. He could have gone out to Persia as a secret agent of the British government. As an ostensibly private citizen, he could have obtained the concession at a much lower cost than if the Shah's ministers knew they were dealing with another government; this would also have prevented the Russians from taking umbrage at the extension of British influence in a sensitive borderland. That, at least, would explain why D'Arcy surrendered control of the vast reserves he found. But the full story of how Britain gained control of Persian oil is still one of the larger mysteries of international oil and remains locked in the archives of the British Secret Service.

9.

The Kaiser's Pilgrimage

It was the dream of a great Eastern Empire. It was born at Haidar
Pasha and there it died. Over the station was a great clock. Above it
a twisted girder and a broken chimney stood gaunt up against the
sky. The clock had stopped at 12.31 . . . the symbol of a great idea
caught by the throat and its neck broken.
　　　　　　　　　　　　— Harold Armstrong, *Turkey in Travail*

In 1871 a party of German geologists poked around the *villayets* (districts) of Baghdad and Mosul in the Turkish province
of Mesopotamia, now Iraq, and brought back to Berlin glowing
reports of oil seepages which were being worked by Midhat
Pasha, the military governor, for his own modest profit. Some
years later the Germans began building a railroad to Baghdad
while German scholars considered that the town of Hit, on
the Euphrates, had been a source of bitumen for thousands
of years and Herodotus had recorded that it was used on the
walls of Babylon; that in Genesis it was written that a similar
substance was employed in making mortar for the Tower of
Babel; that the people who lived in the marshes of southern
Mesopotamia had used pitch in making their boats.

All these were part of the decision of Kaiser Wilhelm II to

visit the Holy Land in the autumn of 1898 as a "simple pilgrim." It had been six hundred years since the Crusaders, many of them German, had been expelled from the Holy Land; the Kaiser would be the first great Christian ruler to set foot in Palestine. The All-Highest hoped and trusted that other rulers would not believe he was mixing religion with realpolitik, or suspect that his visit to Jerusalem and Constantinople had anything to do with Germany's vaunted *Drang nach Osten*, the Drive to the East.

The Kaiser was not a very subtle man; his motives were held up to a searching examination everywhere, even Germany, where the police confiscated copies of the satirical weekly *Simplicissimus* because it remarked that "Golgotha will not only be able to boast of hearing the last words from the Cross but the first words of Wilhelm."

The French and Russians, with their own ambitions in that part of the world, let Berlin know they were displeased by the pilgrimage, and Pope Leo XIII reminded the Kaiser that France traditionally was the "protector" of the Catholics in Palestine, the Hohenzollerns being Lutheran. No one quite matched the Dowager Empress Marie of Russia in her outrage at the spectacle of the spike-helmeted Kaiser, wearing the white uniform of the Teutonic Knights, posing as the First Gentleman of Christendom. The pilgrimage, she wrote her son, Czar Nicholas II, was revolting, "all done out of sheer vanity, so as to be talked about! That pilgrim's cloak, that pose of Oberpastor, preaching peace on earth in a thunderous voice as though he were commanding troops, and she [Empress Augusta Victoria] wearing the Grand Cross in Jerusalem, all this is perfectly ridiculous and has no trace of religious feeling — disgusting! And further, what a pretty sight when they were both kneeling on Mount Sinai and are being blessed by their children's tutor, expressly brought along for the purpose!"[1]

Not at all abashed by the criticism — could anyone expect the modern Emperor of Germany to set out on foot, wearing a homespun cloak and carrying only a shepherd's staff? — he and his retinue, including Foreign Secretary Baron von Bülow and 120 other high government officials, functionaries, and flunkies, departed from Potsdam station for Venice. The "simple pilgrim" and his companions traveled in an eleven-car special train carrying 110 pieces of the royal luggage. They spent a night in Venice as guests of the King and Queen of Italy, then sailed for Constantinople on the royal yacht *Hohenzollern*.

The real purpose of the visit was transacted in Constantinople, where German officers were training the Turkish army, German engineers and businessmen were taking a firm grip on the Turkish economy, and German diplomats were constantly at the ear of Sultan Abdul Hamid, who was in disgrace with the rest of the world for permitting if not encouraging the Armenian massacres of two years before. The Kaiser and his advisers were intent on extending German influence across the Ottoman Empire to the borders of India. A German-Turkish love feast had been ordained; Turkish shore batteries fired salutes and there were answering salvos from German warships; thousands answerable to the Sultan's secret police turned out to cheer the German emperor and empress on their way to Yildiz Palace.

On the night of the Kaiser's arrival a state dinner was given at the Yildiz Palace at which the German emperor beamed with satisfaction and even the Sultan seemed to relax a little. Abdul Hamid presented the Kaiser with a Damascene sword, the Kaiserina with a diamond necklace, and the whole German people a toast to the success of the German-Turkish collaboration. What the Kaiser really had in mind, as he surveyed that glittering and obsequious assemblage, was Turkish vassalage, a stepping-stone toward world domination, the design of which was succinctly described by Henry Morgenthau, Sr., when he was U.S. ambassador to Turkey and watched the fruition of the plan forwarded that night at the Yildiz Palace: "For twenty years the German Government had been cultivating the Turkish Empire. All this time the Kaiser had been preparing for a world war, and in this war it was destined that Turkey should play an almost decisive part. Unless Germany should obtain the Ottoman Empire as its ally, there was little chance that she could succeed in a general European conflict.[2]

During the next few days, the Kaiser reviewed the Sultan's dispirited army and watched the German flag hoisted to the top of the Galata Tower beside the Turkish ensign. The serious work was done behind closed doors, however, while the Kaiserina and her maids of honor, smiles masking their Prussian Lutheran horror, toured the Sultan's harem. The emperor and his advisers conferred with the pashas who formed the Sultan's government over extending the Anatolian Railway and laid the groundwork for vast concessions four years later.

Business done, the Kaiser and company sailed for Haifa and went through the rigamarole of establishing the All-Highest as an earnest pilgrim, of making propaganda in the Christian world by displaying Wilhelm, booted, spurred and sabretached, following the footsteps of the Prince of Peace. No matter that *Punch*, noting that Cook's travel agency was in charge of the Holy Land tour, sneered at the Kaiser and his party as "Cook's Crusaders." They rode in carriages down the coastal road to Jaffa with an escort of Turkish cavalry, some of them no doubt descendants of the warriors who rode with Saladin. On October 29 this small army, with the Kaiser wearing all his hardware and ribbons, topped by a helmet surmounted by the double eagle, invaded Jerusalem with trumpeters heralding their advent. He made a whirlwind inspection tour of the Church of the Holy Sepulchre, spent ten minutes with his head bowed at the presumed site of Calvary, and consecrated the Church of the Redeemer which had just been restored at Lutheran expense. He also drove up the new road, with its hairpin bend, up the Mount of Olives. The imperial mind at that moment seemed to be centered on more mundane matters than the passion and sacrifice of Jesus Christ. The Kaiser was displeased by the lack of military engineering in building the road, and according to Mrs. Elizabeth Spafford Vester, an American who had spent most of her life in Palestine, he complained to his Turkish hosts that "the bend was far too sharp and narrow to allow cannon to pass that way."[3]

Palestine did not, in fact, please His Germanic Majesty. It was fun swanking around with fifty mounted Knights of St. John clattering at his heels and a Turkish band clanging its cymbals wherever he went, but he grumbled at the "excessive heat and the discomfort of travel" in Palestine and the flies and mosquitoes showed no proper respect for even the most imperious personage. He decided to curtail his pilgrimage after making quick side trips to Beirut, Maalbek and Damascus. He sailed home to find the less patriotic of his subjects snickering over a special edition of the Parisian journal *La Rire*. Under the caption "The All-Highest Goes to Jerusalem" was a cartoon showing the Kaiser riding into Jerusalem on a donkey as Christ had.

To posterity Kaiser Wilhelm II would appear a most abject specimen, but there was nothing foolish about his concept of German military and industrial power stretching eastward and engulfing the Eurasian continent. He needed just two things. One was Constantinople. "If Germany could hold Constantinople," a British journalist observed, "she might, in fifty years, hold Cairo, Baghdad, Jerusalem, Basra, and perhaps Moscow, Delhi and Calcutta."

The other necessary ingredient was oil.

Fourteen hundred miles from Constantinople, its administrative capital, lay the land of the Iraqis and all that remained of Babylon and Ninevah — and a suspected treasure in oil-bearing sands sharing the basin of the Baku and Persian fields. The land itself, the Kurds, and other Arabs who populated it, were as inhospitable as anything on earth; the few Westerners rash enough to travel there regarded it as a suburb of hell. "Call it what you will, 'Mesopotamia,' 'Irak,' 'the cradle of civilization,' " wrote a British traveler, "it is no more than an empty, dusty, barren desert with two great rivers ribbed with strips of green fields and with marshes."[4]

The effort to dominate that distant province between the Tigris and the Euphrates, with only oil seepages to recommend it to any civilized nation, resulted in a concentration of German resources in the Middle East. It also brought the Germans into conflict with the British, who were a little slower in recognizing the potential of the Mespot, and eventually a free-lancing American admiral (retired) who had caught the scent of oil.

The focus of all the plotting on the Golden Horn was Sultan Abdul Hamid, who was willing to sell his inheritance — the Ottoman Empire — in bits and pieces to any foreigner who came along. His throne was rickety, the lands he ruled were peopled by many races, a virtual compost heap of fallen empires dating back to antiquity. He had ruled for years by setting one minority against another. His tax-collecting bureaucracy was the most voracious this side of China. Most of the money collected for the privy purse, according to a variety of accounts, which agree on that subject, went to maintaining a constant turnover in the imperial harem.

In the West Turkey was known as the sick man of Europe, but to his subjects Abdul Hamid was still the King of Kings, Caliph of Caliphs, Shadow of God upon Earth, Arbiter of the World's Destinies. Whenever the Turks became too restive, they were encouraged to massacre their countrymen — the Christians, mostly Armenians and Greeks, who had populated the country long before the Turks arrived on their trek from Central Asia.

Long before that, the For Sale sign was up in Turkey. The Germans, like the French, had been squeezed out of the race for oil resources and were determined to find a supply they could control. The German High Seas Fleet wanted to be oil powered. The army had long been interested in motorization. The steel magnates of the Ruhr, the chemical trusts, and the electrical combines of Rathenau and Siemens-Schuckert, as well as the trading firms whose operations reached into Asia and the South Seas, all demanded that Germany become an oil-producer. She could not depend forever on the low-grade stuff she extracted from lignite, the imports from the Galician province of Poland, and the Ploesti fields in Rumania, and she was worried by her increasing dependence on Standard and Royal Dutch Shell, with their monopolistic jiggling of the price structure.

Thus the potentialities of Ottoman Turkey were more attractive to Germans than to their rivals, at first. Opportunity to open up the oil resources of the eastern *villayets* of Turkey appeared in 1888 when an agreement was signed with Turkey for the construction of the Anatolian Railway. The first stretch was built from Haidar Pasha station in Scutari, across the Bosporus from Constantinople proper, to the ancient city of Konya. But that was only part of the German plan for a *Bagdadbahn*. The German interests interlocked through the Deutsche Bank, which controlled the Anatolian Railway Company, and were openly an arm of German foreign policy. After the Kaiser's visit in 1898, the railway concession was expanded. Now it would be the Berlin-to-Baghdad Railway, which would penetrate the presumed oilfields around Mosul and Kirkuk and proceed all the way to the Persian Gulf.

And by the terms of the new concession the Germans acquired the mineral, including oil, rights to a strip of twenty kilometers on both sides of the railroad. The Germans secretly congratulated themselves on a coup of the greatest magnitude. They hadn't counted on the acute perceptions of Sultan Abdul Hamid.

The Sultan soon decided to investigate whether he had conceded too much to the Germans. The Minister of the Civil List, Hagop Pasha, and the Minister of Mines, Selim Effendi, were assigned to find out just how valuable mineral concessions in Mesopotamia might be. There were no Turkish experts available and they couldn't trust any foreigner, so they recruited an Armenian child prodigy in the oil business named Calouste Gulbenkian. His father was a leading kerosene importer. Calouste Gulbenkian, who was graduated from King's College, London, with a first-class degree in civil engineering at the age of nineteen, toured the Russian oilfields, wrote a series of articles for the *Revue des Deux Mondes*, and published a lengthy book based on those articles before he was twenty-one. It was that book which attracted the Minister of the Civil List and the Minister of Mines.[5]

Hagop Pasha and Selim Effendi asked young Gulbenkian to gather all possible information on oil prospects in Mesopotamia. No Armenian could be overly concerned for the Sultan's privy purse, so he dogged the assignment. "I elaborated a comprehensive report," he recalled in his *Memoirs*, "which was nothing else than a compilation of various travellers' books, principally of reports made by Colonel Chesney on his East India missions, and particularly from what I had heard from different engineers of the Anatolian Railway Company who had been in Mesopotamia." Evidently the German engineers had been indiscreet enough to tell the young Armenian of the oil seepages they had noted along the projected right-of-way.

"Whatever its value," Gulbenkian wrote of his report to the Sultan's ministers, "it prompted the Minister of the Liste Civile to obtain possession for the Sultan of immense tracts of land in different provinces of Mesopotamia. Telegrams were sent to the Governors from the Palace for that purpose. Very little money passed for the purchase of these territories. The owners ceded when they were told that the Governors were sending numerous *tapous* [official certificates of landownership] transferring Government lands to the Liste Civile without any payment."

Gulbenkian, too, got cavalier treatment and must have congratulated himself for not putting more effort into his report, because his reward was nothing more than a handshake. "The Minister of the Liste Civile thanked me profusely for the services which I had rendered in making the report and I shall not forget what he told me at the time: 'My boy, you ought to be very proud because you served the Treasury of His Majesty, and to serve His Majesty's Treasury is to serve your conscience!' "

The Sultan now had control of the Mosul-Kirkuk region, but neither he nor his ministers knew how to exploit it. If they had been able to develop it, they could have changed history — perhaps for the better in many ways. Instead the Sultan set off an Anglo-German rivalry for concessions in the oil-bearing provinces which cost hundreds of thousands of lives. The Germans had the edge because they were building the railroad across Turkey and had infiltrated most strategic areas of the national life. "Haidar Pasha," wrote an Englishman, "begins the eastern section of the great railway planned from Berlin to Baghdad. From here along the Marmora shore to Eshki-Shehir and then by Konya to the Cilician Gates and down to Aleppo and Mosul, the railway follows the route along which for centuries trade has travelled and along which many of the great conquerors have marched to the dominion of the world . . . The Germans had seen that whoever holds this route may threaten and dominate the whole Near East . . ."[6]

Most of all the railroad was the wedge by which the Deutsche Bank hoped to pry open the door to Mosul. The Germans in 1904, after much maneuvering and payment of *baksheesh*, obtained a year's option on the right to explore for oil in the Mosul-Kirkuk region under the terms of the Turkish-German Railway Convention. The agreement provided that if the Germans struck oil they would receive a forty-year concession. German drillers then set out to explore their very limited concession and apparently sent down test drills. In Ottoman Turkey, however, an option was not likely to mean what it said. The Sultan interpreted such contracts to suit himself. When American and English hopefuls arrived on the scene, he was prepared to grant them concessions which would obviously have overlapped the Germans'.

The first American to venture into the quagmire was Rear Admiral Colby M. Chester (ret.), whose interest testified to the continuing affinity between the naval profession and petroleum. Admiral Chester had helped subdue the Spanish fleet during the Spanish-American War. On retirement he accepted a commission from the New York Chamber of Commerce to investigate property damage of Americans during the Armenian massacres. Described as "colorful and swashbuckling," he made a success of that mission, during which he heard of the oil bonanza waiting in the Mesopotamian deserts. Chester promptly succumbed to a syndrome familiar to those whose lives had been changed by the worldwide search for oil.

He returned to the United States on completion of his assignment and organized a mini-cartel to obtain a Turkish concession for the building of railroads and other facilities and exploring for oil. For this project he was given the financial backing of the New York Chamber of Commerce, the New York Board of Trade, and the American Transportation Association, as well as the moral support of the State Department. America suddenly acquired a fascination with the strategic possibilities of the Ottoman Empire to match the contemporary craze for what interior decorators called Turkish cozy corners.

Chester was the pioneer of that rather stealthy American approach to the strategic straits between Europe and Asia. He returned to Constantinople bearing promises of American capital to revitalize the empire, without at the same time alarming the Turks, as the Germans did, by appearing in such numerical and psychological force. On his return in 1908, indeed, he immediately closeted himself with the various *baksheesh* collectors and patiently worked his way up the pecking order to the Yildiz Palace. His scheme was embodied by the Ottoman-American Development Corporation, an enterprise that was to struggle on for the next twenty frustrating years.

Altogether the prospects for American venture capital were

not exactly glowing with promise when Chester finally approached Sultan Abdul Hamid with his offer. An underground movement directed by the Committee of Union and Progress, actually a league of secret societies, was rumbling away in the provinces. Until then, too, American capital invested in Turkey had been a losing proposition; riding at anchor in the Bosporus was an American cruiser which served as a reminder of American displeasure and suspicion.

The ruddiest of optimists, Chester pressed on with his scheme. He and the Sultan got along beautifully. Abdul Hamid was receptive to Chester's promises that his company would build railroads, bridges, even whole towns. In return all that the Ottoman-American Development Corporation asked was the privilege of poking around Armenia and Mesopotamia to see if there was oil in those provinces. The Sultan ordered his Ministry of Mines to draw up a concession for Chester's company.

That same year, 1908, other concessionaires approached the Sultan. Calouste Gulbenkian had returned from abroad as a representative of Shell, quietly opened an office and moved stealthily to obtain his own concession. William Knox D'Arcy also entered the lists. He had just struck his great gusher in Persia and formed the D'Arcy Exploration Company as a subsidiary of Anglo-Persian — and just possibly as a front for the British Admiralty and Secret Service. If there was oil in Persia, the basin might well extend across the border into Mesopotamia. So he sent his assistant, Marriott, to Constantinople to begin the laborious process of bribing his way through the Ottoman bureaucracy.

The story of a similar Belgian concession, as later gathered by American naval intelligence, was equally enlightening on the prevailing business ethics. At the same time the Sultan and his officials were handing out concessions to the British, Germans and Americans, a Belgian engineer named Paul Groscopps appeared in the Turkish capital. An odd circumstance came to his attention: for all the feverish whispering about a vast oil dome under the Mosul sands, no one seemed to be doing much about it. Groscopps decided to find out for himself. He endured great hardships to make a thorough survey of the area and returned certain there was oil in exploitable quantity.

"On the strength of this report," American intelligence ascertained, "a Belgian company was formed to work these oil fields. The company paid 40,000 pounds sterling [$200,000] as *baksheesh* to a member of the Sultan's household in order to help obtain the concession they demanded from the Turkish government . . . At this time the Turks were leaning toward the Germans and practically promised a concession to the Germans if the Belgian company should not succeed."[7]

Then came the Young Turk revolution. At first the revolutionists promised to convert Turkey into a modern democratic state in which all minorities would be justly treated and parliamentary rule would be established. Apparently they had heard of the Marquis of Salisbury's adage, "To reform Turkey means to destroy it," for they retained the old bureaucracy and, after sending Sultan Abdul Hamid into exile, ruled through an undemocratic and secret Council of Seven. Within a few years they guided Turkey into two ghastly Balkan wars.

Admiral Chester, flying the American colors, took the lead in establishing amiable relations with the new "progressive and enlightened" Young Turk regime. In 1909, just after the revolution, he persuaded the Ministry of Mines to confirm in writing that he had obtained the Mosul concession. Meanwhile the competition was warming up. The Germans were insisting that they receive the go-ahead. The British government now was thoroughly alarmed by the progress of the Berlin-Baghdad line advancing toward the Persian Gulf. It decided to match the German effort in Turkey. Calouste Gulbenkian's intrigues laid the groundwork for the British-controlled National Bank of Turkey. The British government, he wrote, believed that the Young Turk revolution provided "a first-class opportunity to resume energetic activity in the Near East . . ."

With cosmopolitan nonchalance, Gulbenkian was serving simultaneously as an official of the Turkish government and as director of a British enterprise secretly carrying out the purposes of British foreign policy. Much of his enthusiasm for this role was supplied by his dislike of Germany, whose grab for Mosul might well have succeeded if Gulbenkian's report on its potential had not convinced the Sultan to appropriate control of the region for himself.

Gulbenkian's colleagues, following the pattern set by the Germans and Admiral Chester, insisted on backing a variety of British-owned enterprises in Turkey. Gulbenkian argued against this course, foreseeing that the National Bank would only squander its resources in an economy so ramshackle it was incomprehensible to any Westerner. Far better, Gulbenkian believed, to keep an eye on the main chance: Mosul oil. "I emphasized all along that purely banking business in Turkey was not at all remunerative, owing to the fierce competition of the German, French and Italian banks, who accepted such risks as we could not entertain."[8]

It was Gulbenkian, by his own account, who kept the National Bank concentrating on the possibility of edging into the oil picture. A scheme had to be worked out whereby the chief claimants to the Mosul concession stopped elbowing each other and combined to apply pressure on the Turks to grant a concession that meant what it said. The problem was to make the Germans realize the deadlock would continue if the Turks were allowed to play them off against the British.

With gentlemanly relish Gulbenkian would recount the subtlety with which the deal was finally arranged with the Germans as partners in the National Bank of Turkey. A limited liability company was formed with the Deutsche Bank receiving twenty thousand shares "in consideration of the [Anatolian] Railway's mining rights [20 kilometers both sides] and the *Lettre Vizirielle* [promising German preferential treatment regarding mining rights]." That gave the Germans a one-quarter interest in the Turkish Petroleum Company. Twenty-eight thousand shares went to the National Bank of Turkey and thirty-two thousand, the largest allotment, "were put at my disposal for myself and the oil group, *the disposal of which was left to me.*" Gulbenkian had intended that of the thirty-two thousand shares passed to his control, twenty thousand would be held by Royal Dutch Shell, twelve thousand by himself.

He soon learned that the British government had not interested itself in the scheme merely to smile benevolently in the background. Anglo-Persian was Whitehall's creation, Royal Dutch Shell a partly foreign firm, and Gulbenkian himself merely a nimble Levantine trader. The whole deal was rearranged when Gulbenkian was informed by Alwyn Parker, head of the Near Eastern Department of Britain's Foreign Office, that "it had been decided that I should transfer my shares at once. The style was somewhat peremptory." Anglo-Persian must hold a majority interest in the Turkish Petroleum Company even though the whole scheme had been concocted by Gulbenkian as Royal Dutch Shell's representative. To Gulbenkian then fell the unpleasant duty of telling Henri Deterding that he had been diddled. "Mr. Deterding got into a state of frenzy. He became wild and stated that if I should decide to part with my shares without his consent, it would mean a definite rupture between us."

It was easy enough for Deterding to defy the British government; he had the support of Holland. Gulbenkian was supported by nothing but his supple intelligence. As an Armenian he knew how to bow to superior force, and besides he believed that Deterding's rage was "altogether non-academic — particularly insofar as he hated the Chairman of Anglo-Persian, Sir Charles Greenway [later Lord Greenway]."[9]

The British members of the Royal Dutch Shell group, still smarting over his ruthless takeover, were not entirely displeased at the way their government had outmaneuvered Deterding. Referring to the realignment of Turkish Petroleum demanded by the British government, Sir Robert Waley Cohen, a Shell director, remarked in Pecksniffian tones: "We do not believe in mixing up politics with business: it leads sometimes to corruption, always to inefficiency, and tends to convert what should be mere commercial rivalries into national animosities — a very serious disadvantage."[10]

On March 24, 1914, a conference was held at the Foreign Office in London to determine the exact ratio of holdings in Turkish Petroleum. The site of the meeting was significant, demonstrating that the British government was in the oil business as a direct participant. The decision reached at the meeting also reflected the governmental role. Anglo-Persian got fifty percent of the stock, the Deutsche Bank held onto its twenty-five percent, and the other quarter interest went to Royal Dutch Shell. For services rendered, Gulbenkian received two and a half percent each from Shell and Anglo-Persian, thus his sobriquet "Mr. Five Per Cent."

10.

A Tale of Two Admirals

> We will steal nothing from others.
> We will allow no others to steal from us.
> We are against others who steal from others.
> — Richard Washburn Child

To a considerable extent the outcome of World War I was shaped by the belligerents' unequal access to oil. Aside from making more enemies than her armies could deal with, and producing too many field marshals and too few able diplomats, Germany's main difficulty was that she never had enough oil to keep her war machine running smoothly. The multifront war she conducted against encircling enemies was a military epic, but she was forced to undertake operations in search of oil that warped her strategy and sapped her strength. Whole armies had to be shifted in the Balkans and Middle East to satisfy her oil thirst. Her tremendously efficient forces were able to knock out the Russians while fighting the French and British to a standstill on the Western Front but elsewhere they were called upon to undertake costly operations to protect the relative trickle of oil from Galicia, to invade Rumania and seize the Ploesti fields.

Even with the British command of the seas and the inflow of oil from Asia, the Middle East and America, the Allies often were hard pressed and had to establish an Inter-Allied Petroleum Council to ration themselves. Forty-five percent of Britain's navy had been converted to oil-burning boilers when the war broke out, and its fuel consumption rose from 130,000 tons a month in 1914 to 330,000 tons in 1917. And German submarine warfare so threatened the British oil supply during the later stages of the war that the Allied shortage became almost as severe as the German.

Several of the most ghastly slaughters of the war were directly related to the urgency of maintaining a steady flow of fuel oil to the navies and gasoline to the partly motorized armies and the air forces. Britain launched an expeditionary force against the Dardanelles in 1915, resulting in the bloody futility of the Gallipoli campaign. The seizure of Constantinople would probably have overturned the Young Turk government; it would certainly have opened Allied access to the Russian wheat crops and Baku oil, permitted munitions shipments to Russia which might well have kept her in the war, and forestalled the Bolshevik Revolution.

Meanwhile, the Turks made their own ill-prepared attempt at capturing Baku and its oil reserves. An army of ninety thousand was led into the high passes of the Caucasus by Enver Pasha, the regnant Young Turk who had brought about the German alliance and who was the prime mover of Pan-Islamism, with the aim of turning the Russians' southern flank and taking Baku. The sturdy Anatolian infantry, which fought so bravely at Gallipoli, was ill equipped for mountain warfare and winter campaigning, and they reeled back under the Russian onslaught. Only twelve thousand survived the mountain battles and most of those died of spotted typhus sweeping their tentless bivouacs.

Strapped as she was for battalions to shore up the Western

Front, Britain managed to spare the troops necessary to insure that in any postwar settlement she would have a clear, blood-sealed claim to the oil resources of Mesopotamia. Such rights, benefiting those who held large blocks of stock in Anglo-Persian and Turkish Petroleum, were won through the death and incredible suffering of the troops who were flung into the deserts to secure the Persian oilfields and stake out a claim on Mosul. The experiences of one of those unwitting warriors in the unofficial service of the oil industry, the sacrifices that underlie the enormous profits since extracted from the oil domes of the Middle East, are wryly related in an obscure memoir by Captain Harold Armstrong, a survivor of the 147-day siege at Kut-al-Imarah.

Indian army divisions under the command of General Sir Charles Townshend crossed Persia, invaded Mesopotamia, took Basra, headed for Baghdad, Mosul and Kirkuk, and then floundered. Its operations, falling under the direction of the Indian Office, were handicapped from the start by a wretched mismanagement of the logistics along their long supply line back to India; they lacked artillery, desert-worthy vehicles, ammunition, food and medicine; and the whole force was undermanned. At ancient Ctesiphon, on the approaches to Baghdad, Townshend and his army, actually only the Sixth Division reinforced, ran up against a Turkish force a few thousand stronger. The Turks, however, were commanded by the exceedingly skillful Field Marshal Baron Colmar von der Goltz, who defeated Townshend at Ctesiphon and sent him reeling toward the oasis of Kut-al-Imarah, where he was besieged while another "army" was dispatched from India to his relief.

The sufferings of Townshend's troops at Kut were all but incredible. The town itself was only a collection of mud huts, soon surrounded by British trenches and beyond them the Turks. Winter rains slashed down on the unsheltered men, the Tigris rose and flooded the troops out of their trenches. Captain Armstrong would remember those endless days and bitter nights as a "dull, grey monotony. It became as eventless as a schoolboy's diary. There was no rest, no going back to comfortable billets as in France, but always the crack and flip of snipers' bullets and the drone of shells . . . Food began to be scarce and communiqués from General Headquarters increased in numbers and in promises, till the troops laughed at each new one . . . The world became full of great evil blue flies . . . Lice came by the million and crawled in indecency. Dysentery and scurvy and enteritis, which is little less than cholera, killed the men. Despair and monotony and hunger got hold of us. There was disease, starvation, desertion, crime, despair, and over all the drone of the 40-pound shells and the crack of snipers' bullets . . ."[1]

General Townshend, in a last desperate effort to escape from the trap, tried to bribe the enemy with an offer of £2 million carried in his baggage wagons. The end finally came in April 1916, after the British held out for 147 days. Britain's effort to snatch the Mespot oil lands (undertaken just about the time Turkish Petroleum's controllers were seizing the Deutsche Bank's twenty-five percent share as enemy property) cost the empire almost forty thousand troops. "The Mesopotamian mess," Lloyd George would call it, "the paradise of the steel helmet." Actually it was the paradise of the dreamed-of oil derricks, the attainment of which was allotted to generals unprepared for that kind of campaigning.[2]

And it was hell for the thousands of survivors who had to march sixteen hundred miles across deserts and mountains and through Arab mobs howling for their blood, with a Turkish prison at the end. Captain Armstrong recalled that he was possessed only by "a dull instinct that I must go on . . . The training of the public schools, the veneer and polish of modern life and civilization disappeared, and we were primitive in our dealings with one another." At the village of Tekreet the column of British prisoners came across survivors of a previous batch of their captured comrades. "They were dying of dysentery; and there they lay uncared for under the pitiless June sun. When we helped them to crawl in the shade under the cliffs the Arabs stoned them out again under the sun. Later we heard that our men came here by the hundreds, until this beach was black with men crawling because they could not stand. Under the raging sun they died of dysentery and enteritis, while the Arabs gloated over them and looted them . . ." When the survivors of that death march finally reached the prison camp at Kustamouni near the Black Sea, they looked so much like "half-wild animals" that the guards were terrified of them. Needless to say, Captain Armstrong and his fellow prisoners were not among those who half swooned with delight at the romanticization of the Arab world by Colonel T. E. Lawrence or who fell in with his grandiose plan to hand over most of the Middle East to the Arabs, minus, of course, the oil underneath their slippered feet.

By the end of the war British forces finally succeeded in grasping the oil-rich prize of the Mespot after that theater, as British military historian Cyril Falls has written, "was allotted a disproportionate strength from Britain's war potential."[3] General Sir Edmund Allenby took it, but only after an apparently accidental explosion logistically crippled his Turkish and German opponents. On September 6, 1917, the munitions about to be forwarded to their desert army blew up at the Haidar Pasha station in Constantinople. Captain Armstrong, surveying the scene later as a staff officer with the British army of occupation wrote that the German hope of seizing an oil-based empire in the Middle East was born and died there.[4]

Even the admiring Captain Falls, in his history of the final Mesopotamian campaign, had to conclude that it "witnessed an undignified rush to secure Mosul, with its oil potential, before the Turkish armistice came into effect. Mosul was not actually secured until after the armistice had been signed and the legality of its occupation was more than dubious."[5]

In view of oil's impact on the fortunes of the First World War, the British might have been forgiven for clutching at their clouded title to Mosul. Oil was credited with winning the battle of Verdun for the French, who were able to keep a steady stream of trucks and troop convoys pumping life into the sector in 1916. "A drop of oil is worth a drop of blood," Clemenceau remarked. A year later the oil shortage was so desperate on the Western Front, with the last series of German offensives in the offing, that the French war leader dispatched an appeal to President Wilson: "A failure in the supply of petrol would cause the immediate paralysis of our armies, and might compel us to a peace unfavorable to the Allies. Now the minimum stock of petrol computed the French armies by their Commander-in-Chief must be 44,000 tons, and the monthly consumption is 35,000 tons. This indispensable stock has fallen today to 28,000 tons, and threatens to fall to almost nothing if immediate and exceptional measures are not undertaken and carried out by the United States. These measures must be taken without a day's delay for the common safety of the Allies, the essential condition being that President Wilson shall obtain permanently from American oil companies tank steamers with a supplementary tonnage of 100,000 tons . . . The safety of the Allied nations is in the balance. If the Allies do not wish to lose the war, then, at the moment of the great German offensive, they must not let France lack the petrol which is as necessary as blood in the battles of tomorrow."[6] Standard and other American oil companies, a fleet of tankers and U.S. destroyer convoys built up the Allied stocks behind the Western Front to 1.5 million tons by April 1918, and victory was secured. Lord Curzon later testified that the "Allies floated to victory on a sea of oil."

On the enemy side, the situation was reversed. Germany had no ally to which she could fly distress signals. After the drawn battle of Jutland, the Kaiser's Grand Fleet was immobilized, partly out of fear of another encounter and partly because of the shortage of fuel oil. The movement of German armies was hampered by a similar lack for their trucks and motorcycles. War production was slowed by a shortage of lubricants, kerosene was severely rationed on the home front, and the exploits

217

of the Red Baron and other airmen had to be performed in planes fueled by benzol, an inferior substitute for gasoline.

The strategic necessity of finding oil diverted German troops from more urgent operations to Rumania, where Ploesti would replenish the stocks of the Europeanische Petroleum Trust. "As Austria could not supply us with sufficient oil," General Ludendorff wrote, "and as all our efforts to increase production were unavailing, Rumanian oil was of decisive importance to us. But even with the deliveries of Rumanian oil, the question of oil supplies still remained very serious and caused us great difficulty, not only for the conduct of the war but for the life of the country. The stocks of the Caucasus opened a more favorable prospect for us in 1918."

The Caucasian prospect — the oil of Baku — may have been one factor in Ludendorff's decision to send Lenin and a party of Bolshevik revolutionists to St. Petersburg in a sealed train from their Swiss exile. If so, it paid off. Shortly after the revolution began, it quickly spread to the Baku oilfields, where Stalin and other agitprop specialists had been working for years. The Czarist governor was chased out, even as German-Turkish forces began an offensive in the Caucasus with Baku as their objective. For a few brief weeks, Germany at last possessed the prize which long eluded her, an unlimited oil supply; she took over the Baku-Batum pipe and railway lines, but before the oil could flow toward Germany the war ended.[7]

For oilmen the real war was just about to begin.

The United States established a naval presence a half-century ago in the eastern Mediterranean, at the end of World War I, when the U.S. Naval detachment appeared in the Bosporus. It consisted of the station ship *Scorpion*, formely Sarah Bernhardt's yacht, eight destroyers, and six sub-chasers, which soon began scooting around the Sea of Marmara and the Aegean and the Black seas as though in their home waters.

In command of all this sudden expansion of American naval power and commercial interest was a shrewd, tough-minded, ruddy-faced, square-jawed rear admiral named Mark L. Bristol, of the American sea-dog variety, which is to say that he was hostile toward and suspicious of the British.

Admiral Bristol, born in 1868 and a serving officer in the years when the United States was just beginning to flex its naval muscle and build a steel-hulled navy, had participated in the Spanish-American War and the Vera Cruz landing. For three years he had been in charge of developing naval aviation. In 1917 he had commanded the battleship *North Carolina* on Atlantic convoy duty. In 1919 he was given command of the eastern Mediterranean detachment and also appointed U.S. High Commissioner to Turkey. He wore two hats, civil and naval, and did not hesitate to use the wide powers they bestowed. The United States, rather cagily, had refused to declare war on Turkey, even though Turkey's allies were her enemies. She remained sympathetic to the Turks even while her former allies were dismembering the old Ottoman Empire. Britain and France were bent on assuming "mandates" which gave them Mesopotamia and Syria; Italy was claiming a chunk of Turkish territory; and Greece would soon invade Anatolia. The other victors were urging that the United States establish a mandate over Armenia, the landlocked scene of genocidal massacres during the war.

In a conference of high commissioners, Bristol coolly proposed instead that the United States assume a mandate over all of Turkey.

"What?" exclaimed Admiral de Robeck, the British Commissioner, whose monocle popped out of his eye. "And we'd give up Iraq and Palestine, that we've shed our blood for?"[8]

The victorious allies thus tried to set up a sort of ratio between the amount of blood spilled and the amount of oil land each was entitled to as recompense. America had come into the war so late she deserved to be placed below the salt at the victory table. When Robert Dunn, a former war correspondent, was assigned to Admiral Bristol as his staff intelligence officer, the latter told him that there was no cooperation with the

British. The British, Dunn noted, "never got straight why America was here, anyway. Yet every missionary in Anatolia came from our Mount Holyoke or Oberlin. All the tobacco of Samsun and Smyrna went into U.S. cigarettes, and Standard Oil kerosene packed most camel trains out of Trebizond."

And, of course, American oil concessionaires, including the indefatigable Colby Chester, were still hanging in there with their hopes sighted on Mosul. For the next decade the two admirals, one active and one retired, were deeply involved in the American effort to reach the Middle East reserves.

In America a near-panic was running through the oil industry, which had almost exhausted itself in supplying the Allied demand. Mexican wells were spouting salt water. The domestic reserves, it was believed, were insufficient to keep American companies in world competition. In 1917–1918 the United States had supplied eighty percent of the Allied requirements, even though the German U-boat toll on its tankers was so high that for a time in late 1917 the British Home Fleet was all but immobilized for lack of fuel oil. Now that the war was over, the British were aggressively elbowing aside the Americans as well as all other rivals for the greatest proven reserves.

The British were assuming a mandate over Iraq and Palestine, the French over Syria (through which pipelines from Iraq would run), and both had formed an "Empire exclusion policy" which was designed to freeze out Americans in particular. "During the months after the Armistice," John A. De Novo has written, "the British had refused to allow geologists of the Standard Oil Company of New York to investigate its claims obtained in Palestine prior to the war, and soon they excluded from Mesopotamia American geologists eager to investigate oil possibilities there. The diplomatic exchanges during 1919 and 1920 resulting from these cases . . . lent color to the fears that the British, in carrying out their alleged monopolization, were discriminating against American oil interests."[9]

If that wasn't reason enough for the United States to formulate a more self-interested attitude toward the disposition of oil-bearing territories, there was the rather gloating article written by a London banker, Sir Edwin Mackay Edgar, which predicted an all-out victory by British interests in the world oil competition: "While America is exhausting her supplies at a prodigal speed, we are getting a firmer grip upon the world's oil reserves . . . I should say that two-thirds of the improved oil fields of Central and South America are in British hands." The Shell group, he noted, now included interests — often virtual monopolies — in Asia, the Middle East, Russia (although that claim was dubious and subject to violent change), and even the United States.

As for the coming bonanza in the Middle East, Sir Edwin wrote, "We shall have to wait a few years before the full advantages of this situation shall begin to be reaped; but that the harvest eventually will be a great one, there can be no manner of doubt. To the sum of many millions of pounds a year, Americans before long will have to purchase from British companies and to pay us in dollar currency in progressively increasing proportion, the oil she cannot do without and is no longer able to furnish from her own store."

There were apparently no bounds to Sir Edwin's *hubris*, which only reflected that of his colleagues in London's financial district and at Royal Dutch Shell headquarters in London and The Hague. "With the exception of Mexico, and to a lesser extent of Central America, the outer world is securely barricaded against an American invasion in force. There may be small, isolated sallies, but there can never be a mass attack. The British position is impregnable. This is no revelation. The United States experts have been well aware of this situation for more than a year. But Congress and public opinion were not on their guard.

"The [American] public at large, convinced that America is an immense reservoir of petroleum, and never having seen its engines stop for want of oil, took it for granted that petroleum

221

is a product which grows naturally, like apples on an apple tree. Unfortunately for them — and fortunately for us — their eyes have been opened too late."[10]

Nor was this an isolated case of British self-confidence over their ability to gain control of most of the world's oil reserves. The London *Financial News* on February 24, 1920, estimated that Britain's "present command of the world's oil resources runs to no less than seventy-five percent of their entirety, compared with two percent when that country entered the war."

About the same time Sir Henri Deterding, who as a citizen of the neutral Netherlands, had carefully conserved Shell's supplies while Britain was begging for American help in keeping its Home Fleet in operation, was making the same sort of boasts in his 1920 annual report. He congratulated himself on his company's policy of scattering its production facilities throughout the world. (Not least in the United States. He had invaded the California fields, had taken over the Roxana Petroleum Company in Oklahoma as a subsidiary — and to top it off he had persuaded the Americans to finance his attack on their oil reserves. A syndicate headed by Kuhn, Loeb and Company sold large blocks of Deterding's stock, which was snapped up by American investors. This income allowed Deterding to continue expanding his operations.)

"It hardly needs to be mentioned," Deterding stated in his report, "that the American petroleum companies have also realized, although too late, that it was not sufficient to have a large production in their own country . . . It goes without saying that we are now reaping the benefits resulting from this advantageous position . . . We must not be outstripped in this struggle to obtain new territory. Our interests are therefore being considerably extended; our geologists are everywhere where any chance of success exists."

The rest of the world had not yet realized that baiting American capital could be a dangerous business. In Congress demands were made that the government protect our oil enterprises abroad, and the State Department replied with a document charging that Britain was trying to freeze out American interests. "The policy of the British Empire is reported to be . . . the exclusion of aliens from the control of the petroleum supplies of the Empire and to endeavor to secure some measure of control over oil properties in foreign countries."[11]

The San Remo Agreement of April 1920 only confirmed American apprehensions that Britain and France, as the major Allied powers, intended to freeze out the United States. No mention at all was made of any American rights or privileges. A British-controlled company was to take over all the oil reserves in what was now Iraq, France would receive the old Deutsche Bank twenty-five percent share of holdings in the Turkish Petroleum Company and would agree to build pipelines across Syria. The United States could only proclaim the validity of the Open Door concept, which had worked so well for the participating powers, particularly the United States, in China before the war.

Finally the State Department angrily demanded of the British Foreign Office whether the United States was not entitled to share in Middle East concessions as one of the "usual consequences of association in war." This ploy was briskly deflected as sheer hypocrisy. The two leading British oil historians of the period put it this way: "How the mighty had fallen! The United States had originally set a fine example of charity by virtuously declining to take a mark of German reparations or a square mile of the German colonies, but after four years was found making an exception to its self-denying ordinance in the case of the oil fields in Mesopotamia." The American policy had advanced, they asserted, from the economic-equality principle of the Open Door to the "lower note of 'sharing the swag.' "[12]

There was talk of promoting a boycott of Shell in the United States, but it was discarded because of the danger of a counter-boycott. And eventually the British, recovering their traditional suavity, sent Sir John Cadman, one of the architects of the Anglo-Persian deal, to Washington to suggest that a com-

223

promise might be worked out. But that would take more than a half-dozen years of bluffing, maneuvering and bargaining in London, The Hague, Lausanne, Washington, Istanbul.

That was the background to Admiral Bristol's mission to Istanbul.

Istanbul in the early 1920's like Berlin in the 1960's, was the espionage capital of the world. The city was overrun by agents operating for or against a Free Armenia, the White armies in Russia, the Soviets, the Greeks, the Allied Occupation, the Turkish nationalists supporting Kemal Ataturk. To Robert Dunn of U.S. naval intelligence Istanbul was "a wide-open town, old Arizona style." Within a short radius, the Whites and Reds were fighting it out in southern Russia, the Greeks were battling the Turks, the desert tribes were struggling against the French and British. Naturally the U.S. and British intelligence men took a keen interest in each other's activities. "War censorship and intelligence work gave one a certain carelessness about the mails," as Dunn put it. "Often useful were the gray manila envelopes printed 'On His Majesty's Service' which could be lifted in office or mess. You couldn't let the admiral in on breaking the Foreign Office code. But our destroyers took carbons of dispatches from the British high commissioner in Georgia . . . I'd pick them up from mailbags, steam covers open over the teakettle in the embassy kitchen. Then my yeoman resealed and sent them on . . . For expert cracking they went on to Washington . . ."[13]

Judging from the entries in what he aptly called his war diary, Admiral Bristol soon learned that the largest part of his effort would be concerned with oil concessions. That log shows him conferring almost daily with someone or other connected with the search for a way to obtain an American share. Even such a preposterous figure as one Rustem Neghib Bey, who represented the false hope of establishing an Assyro-Chaldean republic, had to be given audience at which raw intelligence could be gleaned.[14]

There were two American interests ready to exploit whatever share in the Mosul fields could be obtained. Besides the Chester concession, which had priority, Standard Oil was on the scene and doing its best to make up for its tardiness. Standard even tried to buy the Mosul claims being pressed by the heirs of the late Sultan Abdul Hamid. Failing that, it was content to bide its time knowing the State Department secretly favored its cause. Standard built a refinery at Selvi Bournu, just above the Bosporus, and when a fire started there under "suspicious circumstances," Admiral Bristol sent men from his ships to put it out and stationed naval guards over the property.[15]

Bristol did not favor his old Spanish-American War comrade, Admiral Chester, over Standard Oil, but helped both rivals impartially. Rather naively, perhaps, he hoped that the two American factions could get together and jointly press the Mosul claim. He did not sense that Standard was determined on getting its foot in that door without cutting in Chester and his New York backers. Standard maintained its standoffishness even after Admiral Chester came to an agreement with the new government of Turkey under which he was given a 99-year railway, oil, and mineral concession covering twenty kilometers on either side of a 2,400-mile right-of-way. The new concession not only covered the former German rights but untapped fields in the *villayets* of Van, Bitlis and Erzerum. The new contract called for Chester's building railways and port facilities worth $1.5 billion.

Standard may have known that Chester was undercapitalized for such a huge project; certainly it was confident of its influence with the new Republican (Harding) administration. A hint of its self-assurance was contained in Bristol's exchange with Dr. Victor Heiser of the Rockefeller Foundation. Now thoroughly pro-Turk, Bristol berated Dr. Heiser because the foundation had just given the city of London $5 million for a new hospital but rejected a plea for funds for the American Hospital in Istanbul. Heiser, he wrote, "set forth that the political conditions here were such that the Rockefeller Foundation

225

did not feel justified in going ahead with any work in Turkey."
Bristol may have wondered what "political conditions" had
to do with a supposed philanthropic exercise.[16]

He exerted every bit of his influence toward bringing the
Chester project and Standard Oil together so they could present a united American front; he saw it as a "combined operation" in the military sense. In his war diary he recorded a
conversation with Admiral Chester in May 1922, in which he
advised Chester to discharge a certain Canadian employee who
may have been infiltrated by the British. Chester, he wrote,
agreed that "different American interests seeking to do business in Turkey should combine for a common interest and
not compete with each other."[17]

During the winter and spring of 1922–1923 Admiral Bristol
spent much of his time commuting to Switzerland as an
official American observer at the Lausanne Conference, where
the territorial limits of a Westernized Turkey were set, but he
continued to press for a recognition of American aspirations
in that part of the world. On October 5, 1923, he held a frank
and sometimes ill-tempered discussion with the Acting British
High Commissioner in Istanbul, Neville Henderson, and a
British admiral named Webb. Bristol and Webb went at it
quarterdeck style while Henderson as a professional diplomat
tried to preserve decorum.

"Why are you always talking about America's rights in
Turkey?" Admiral Webb growled at Bristol. "You did not send
an army here and spend money and lose men."

About the same time the U.S. High Commissioner was dis-
creetly promoting the Chester project, and the American public
was being informed of its new ventures in the Middle East,
liberals back in the States began protesting that the navy was
taking too great an interest in the Chester concession, presumably because it wanted a fuel supply for the destroyer
division based on Istanbul. "There is no reason," remarked
the liberal Democratic New York *World*, "why the State Department should make itself the promoter of the Chester busi-

ness enterprises . . . Certainly the American people have no more interest in taking up the Chester concessions diplomatically than they would have if the Admiral was proposing to open a candy store in Piccadilly" — thereby exhibiting a stubborn indifference to the relative strategic value of petroleum and bonbons. An American magazine was also somewhat startled by the report of a traveling correspondent that under Admiral Bristol's benevolent eye, "American destroyers are entering Turkish ports with 'drummers' as regular passengers, and their fantails are piled high with American samples. An American destroyer has made a special trip at thirty knots to get American prospectors into a newly opened field." The U.S. navy flotilla at Istanbul was openly assisting American business in Turkey and turning over all "information of commercial activities obtained by naval officers in their frequent trips around the Black Sea."

The admiral's war diary bears out reports that aboard the station ship *Scorpion*, wearing his naval hat, or ashore at the U.S. embassy in the Pera quarter he was a vigorous exponent of American interests, which he conceived to be part of his duty. His intelligence officer, Robert Dunn, related that when he traveled on a destroyer to the oil port of Batum they were accompanied by a "Socony [Standard Oil of New York] vice-president who'd been on the Anglo-American war oil board and was the only U.S. civilian I'd seen with the British fleet when the Germans surrendered theirs."[18]

During the period when the great powers were settling the Mosul question in secret negotiations, Bristol was being assured of the eventual success of the Chester project. On June 3, 1923, he recorded a conversation with Julian E. Gillespie, U.S. trade commissioner, that Prime Minister Raouf Bey of the new Turkish republic told him in Ankara: "Turkey will never grant a concession for a pipeline in the Persian fields until the Chester people have built their [Turkish] railway to the Persian frontier. *Now go and tell your Standard Oil friends that.*" There was no conflict, Raouf Bey maintained, between the claims of Sultan Abdul Hamid's heirs with the provisions of the Chester concession to "build a railroad from Mosul to Suleimanie and for mineral rights on both sides of the proposed railway. *We have given Chester a concession and we are going to stand behind it.*" The Turkish Prime Minister also told Gillespie that the logical way for the British to exploit their Persian fields was through a pipeline across Turkey, and that gave Turkey a certain amount of control over British activities.[19]

A little earlier Bristol had also held an encouraging conversation with a New York banker who was pumping fresh funds into the Chester project. The banker admitted that the more powerful financiers in America, possibly because they'd got the word from Standard Oil, were wary of the project, which he believed would eventually absorb $2 billion in venture capital. Bristol told the banker he was promoting Chester's scheme because "if Americans handled this project they could pretty nearly dictate to the Turkish government regarding laws for the best development of Turkey in the future."[20]

At the conference on Near Eastern affairs in Lausanne the final terms with Turkey were arranged and the spoils of Mosul allotted. The United States sent a delegation of observers — Richard Washburn Child, the U.S. ambassador to Rome; Joseph C. Grew, and Admiral Bristol — who did not hesitate to move from observation to participation.[21]

Lord Curzon for Britain, Mussolini for Italy, Poincaré for France, Venizelos for Greece, and Ismet Inonu for Turkey were among those grouped around the conference table in an effort to arrange a final peace settlement. The wrangling went on for months, usually in temperate diplomatic tones but occasionally in acrimony. "It is my great wish," Ambassador Child, the ranking U.S. delegate, confided to his diary, "to establish here the principle of the Open Door in the Near East . . ."[22]

The urbane Harold Nicolson, a member of the British delegation, complained of Child that "He was typically American in his conviction that the whole Lausanne Conference was a plot on the part of the Old Diplomacy to deprive American company promoters of oil concessions." The British, on the whole, were very unhappy with the United States and simply wouldn't yield in the matter of the Chester concession, which was significantly ratified by the Grand National Assembly of Turkey while the second session of the Lausanne Conference was in progress. If the Turks and the Americans were allowed to get away with that, the acquisition of Iraq might be rendered all but meaningless.

From the earliest history of the oil industry, it always turned out that control of transportation was essential to the development of any lucrative oilfield. By the terms of the Chester concession, an American-built railway net, pipelines, and port facilities would cover eastern Turkey right up to the proposed Turkey-Iraq boundary. Furthermore the forty-mile band along the right-of-way would run right through the Mosul-Kirkuk region which the British were claiming for Iraq. And if Mosul was carved out of Iraq and handed back to Turkey, "the resulting economic complex would be so pervasive as to make eastern Turkey and Mosul impenetrable to competition."[23]

Nor was the State Department prepared to go all out against the British for the sake of the Chester concession, about which it was increasingly dubious. Its position, as summarized by the American diplomatic historian Waldo H. Heinrichs, Jr., was that "the Chester undertaking offered little hope of success."[24] It was prepared to wave aside the purely legal consideration that the Chester concession had been ratified by three successive Turkish governments.

And there was the undeniable fact that something more was involved than deciding which American group was less "speculative" or "questionable." The group that won out — Rockefeller's Standard, Mellon's Gulf, with Andrew Mellon then occupying the post of U.S. Secretary of the Treasury — simply possessed incomparably greater political influence than Colby Chester and his supporters.

More than a hint of conflict of interest was charged when the American section of the Lausanne agreements came up for Senate ratification. An opposition group headed by James W. Gerard, the wartime ambassador to Berlin, tried to block the treaty in the Senate, claiming that it was part of a conspiracy to enable American oil companies to "grab vast oil deposits."[25] That charge was amplified in a letter from Vahan Cardashian, attorney for an Independent Armenia movement, to Senator William E. Borah of the Foreign Relations Committee:

"I charge that two members of the President's Cabinet bartered the Armenian case at the Lausanne Conference and conspired to effect the expulsion of nearly 1,000,000 Armenians from their ancestral homes, for a share in Mosul oil, and that they are now scheming to seize possession of the oil deposits in the deserted homes of their victims. I charge that these men and their confederates in this outrage have used and are now using the Department of State as their willing tool to carry out their infamous design; and that the Department of State, in an effort to cover up the tracks of those who have dictated its policy in this respect, has resorted to misrepresentation, intrigue, and even terrorism and has flooded the land with shameless and irresponsible propaganda . . .

"Under these circumstances, what, then, is the motive, the purpose behind the Turkish policy of the Department of State? I charge that it is oil. An administration which has surrendered legitimate American rights and then has had the impudence to fill the air with irrelevancies, wild insinuations and falsehoods to divert attention from its disgraceful policy; an Administration which had deliberately trampled upon the Constitution of the United States in its conduct of foreign relations — such an Administration . . . has not hesitated to sell out the Armenian people and their homes for oil, in the interest of a privileged group . . ."[26]

During the final stages of the Lausanne Conference the British tried to slip through an article which would have validated the Turkish Petroleum Company's concession, even though it had never been ratified by the Turkish parliament. Acting as "observers," and stiffened by a 1,783-word cable from Secretary of State Charles Evans Hughes, the American delegation worked on the chief Turkish delegate, Ismet Inonu, to hold out against the British. At a final session lasting seven hours and breaking up at two o'clock in the morning, Inonu emerged from the conference table after receiving "treatment which would make the third degree in a Harlem police station seem like a club dinner." But he had refused to accept the article in the draft treaty the British wanted. They would have to prove their case before the Council of the League of Nations.

That body finally, in 1925, awarded the oil district around Mosul to Iraq and placed that newly created nation under a twenty-five-year British mandate. The British installed the former Emir Faisal, a protégé of Colonel Lawrence, on the Iraqi throne. Iraq promptly granted the Turkish Petroleum Company a seventy-five-year concession to develop its oil resources. Not unexpectedly there was an uproar in Turkey over the League's decision, but Britain prevailed through an artifice characteristic of its diplomacy in that period. The details were supplied by Henri de Jouvenal, former French High Commissioner in Syria, in an article written for an American periodical a year later: "Early in 1926, when the League's decision on the Mosul question nearly precipitated an Anglo-Turkish war, England offered Cilicia [a Turkish province] as a bait to Italy. I was present in Angora [Ankara] at the time, attempting as High Commissioner in Syria to negotiate a treaty of neighborliness with the Turks. Personally I have not the slightest doubt that the fear of an Italian landing in Cilicia hastened an arrangement between the British and Ottoman [sic] Governments whereby Italy was cheated of a military adventure."[27]

The United States went along with the settlement of the Mosul question, which had been an irritant for more than a quarter of a century and undoubtedly had helped bring on World War I, because an American consortium was given a large share of the loot. The American entry had been engineered partly, perhaps mostly, through the statesmanship of Calouste Gulbenkian, who had already brought the French into the winning combination; it was the only way to keep the peace. "Personally," he wrote, "from the inception of the American crisis, I had held the opinion, taking the broader view, that it was sounder and higher policy to admit the Americans into the Turkish Petroleum Company, instead of letting them loose to compete in Iraq for concessions when in reality the Company had a very weak grip there. The oil groups are always tempted to seize what they see before them without looking ahead or following broader policies of collaboration."

He advised Sir William Tyrrell to impress on Royal Dutch Shell and Anglo-Persian that "it was in the national interest that the Americans should be admitted as soon as possible — that, whatever the rights or wrongs of the matter, it was far more practical politics to make room for the Americans in the Mesopotamian fields."[28] Gulbenkian understood the relation of national power and prestige, which the United States had won through participation in World War I at its most critical stage. Morality, even legality, had nothing to do with the case. The Chester concession, after all, had the firmest moral and legal claim to participation in the Mosul development, but it was more powerful American interests that took the prize.

The crux of the negotiations was how large a share of Turkish Petroleum the Americans should be granted. Walter C. Teagle, president of Standard Oil of New Jersey, argued as their spokesman that the U.S. participants should have an equal footing with Shell and Anglo-Persian, and his views finally prevailed.

In the settlement of 1925 Anglo-Persian, Royal Dutch Shell, Compagnie Française (representing the French interests) and the American consortium each received a 23¾ percent interest in Turkish Petroleum, and the tenacious Gulbenkian was still in for 5 percent. It was another victory for the Rockefeller interests, which arrived late on the scene, let other men sweat and connive, and then walked off with the winnings. Their drillers operated in Washington and on Wall Street; they along with the Mellons tapped the prestige won by American soldiers on the Western Front. Standard accepted its inevitable victory with modesty and discretion, even tried to play down the enormity of the prize. It was all a triumph of the virtuous American trade policies. The Standard Oil house organ cited the benefits of "friendly international cooperation . . . For the first time there has been negotiated what promises to be a practical Open Door policy in which four great nations take equal participation in one field."

It wasn't all gravy, Standard's mouthpiece sighed: "Even those varied interests are not to have in combination anything approaching exclusive rights in this vast area. On the contrary, provisions incorporated in the Government grant specifically forestall this. It is provided that the Turkish Petroleum Company may select any 24 plots, each of eight square miles, for development. Four years from the date of the Convention all the geological and other information covering the areas to be offered competitively is to be made public for the benefit of any individuals or companies that may wish to enter the territory, and the Turkish Petroleum Company must sell to the highest bidder, under Government supervision, in tracts of eight square miles which have been indicated by the Government or outside parties. This procedure will take place each year by the successive offer of a further 24 plots annually. When the relative size of the 24 pieces (192 square miles) to be reserved by the Turkish Petroleum Company and the area of the concession (89,000 square miles) granted by the Iraq Government are considered, it will be seen that the international group has made a doubtful bargain unless good fortune attends its exploration work."[29] The article also emphasized the costs of drilling at great distances from railheads and the necessity of building a 700-mile, $50 million pipeline.

The international combine lost no time in sending its drilling crews into the sweltering desolation of the Mosul-Kirkuk

233

area. Its geologists determined that there were three huge pools in the area, and the drillers began operations in April 1927 at Palkhana, where oil was struck at 1,329 feet. Another hole bored at Quiyara produced five thousand barrels a day from its seepage pool alone. Then in June 1927 a thunderous gusher came up at Baba Gurgur, the "Burning Fiery Furnace," near Kirkuk. Ninety-five thousand barrels daily roared up to the surface. One of the greatest producing fields in the world had just been brought in, and the Baghdad correspondent of a London financial journal could not help boasting that "We shall have the satisfaction of knowing that three enormous fields situated within close proximity of each other, and capable of supplying the oil requirements of the Empire for many years to come, are being almost entirely developed by British enterprise."[30]

Meanwhile twenty years of hopes deferred and efforts frustrated were coming to a sorry close for Colby Chester and his associates. They never managed to raise the necessary capital to build up the Turkish economy; without Mosul oil their concession was all but worthless. According to one source, "Standard, with its hope of sharing the Mosul riches through the Turkish Petroleum Company, later was charged with helping to choke off the Chester credit supply in Wall Street."[31] The Chester project quietly folded.

Its epitaph fittingly was supplied by Raouf Bey, the former Turkish Prime Minister, in a conversation with Admiral Bristol during which his "earnestness was most apparent" to Bristol. "You can see how it breaks my heart to see the Chester project become a failure," Raouf Bey said. "I looked for the Chester project to be a means by which the young men of Turkey could have work of all kinds and earn their living and develop to be real men and not be looking to the government to help them, as was the case in the old days under the old regime when practically everyone was living off the government as functionaries."[32]

The now obscure history of the Chester concession could

serve as a diagram of how the international oil industry operates. Certainly Chester's claim was stronger than Turkish
Petroleum's. Yet it amounted to nothing in the scales of power
politics. The sanctified Open Door was a means of egress only
to those with a favored position in Washington and Wall
Street.

The sufferings of the retired admiral were neatly balanced
by the lusty enjoyment of Calouste Gulbenkian of his position
as the binding agent in the Turkish Petroleum deal. Gulbenkian lived in Paris and reveled in his collections of paintings
and mistresses. "Mr. Five Per Cent" was probably making more
out of the consortium than any other individual, since Deterding, the Rockefellers, the Mellons, and other participants
shared only in the corporate dividends. Gulbenkian's five percent was pure gravy and he sopped it up with relish. He was
a cautious sybarite who was determined to live long and in
the utmost comfort. A private Handley-Page twin-engined
plane was available whenever he felt the urge to travel. Yet
never in his life would he visit the wells of Mosul which provided his immense fortune.

Gulbenkian kept one eye on the balance sheets and the other
on Deterding, whom he knew to be a tricky customer. A Deterding squeeze play alerted him to the fact that the Dutchman
was eyeing his five percent with a covetous gleam. Gulbenkian
wanted to draw his share of the Iraq proceeds in cash, but
Deterding insisted that his payment, like that of the other
participants, must be in crude oil. But what would Gulbenkian, with no marketing system of his own, do with his thousands of tons of unrefined oil? Deterding's partners naturally
joined in attempting to reduce or eliminate Gulbenkian's
share. Gulbenkian, however, could also pull strings at the
British Foreign Office, which announced that if the partners
in the consortium couldn't settle their differences the head of
the Treasury would step in and they would have to accept his
arbitration. No one wanted governmental interference. Gul-

benkian was permitted to sell his oil quota to Compagnie Française.

The personal relations between Gulbenkian and Deterding were even more embittered when the Dutchman became jealous of the former's attentions to Lydia Pavlovna Bagratumi. The lady's husband, General Bagratumi, might more properly have been enraged but he was occupied by the affairs of the Free Armenia movement and his wife had become Deterding's mistress. "On subsequent social occasions," Gulbenkian's son Nubar has recalled, "Deterding jumped to the conclusion that Father was trying to cut him out in Lydia's estimation. She was certainly an attractive woman and as she and father spoke the same language, they undoubtedly talked a lot together, and Deterding became jealous. Father was not really interested in Lydia, but Deterding's dismay amused him: especially when Deterding started heaping literally hundreds of thousands of pounds worth of jewelry on her — in the mistaken belief that his imaginary rival was up to the same game . . . When Deterding and Lydia were free to marry, Father said good luck to them . . ."[33] Lady Deterding herself later denied the scandalous rumors that she was the beneficiary of a jewelry-buying competition. She was pregnant at the time, she said, and besides "Gulbenkian could be charming, if he liked, but . . . he was not the type of man who gave away something for nothing and I certainly received nothing from him." The scandal, aside from speculations on how the oil world would have been rocked if Deterding and Gulbenkian faced each other over dueling pistols in the Bois de Boulogne, offered an interesting sidelight on the sociology of the dinosaurs who trampled through the international jungle of concessions and consortiums.

Despite the bad blood between two of the chief entrepreneurs, it was Gulbenkian who hammered out the famous Red Line Agreement which formed the basis for peaceful coexistence among the major oil-producers in the Middle East. During the months after Baba Gurgur started spouting, the

American members of the cartel began exhibiting a keen appetite for a larger share and a desire to bring in American drillers to exploit the surrounding districts. That was the American way: get in fast, in strength, and pump out everything in reach. But it wasn't the conservative British or cautious French way, and the Americans were firmly informed that they would have to play by the rules. The original concession, it was pointed out, forbade such overdevelopment by the separate partners. The Americans replied that the Turkish Empire no longer existed and that an agreement drawn up with a defunct grand vizier no longer had any legal force; that any restraint of competition would be interpreted as monopolistic in Washington.

Thus a conference had to be called to define just what the Ottoman Empire had included — there had always been doubts about its loosely drawn boundaries — and to curtail competition among the members of the group within those vanished borders. "It was," as Gulbenkian stated, "inherently eyewash that the whole world could participate in the exploitation of oil in Mesopotamia." The partners in Turkish (later Iraq) Petroleum sat down in London to work out an agreement, which had become even more urgent with Gulf Oil seeking the right to explorations in the sheikhdom of Kuwait and on the Persian Gulf island of Bahrein.

It became a crucial point whether Kuwait and other Arabian sheikhdoms would come under the rules of the Iraq agreement. The wrangling went on for days. Gulbenkian later said he broke the impasse with one authoritative gesture. He called for a map of the Middle East, took a red crayon pencil, and drew a line, saying: "That was the Ottoman Empire which I knew in 1914. And I ought to know. I was born in it, lived in it and served it. If anybody knows better, carry on."[34]

The Americans were satisfied because Kuwait was outside the red line, the British were happy to see that control would be maintained over practically everything else, Bahrein, Qatar, Trucial Oman, Saudi Arabia, all the little sheikhdoms floating

237

on that vast sea of oil. Inside the red-crayoned area the companies would not compete for concessions or hold individual concessions without consulting their partners.

In one stroke the happy few of the Iraq cartel made temporary peace among themselves and built the first of their Maginot lines to keep out invaders. Their own world war ended just ten years after the official one. Their world was now safe for the peculiar democracy of the oil industry.

To celebrate the victory of statesmanship, Gulbenkian chartered a yacht for a Mediterranean cruise with his daughter Rita. One day off Morocco he saw a strange-looking vessel and asked what it was. At the age of fifty-nine, after dabbling in oil since his earliest youth, he had to be told by his young daughter that it was an oil tanker.

IV.

Imperial Visions

11.

The Sinclair Follies

Harry F. Sinclair was the first man to wear silk underwear in the Oklahoma oilfields. The fact that his fellow entrepreneurs remembered this seemingly insignificant preference of wearing silk next to his skin rather than the traditional long woolen underwear tells us something about the man. He possessed a notable tendency to outdo, outbuy, and outbluff everyone else; he flew around the country in a private plane while his fellow magnates were still earthbound; he started up his own major-league baseball in defiance of Judge Landis, and established brass bands in a dozen southwestern towns because he liked the oompah vibrations of the tuba. Life, in brief, taught him there was nothing, up to and including a Cabinet officer, that money couldn't buy.

During the 1920's, while the Rockefellers were quietly consolidating and surefootedly expanding, the bluff, hearty, sybaritic Sinclair was the most spectacular and controversial figure on the American oil scene. He was a man of almost cosmic vision who could picture himself controlling a national administration and leaping continents to become the dominant figure in the petroleum world. That he looked something like a frog, with his popping eyes, his wide mouth and fat cheeks, was no handicap; Napoleonism is likely to appear in the most curious guises. No one understood better than Harry Sinclair the uses of opportunism, the efficacy of pushing your luck for all it is worth. His initial capital, a number of oilmen affirmed, came from insurance he collected when he "accidentally" shot off his toe while hunting.[1]

At the turn of the century Sinclair, born in 1876 in Wheeling, West Virginia, but brought up in Independence, Kansas, was working as a pharmacist. When Independence became the center of the Kansas oil boom, Sinclair caught fire from all the excited talk about overnight fortunes, and possibly with the stake acquired in exchange for his big toe he decided to enter the oil-leasing game. He started out by acquiring "backyard leases" in various small towns, traded or sold them to the larger companies, and developed a nice smell for oil-bearing properties. Buying and selling options, however, was a small-time operation. The big money was in producing and if possible refining the product.

It was a wide-open field then, with the Oklahoma Territory to the south, still a decade away from statehood, the happy hunting ground of the independent oilmen. The trick was to con the Cherokees and Osages out of the mineral rights to their tribal lands before their supposed protector, the Bureau of Indian Affairs, could take measures against the practice. One method was to persuade an Indian under the age of twenty-one to pledge his mineral rights in exchange for small sums or trinkets, then keep a close eye on the stripling until he reached his majority and could be properly fleeced. Sinclair was adept at dealing with the Indians and on one occasion was able to combine his oil and baseball interests. A young Indian with a promising leasehold, who loved baseball, was tucked away on one of the teams sponsored by Sinclair and kept busy on the diamond until he was old enough to sign over his property.

Until the spring of 1905 Sinclair was only one of a score

of hard-driving opportunists working the Oklahoma Territory. His break came one spring morning that year. A collaborator named Pat White had been buying leases around Flat Rock Creek near Tulsa because it was close to several producing wells at Red Fork. White didn't have the money to drill so when he heard of a new strike nearby he hurried over to the Robinson Hotel in Tulsa where Sinclair stayed.

He knew Sinclair, a late riser, would fly into a rage if awakened before the sun was high over the prairies, so he paced the floor outside Sinclair's room until Sinclair got up and went down the hall to the bathroom. Sinclair, then twenty-nine, listened with scant interest while White stammered out his news of a "big strike." His bladder, Sinclair growled, had priority over business talk. His heavy-set figure proceeded majestically to the bathroom.

"All right," he snapped at White as he emerged from the bathroom, "What's up? What's on your mind?"

"They've got oil in that well out on Flat Rock Creek," White excitedly replied. "I've got a bunch of leases lined up but I've got to have about twelve or fifteen thousand dollars to close the deal. Are you in?"

"Let's go out and have a look," Sinclair replied. "If it looks good I can raise the money."

They raced out to Flat Rock Creek, it looked good to Sinclair, "and that," Sinclair said later, "was the beginning of the White and Sinclair Oil Company, which at one time was the largest independent oil-producing firm in the world."[2]

Their first well came in on July 25, 1905, and from then on Sinclair showed an amazing aptitude for parlaying his bets in all directions. Before he was forty he was believed to have made his first $50 million. He was the first man to sell oil bonds on Wall Street and financed his expanding enterprises largely through New York financing. He speculated in grain. He organized and backed the outlaw Federal League in a brazen attempt to take over a sector of baseball in competition with the American and National Leagues. His racing stable produced Zev, the winner of the Kentucky Derby in 1923. His drillers appeared all over the map, working concessions in West Africa, Mexico and Costa Rica.

By 1920, still vigorous and venturesome in his mid-forties, he was dreaming the improbable dream of all independents: to "get bigger" than the Rockefellers and shoulder aside Standard Oil.

The results of the national election of 1920 were most pleasing to the oil industry as a whole, but particularly to Harry Sinclair and Edward Doheny, both of whom enjoyed considerable influence with the incoming administration. President Warren G. Harding was regarded as highly sympathetic to the oil interests and several of his Cabinet appointments indicated that the industry would be tenderly treated in considerations affecting it domestically and internationally. The lineup in Washington might almost have been selected by an oil industry committee: Secretary of State Charles Evans Hughes, former counsel to Standard Oil; Secretary of the Treasury Andrew W. Mellon, owner of the controlling interest in Gulf Oil; Secretary of the Interior Albert W. Fall, long the Senate's most vociferous champion of the industry, and particular friend of Sinclair and Doheny; Secretary of the Navy Edwin Denby, a Detroit lawyer, whose chief administrative trait appeared to be gullibility, whose department was in charge of the sizable naval oil reserves.

The scandal and the tragedy of the Harding Administration, which promised to restore "normalcy" to the nation after the adventurism of Woodrow Wilson, is easily described and documented. It was exhaustively placed on the record of congressional investigations and court trials. What isn't so easy to penetrate is the mystery of the human motives it involved; principally why two very wealthy men like Sinclair and Doheny should have risked so much for the "stealage" connected with what generically became known as the Teapot Dome scandal, successor to the Credit Mobilier as the paradigm of American political corruption.

The answer perhaps lies in a most pernicious psychosis afflicting oilmen when they reach a certain level of attainment — a ravening appetite for more of the same. The geometric progression of ambition, similar to that which led Napoleon to his reckless invasion of Russia, may overcome all men of conquest. Because of the quasi-military aspects of the oil business — the reconnaissance by geologists, the cloak and dagger operations often necessary to secure concessions, the reconnaissance in force by drillers, the occupation of territory when a rich field is exploited — oilmen may succumb all the more readily to the Napoleonic syndrome. It is not merely a question of more wealth or more power but the spectacle of all those wells sucking oil out of the earth, those leagues of pipelines, those platinum-colored refineries and petro-chemical plants gleaming in otherwise forlorn landscapes. Enough is never enough.

The Teapot Dome case epitomized that obsessive lust. More, almost from the establishment of the naval reserves, it exposed the curious theory of the oilmen that they had a right to oil wherever it might be found, whomever it belonged to (including the nation itself), whatever the conservation aspects involved, regardless of the national interest or even the security of the United States and its armed forces.

Executive orders issued by President William H. Taft established the reserves. In 1912 it was ordained that certain lands be set aside for the navy, which had just converted from coal-burning to oil-burning ships. Naval Petroleum Reserve No. 1 was 38,969 acres located at Elk Hills, Kern County, California. Reserve No. 2 consisted of 29,341 acres at Buena Vista Hills, Kern County. Reserve No. 3 was 9,481 acres located at Teapot Dome, Natrona County, Wyoming. The reserves were established to make certain that the navy would always have a supply of oil, even if other sources within U.S. territorial limits dried up. They could also be used by the federal government as a bargaining point with the oil industry; for if prices rose too high the government could always threaten to refuel the navy from its own reserves.

Throughout the Wilson Administration there were repeated pressures from the oil industry to allow private interests to obtain leases in the three naval reserves, and Secretary of the Navy Josephus Daniels later recalled staying in his office all night on occasion, watching legislation offered in the closing sessions of Congress and "fearing that some act might be passed that would turn over these invaluable oil reserves to parties who laid claim to them without even decent shadow of title."[3] The Wilson Administration was successful in resisting all claims by the oil industry that the navy was losing valuable amounts of oil in its reserves because of drainage into adjacent private fields.

The new Secretary of the Interior had always, as Senator from New Mexico, advocated that the naval reserves be turned over to private exploitation as rapidly as possible. Fall's first step was to persuade President Harding and Secretary of the Navy Denby, both amiable dolts, that control over the naval reserves should be transferred from the navy to the Interior Department. The negotiations through which the transfer was effected were handled by Assistant Secretary of the Navy Theodore Roosevelt, Jr., who had recently been a director of the Sinclair oil companies and whose brother Archibald was a vice-president of one of those companies. On May 31, 1921, President Harding signed an executive order for the transfer. Meanwhile, Fall was placating the navy by working out a scheme by which the oilmen benefiting from the privilege of tapping the naval reserves would build a huge storage facility at Pearl Harbor for the newly established Pacific Fleet.

In April 1922, in return for such considerations as would allow him to satisfy his ambitions to acquire baronial ranch lands in his native state, Secretary of the Interior Fall proceeded to lease the Elk Hills and Teapot Dome naval reserves to Doheny and Sinclair.

Several months before, Sinclair had prepared for the hand-over. On February 28, 1922, he had incorporated, in Delaware, the Mammoth Oil Company, the sole purpose of which was to exploit the Teapot Dome reserve. Its stock was owned entirely by Sinclair. He then proceeded to clear his very clouded title to the leasehold by paying $1 million to several parties with otherwise worthless claims to the same property.

On April 7, 1922, Secretary Fall signed the lease, which gave the Mammoth Oil Company the exclusive right to extract oil and gas from Teapot Dome for the next twenty years. In return the government was to receive royalties ranging from twelve and a half percent on wells producing less than fifty barrels a day to fifty percent on those producing more than a thousand barrels daily. The average payment to the government was between sixteen and seventeen percent (about the same deal backward Persia got, years before, from the British). The Teapot Dome reserve was estimated to contain 135 million barrels, about eighty-four percent of the proceeds from which would go to Harry Sinclair in return for his bribes to the Secretary of the Interior. Sinclair frankly stated in January 1923 that he expected the value of Mammoth Oil Company's stake in Teapot Dome would run to "a greater amount than $100,000,000."[4] Competitive bidding for that lease, it was estimated, would have brought up to $50 million more into the U.S. Treasury.

On April 25, 1922, Secretary Fall made his old friend Edward Doheny equally happy by signing a contract allowing his Pan-American Petroleum and Transport Company to extract oil from the Elk Hills reserve in return for building storage tanks for the navy at Pearl Harbor. Two subsequent concessions from Fall considerably sweetened the pot. Doheny's company would not only be allowed to take 6 million barrels of crude oil from Elk Hills, but in return for building a pipeline to and a refinery at San Pedro, California, for the navy

247

it would be given a lease on the whole reserve for the next fifteen years with the right to take out as much oil as it pleased. The prize would be worth almost exactly as much to Doheny as the Teapot Dome lease was to Sinclair. The oil deposits at Elk Hills were estimated to total somewhere between 75 million and 250-million barrels. "We will be in bad luck," Doheny later testified, "if we do not get $100,000,000 profit. But that will depend on the price of gasoline."[5]

New Year 1923 found Albert B. Fall a happy man. The deals he had engineered were all neatly — so he thought — completed, and without any passionate outcries from conservationists or government moralists. He could now retire from the public service which he had made so profitable. On January 9, 1923, he turned in his resignation to President Harding, who considered him such a magnificent public servant that he wanted to appoint Fall to the U.S. Supreme Court. If Fall had not been so eager to return to New Mexico with the swag, he might have been not only the first Cabinet officer but the first justice of the Supreme Court to be sent to prison.

To Sinclair the deals which helped pay for Fall's retirement were only part of a much larger scheme. The profits from Teapot Dome, funneled through his wholly owned Mammoth Oil, were to finance a program of breathtaking audacity. In the several postwar years the structure of the oil world was undergoing radical changes from which, he believed, a man of bold vision might profit, might elevate himself to the level occupied jointly by Deterding and the Rockefellers.

Just who would exploit the oil lands of northern Persia and the Mespot still hadn't been settled. In addition, there was Russian oil, which was of incalculable importance. The old concessionaires, the Nobel-Rothschild crowd plus the raffish crew of Armenian and Azerbaijan cutthroats, had been heaved out by the Bolshevik Revolution. The Soviet government knew more about toppling old regimes than making new ones work; it was faced with the problem of selling its oil to hostile Western countries which had established a *cordon sanitaire* around Russia during the years of upheaval, many of them still refusing to grant the Communist state's right to exist. Thus enormous possibilities opened up, and Sinclair believed he was the man to exploit them. Northern Persia, traditionally a part of the Russian sphere of influence, could be appropriated only by someone regarded as friendly by the Soviet Union. Similarly, Russian oil would be marketed and new Russian sources explored by someone independent of either Standard or Shell, both of whom made their tries at obtaining control of the largest oil resources in the eastern hemisphere.

The Russians needed a new friend in the capitalist world, and Sinclair aimed to be that friend, regardless of his own prejudices against Communism. Such a friend, however, would be required to gain two things Russia most wanted from America — credits and recognition. The credits could be swung. But recognition? From a business-oriented Republican administration? In a United States just cooling from the years of the Bolshevik Menace, the raids of Attorney General A. Mitchell Palmer, the deportation of thousands suspected of being Bolshevik sympathizers? It was a desperately chancy game Harry Sinclair now elected to play.

Just how desperate the intrigues for oil rights could become, with assassination the ultimate weapon, was bloodily illustrated on the streets of Teheran, the capital of Persia. There a hard-bitten soldier named Rhiza Khan, the father of the present Shah, was about to seize power. Ex-sergeant of the house guards, now Sirdar of the Persian armies, he was being influenced by a Russian named Einhorn, an Ogpu (secret police) agent stationed in Teheran, to revoke the British protectorate, and along with it the Anglo-Persian and Standard Oil concessions in the untapped northern provinces. An arrangement was being made whereby Sinclair was to receive a concession for exploration rights in northern Persia in return for arranging a $10 million loan for the Persian government.

Sinclair's drillers and engineers had not yet appeared in provinces bordering Russia. Standard Oil had just been advised by Foreign Minister Hussein Ali where it stood with the new government via a memorandum addressed to the State Department: "The Standard Oil Company of New Jersey did not show any inclination to meet the requirements of the law and made no proposals, but the Sinclair Consolidated Oil Corporation submitted terms following closely the conditions laid down in the oil law. The Standard manifesting no further interest in the concession, an agreement was consequently signed last December by the Government and the Sinclair representative in the Teheran district subject to the ratification of the Madjless [Parliament] . . . Now that there is at last a prospect of the northern oilfields of Persia being developed under purely American auspices, the Standard Oil Company of New Jersey advances certain claims on the basis of association with the Anglo-Persian Oil Company, Ltd., in the so-called Khostaria concessions . . . The Standard Oil made the mistake of yielding to the unwarranted contentions of the Anglo-Persian Oil Company. They were repeatedly warned . . . of the strong feeling of suspicion inevitably entertained in Teheran, in view of past experiences, as to British motives and aims . . ."[6]

Six months later occurred the shocking event which indicated, to those who believed that rival oil interests would stop at nothing to achieve their purposes, that even murder by mob was an instrument of policy.

One autumn morning the U.S. vice-consul in Teheran, Major Robert Imbrie, accompanied by a friend named Malvin Seymour, took a carriage to the outer suburbs of Teheran. He brought along a camera to take certain photographs on assignment from the *National Geographic*. They got out of the carriage and Imbrie began taking pictures of a well regarded as holy by the Moslems. The two Americans were suddenly attacked by a howling mob. Both were badly beaten, tried to escape in their carriage, were overhauled and beaten again.

Finally they were rescued by a squad of Persian police, who had been idly watching the mayhem.

Less than an hour later the mob — strangely diligent for a group supposedly inflamed by a sudden rage against infidels photographing a holy place — broke into the hospital and again attacked Imbrie. The American vice-consul was beaten to death, but Seymour escaped through a window.

British press reports soothingly explained that the murder was nothing more than an outbreak of religious fanaticism, that the outraged Moslems had mistaken Imbrie, somehow, for a member of the Bahai sect much hated by the faithful of Teheran.

Then came a Paris dispatch to the New York *Herald Tribune* with quite a different explanation for the incident. Imbrie, said the dispatch, was "assassinated by a mob organized by financiers in the United States and England who thought his influence might swing control of the Persian oil fields . . . to an American syndicate in which the Sinclair group has the major interest." The source of his information, the Paris correspondent of the *Herald Tribune* revealed, was Harold Spencer, whom he identified as an Annapolis graduate of 1911 and "for years British Secret Service agent in the Near East."[7]

The murder of Major Imbrie, for all its momentary fascination, went unsolved, unpunished. The question of why the Persian police had not protected Imbrie went unanswered. It was undeniable, however, that in Teheran and most Middle Eastern cities a mob could be hired for any purpose, from a carefully staged riot to a political murder, after a few hours dickering with the right parties in the bazaar.

If making a deal for northern Persian oil was tricky, the Russian project, obtaining control of Baku's production under license from the Kremlin and exploiting other concessions in the Soviet Union, was surrounded by political and economic minefields. In the hope of securing the prize of Baku, thousands of lives and millions of dollars had already been futilely expended. Even with his Teapot Dome coup, his political clout, and his personal fortune and his immense self-confidence, Sinclair must have wondered in the gray watches of the night what an ex-pharmacist from Independence, Kansas, was doing in that bloody arena.

Turkey had suffered more casualties driving for Baku than on any other front during the war, Germany had spared troops for that effort she could ill afford in the last year of the war, and Britain had made her own smash-and-grab attempt at snatching the same prize from the Red armies. Deterding had tried to obtain a monopoly on Russian oil and failed; so had Standard Oil, for all the anti-Communist proclamations it issued when Baku eluded its grasp.

Could Sinclair succeed where nations and more powerful industrial rivals had failed? He must have pondered the history of those lunges for Baku oil long and hard. At the end of the war a Turkish-German force had taken over for a time when Azerbaijan, the oil province, declared itself independent of Russia. A British outfit called Dunsterforce detached from the Indian army operating in Persia and Iraq, commanded by a General Dunsterville, occupied the city for several weeks, was driven out by the Turks, then reappeared after the Armistice. The British took over the oilfields and pipelines and one statesman foresaw the creation of a "second India" out of the Caucasus and other bits and pieces of Asia Minor. A White Russian army, largely supported and financed by the British, was the only real shield against Bolshevik intentions of reclaiming the territory.

The British occupation lasted until July 1920, when the Communist regime regained power over the Caucasian republics. Meanwhile, both Deterding's Royal Dutch Shell and Standard Oil were hoping to take over Baku as concessionaires. Ever since the Russian Revolution, Deterding, assisted by the White Russian connections of his new wife, had been buying up the dubious ownership certificates of Russian and Armenian émigrés in Paris. This would give him a certain legal standing in taking over the oilfield, but only if the Soviets were amenable.

Standard Oil meanwhile was working out its own program for taking over Russian oil production, assuming the Bolsheviks couldn't manage it themselves. Standard bought out the Nobel interests which had been dominant in Baku almost from the beginning. Naturally it was pleased that Washington refused to join France and Britain in recognizing any of the counterrevolutionary governments in the Caucasus. Washington was opposed to any dismemberment of Russia and had not joined in supporting the White counterrevolution; the expeditionary force it sent to Siberia stayed neutral between Whites and Reds and was largely concerned with preventing the Japanese from seizing the maritime provinces. At the moment this fitted in beautifully with Standard strategy.

If the Soviet Union would regard the United States as a well-wisher, it was apparent that American entrepreneurs would be favored over their rivals from a hostile western Europe. The Soviets appeared to be adopting a policy of "blanket" concessions to a single foreign group which would be expected to quiet the claims of any former owners. As proof of this policy, Louis Fischer has cited the Soviet agreement with W. Averill Harriman "giving him an invaluable contract to the manganese ore deposits in Chiaturi, the richest in the world . . . Harriman had never had any interests in Chiaturi. On the other hand, some twenty-five foreign companies had owned mines there before the revolution . . . When Harriman appeared on the scene to bid for the manganese fields he was, in effect, offering to oust and dispossess all the other concerns which had been operating there for a score of years or more."[8]

With high hopes of elbowing aside Royal Dutch Shell in the secret negotiations conducted with Soviet representatives in Berlin and Moscow for more than two years, Standard headquarters in New York were bedazzled by sugar-plum visions of dominating the world market through control of Russian oil resources. There was a certain urgency behind its Russian ambitions, as a contemporary oil historian noted. "For unless the Rockefeller firm soon finds supplementary resources in Eurasia its hold on the markets of the eastern hemisphere is destined to disappear in the next few years. More than this. If Henry Ford, the General Motors Company and their competitors continue to turn out oil-consumers in the millions as they have been doing — and there is no reason why they should stop — if, furthermore, more and more ships take to burning oil and an increasing number of Diesel engines enter industry, it is not impossible that the United States will, within the next decade, become dependent on Russian oil . . . Consumption is greater than production . . ."[9]

While Standard was taking a soft line toward Russia, Deterding was vigorously, often aggressively pushing his program for Shell's monopoly over Russian production.

By the fall of 1922, however, neither Standard nor Shell had managed to make a deal with the Russians. In mutual exasperation they summoned an International Defense Committee meeting in Paris with sixteen other companies and various Russian claimants. Solemnly, but with one or two crossed fingers, they agreed to boycott Russian oil until the Soviets "rehabilitated on equal conditions to all interested parties their oil rights and properties." Free enterprise, as the Russians were observing with sardonic amusement, was not a monolith but more of a verbal façade. No more than six months after signing the Paris pledge, Sir Henri Deterding was secretly dickering with the Russians. He signed a contract for seventy thousand tons of crude with an option for another hundred thousand. Meanwhile Standard was also secretly negotiating with the "boycotted" Russians.

At that point both Standard and Shell learned to their mutual chagrin that a third party had stepped into the murky picture. Harry F. Sinclair grandly announced that he would act as "Russia's oil salesman to the world."

Even to his rivals Sinclair's chances of making a deal with the Russians looked pretty good. Sinclair's corporate setup, as Louis Fischer noted, was highly adaptable because of its speculative nature and because it was controlled by Sinclair alone. Sinclair was smart enough to realize that an exclusive deal with the Russians would make him the biggest oilman in the world. Furthermore, his chances of nailing down the concession were excellent; he was not burdened by any past dealings, any Czarist connections, any claims to expropriated property — and he had never joined in the blockade.

The claims of those who had been ousted by the Russian Revolution had never aroused any sentimental emotions in Sinclair. He was apolitical. He had come on the scene just at the moment the Communists were in a highly receptive mood, anxious to lease Baku and Grosni. "Finally," Fischer observed, "Sinclair was an American; there was, therefore, a possibility of loans and credits, and possibly even of recognition of Moscow by the American government."[10]

Early in 1923 Sinclair was in high feather as he made plans for a triumphal progress to Moscow. A sizable retinue was organized to enhance his prestige in the eyes of the commissars. Notables were being recruited to attend him in the manner of a samurai prince, including Mason Day, Archibald Roosevelt (son of TR), Robert Law, Jr., E. R. Tinker, William Dewey Loucks, Elisha Walker, Grattan T. Stanford, various mining engineers, advisers, and other satellites.

He particularly wanted ex–Secretary of the Interior Fall to join the party because Fall was President Harding's still trusted confidant and a continuing influence among the Republican majority in the U.S. Senate. Fall, however, expected to be paid on the barrelhead for any services rendered. Sinclair's lawyer had to be dispatched to Fall's Three Rivers Ranch with the necessary inducements. Fall would join the party only if he were paid $25,000 plus $10,000 in expenses. The Sinclair attorney brought along $25,000 in Liberty Bonds, the curious history of which was revealed in subsequent investigations; they also testified to the peccable morality of oil magnates. (The bonds had been funneled through the Canadian-incorporated Continental Trading Company, among whose organizers were Sinclair himself; Harry M. Blackmer, board chairman of Midwest Refining; James E. O'Neil, president of Prairie Oil and Gas; and of all people, considering the antipathy between Sinclair and Standard, Colonel Robert W. Stewart, president of Standard Oil of Indiana. Continental, it was revealed, was a private boodle-sharing operation among Sinclair and the oil-company executives; a device by which stockholders were deprived of their share of the profits. Continental bought 33,333,333 barrels of crude at $1.50 a barrel from the Texas Oil Company, whose operating head was also a member of the insiders' clique, and sold it to Sinclair's companies and Prairie Oil and Gas for $1.75 a barrel. In one year's operation Continental raked in $2 million, which was invested in Liberty Bonds immediately distributed to each of the conspirators. Then Continental was dissolved and all its records destroyed; but the serial numbers of the bonds were kept on file in Washington, and it was through them that investigators uncovered the transaction. Sinclair's payment of $25,000 in bonds to Fall was part of his $757,000 share in Continental's short but profitable history.[11])

Sinclair and his party traveled across the Atlantic in style, taking over two decks of the liner *Homeric*. In London they paused while Sinclair conferred with Leonid Krassin, the Soviet representative, to whom he revealed a grandiose program for taking over not only the oilfields of Baku, Grosni, Emba, Maikop and the Russian northern half of Sakhalin Island off Siberia but building a refinery complex which would monopolize all Russian refining and a pipeline system throughout the Soviet Union. He would be the sole distributor of Russian oil products throughout the world. Then, early in June, Sinclair and his entourage crossed over to France where they boarded a special train, costing $193,000 with all possible luxuries laid on, and steamed directly into

Moscow. There they were greeted with full honors and escorted to a palace near the Kremlin for their month-long stay.

During that time Sinclair and the Kremlin's oil policy-makers agreed on a concession of somewhat less magnitude than Sinclair had envisioned when he paced the decks of the *Homeric* but one which, if he could hold up his end of the bargain, might very well raise him to supremacy in the oil industry. It was, essentially, an entering wedge. If Sinclair could deliver on his promises, he could eventually gain control of Russian oil for marketing aboard; with it, of course, would be coupled his parallel exploitation of the northern Persian fields with Soviet approval and through the agreement with an English-hating new Shah-in-Shah.

For openers, Sinclair would be equal partners with the Soviet oil trust in exploiting the Baku and Grosni oilfields for the next forty-nine years. On their part, the Soviet bargainers obtained Sinclair's agreement to invest $115 million in their oilfields and to float a $250 million loan for Russia in New York. All this was contingent upon Sinclair's following through with the unwritten codicil to their formal agreement — U.S. recognition of Soviet Russia. Such a diplomatic exchange would be necessary, in fact, from Sinclair's viewpoint; he would need consular support and comfort in future dealings with his Russian partners.

Everything hinged on American recognition. Without it, certainly Wall Street would have been reluctant to float a quarter-billion-dollar loan. Could Sinclair swing it, given the anti-Communist sentiment general in the United States? As of mid-July 1923, when the outlines of the Sinclair-Soviet agreement were approved by both parties, the details to be worked out by a Sinclair executive left behind for that purpose, it seemed likely to at least one commentator. "It thus became Sinclair's task, on returning to the States, to persuade the Harding Republicans to swallow their righteous sentiments about Communism and to put recognition through Congress. And it actually seems that Sinclair must have felt reasonably sure that he could perform this amazing feat. Were not Fall, Harding and Daugherty [the Attorney General] his friends? Were there not obligations — of which the shocked nation was yet to learn — cementing this political friendship? Who could bring about the recognition of Russia, in the teeth of all the propaganda, if not Harry Sinclair? That propaganda, though the public didn't realize it, was oil trust propaganda. Was not an 'independent,' high in party and government councils, the very man to smash it? Especially when, by so doing, he would fall heir to former oil trust lands . . ."[12]

But there was another complication, which arose through the very success of Sinclair's mission to Moscow. As sort of a bonus the Soviet oil trust awarded Sinclair a monopoly concession on northern Sakhalin, which formerly had been held and was still claimed by the British-owned Sakhalin Oilfields Company. Northern Sakhalin, however, had been occupied by the Japanese army in token of its Allied status during World War I. To make good his rights to that oil-bearing section of the disputed island, the southern half of which was more or less legitimately held by Japan, Sinclair would have to persuade the State Department and its Standard-oriented overseer, Secretary Hughes, to back Soviet Russia against Imperial Japan and ease out the Japanese occupation forces in the northern half of the island. This Mr. Hughes would prove most reluctant about, though not as reluctant as the Japanese to abandon the only oil source they had for their oil-burning navy.

In attempting to prove out his Sakhalin claim, in fact, Sinclair resorted to a typical bluffing operation. He sent two engineers, J. P. McCullough and L. F. MacLaughlin, to Siberia with orders to survey his dubious new concession. In the middle of the Siberian winter the two intrepid Americans traveled on sleds from Vladivostok to the Amur Valley, then across the frozen straits to the northern end of Sakhalin Island, where several hundred Chinese workmen engaged by other Sinclair representatives had preceded them. As soon

258

as they walked ashore McCullough and MacLaughlin were arrested by the Japanese military and thrown into detention pens with the Chinese laborers. Later the Japanese commandant invited them to dinner and with exquisite courtesy deported them. Secretary of State Hughes refused to become indignant over this affront to the Sinclair interests.

When he left Moscow in July, however, Sinclair had every reason to congratulate himself. He had succeeded in shaking the oil world off the axis that ran from New York to London to The Hague.

Yet he was uneasy. Just before he returned to New York he confessed to a member of his party, amid all the euphoria, that he feared "Nemesis would pursue" him. By that he meant Standard Oil.

Nemesis was indeed on Sinclair's heels. He had hardly arrived back in the States before his bold plan to flood out his rivals with Russian oil collapsed. Whether Nemesis was helped along by Standard Oil, as gossip in the industry had it, is still a matter of conjecture. There were, however, few long faces around 26 Broadway when Sinclair began to get his lumps.

His whole program was based on wishful thinking, actually, in that it depended on his ability to swing Russian recognition and Wall Street financing for a Soviet loan. That, in turn, depended on whether he could persuade President Harding to prevail over his Secretary of State, whom Harding held in almost superstitious reverence. It was an impossible equation: Sinclair's influence over Harding simply didn't equal the Secretary of State's influence over the President.

All that became immaterial a few days after Sinclair returned from Russia. President Harding, junketing around Alaska while Sinclair was hobnobbing with the commissars, apparently had been stricken after eating tainted crabmeat, but seemed to be recovering when the presidential party reached San Francisco on the homeward journey. On August

259

2, 1923, Harding suddenly died in his hotel room. His successor, Calvin Coolidge, moved into a haunted White House. Almost every closet door seemed to spring open and reveal some grinning skeleton, personal or political.

Overnight Sinclair's chances of sewing up Russian oil production disappeared. He had no influence over President Coolidge, and he was about as welcome at the White House or any of the executive offices as a carrier of bubonic plague. Recognize Russia? Secretary of State Hughes would have smiled glacially behind his white whiskers, possibly because, as Louis Fischer remarked, "all his indignant moralistic philippics against Moscow were really a smoke screen for the State Department's desire to obtain satisfaction through denationalization for the Rockefeller interests."[13] After all, on the wall maps at 26 Broadway, Baku was still designated as a Standard Oil property through its acquisition of the Nobel leases and title deeds.

Before the year was out Senator Thomas Walsh of Montana was prying the lid off Teapot Dome, and Sinclair's two particular friends in the Cabinet, Denby and Daugherty, were about to resign at the request of President Coolidge.

In America at the time there was a certain "letdown in public morality," to use a phrase often fondled by editorial writers, but the nation was shocked and outraged when the details of the Teapot Dome scandal were extracted with ruthless persistence by Senator Walsh. Fall had to admit having stealthily acquired control over the naval reserves and having leased two of them to his friends, but he arrogantly maintained that this was his right as Secretary of the Interior.

The unasked question was how the oil-lease scandal happened to erupt with such precise timing, just after President Harding's death and just before Sinclair could start capitalizing on his Russian project. Such investigations usually are initiated by a tip-off of some kind. Two oil historians of that period, Hanighen and Fischer, both voiced the suspicion that the Teapot Dome scandal broke through the public-spirited, though privately voiced, encouragement of Standard Oil.

The results, Fischer commented, "could not have been more favourable" for the Rockefeller interests; "the chief domestic rival of the Standard had shrunk to dwarf stature" through the investigation. Hanighen was even blunter: "Officially, of course, it was Senator Walsh who revealed this combination of shifty politics and oil — the greatest political scandal since the Grant Administration. And his fervor for clean government fully justified him in doing so. But there is no doubt in any oil man's mind that Standard was initially responsible for this exposure of oil corruption, or that it was Standard's trump card against Sinclair. Standard's hands in this matter were clean; those of her competitors were exceedingly greasy. What better way to discredit them?"

All that is speculation. There is no more than suspicion to connect Standard with the Teapot Dome investigation which ruined its most competitive rival. It was also true that Standard for years had labored to make the oil industry more respectable, more publicly acceptable. The pioneering genius of public relations, Ivy Lee, had been lured away from the Pennsylvania Railroad to institute a program to present the Rockefellers as peerless benefactors and philanthropists until it often seemed that every gallon of gasoline that Standard sold was helping stamp out disease, poverty, and ignorance throughout the world. The Teapot Dome case besmirched the whole industry as well as exposed political corruption at the highest levels of the government and the incredible stupidity of a man elected to be the President of the United States.

Sinclair's international operations came unglued even before he had been convicted of anything. Oil concessions, it seems, can be conducted only in an atmosphere of sanctimony, with a flowering of phrases like "developing resources for the public weal." The Soviet deal was canceled out as soon as it became evident that Sinclair could win the Russians neither recognition nor loans. His north Persian concession was also wiped out instanter, but not before rumors of corruption tainted Teheran as well as Washington. On January 14, 1924, just about the time it was revealed that Sinclair had given Fall a $100,000 bribe, a Teheran newspaper charged that the Persian Prime Minister had received $275,000 from Sinclair. It also became known that Sinclair was encouraged to enter the Persian field by yet another Harding Cabinet member — Secretary of Commerce Herbert Hoover, himself a future President. Thus it appeared that Hoover was backing Sinclair while the State Department was supporting Standard, either out of habit or the natural loyalties of Secretary Hughes. A. C. Veatch, vice-president of the Sinclair Exploration Company, wrote the Federal Trade Commission in Washington: "In July of 1921, following up a suggestion of the Secretary of Commerce, the Sinclair Company began its negotiations with the Persian authorities for an oil concession over the five northern provinces, which are stated by the Persian government to be free of any prior claims . . ."[14]

For sheer grubbiness, an American political scandal is rarely equaled. Teapot Dome, involving the payment of a few hundred thousand dollars in exchange for the integrity of a Cabinet officer, was certainly our grubbiest. Yet for all the tawdriness of the Sinclair-Fall-Doheny conspiracy, it did, at least, involve huge sums, as subsequent developments showed. The government took five years to wind up a civil suit for recovery of Teapot Dome, upon which Sinclair was forced to pay the Treasury $12,156,246, the value of the oil he extracted from the naval reserve. On the Elk Hills lease, the government collected $34,981,449 from Doheny. That made a total of $47,137,695 worth of crude oil involved in the two leases. It must be said that Sinclair and Doheny got themselves a bargain when they bought Secretary of the Interior Albert F. Fall.

Fall, Doheny and Sinclair all were indicted, convicted, and

imprisoned briefly. The two oilmen did not suffer greatly, except in self-esteem. Doheny sold his Pan-American Petroleum to Standard Oil of Indiana and left a fortune estimated at $75 million when he died at the age of seventy-nine; more than three thousand persons attended his funeral at St. Vincent's Cathedral, Los Angeles, which he had built. Sinclair died at eighty, in 1956, long retired from his company, on his palatial Pasadena estate. Fall, however, died a poor man after losing the ranch he had sold himself for.

During the several years following the collapse of his paper empire abroad, Harry Sinclair must often have experienced a stab of pure hatred for the corporate maneuvers of Standard Oil. If he was capable of appreciating the irony of it all, he must also have laughed bitterly over the spectacle of Standard and Shell, the Rockefellers and Deterding, gouging each other in their competition for the Russian oil production. Deterding's course, in line with his aggressive character, was to attempt to undermine the Soviet regime; Standard's was to maintain its cool objectivity, its dispassionate attitude toward politics and personalities, and get the oil out the best way it could.

Standard, always adaptable, changed its tactics after the Sinclair deal fell through and the Russians decided to work their oilfields without any outside help or concessions. Leon Trotsky was appointed chairman of the Chief Concession Committee and was a hard-nosed bargainer when it came to negotiating with foreign oil interests. The Russians knew that both Standard and Shell needed Russian oil in their continuing all-out competition. The flashpoint of this commercial war in the mid-1920's was the Mediterranean basin, which Shell had dominated and Standard was now determined to take over. For that purpose Standard would need a nearby source to save shipping costs. In 1926, after the usual lengthy negotiations, Standard signed a contract to buy eight hundred thousand tons of crude oil and one hundred thousand tons of kerosene from the Russian Naphtha Syndicate on consignment to Egypt.

Deterding was outraged at being outmaneuvered by Standard, declared war on the Soviet Union, and published a sneering "open letter" to the Russian oil commissars: "You are so much against the 'bourgeosie'; why then do you want their money. To fight them afterwards? . . . The world of the last century has been developed on credit. The cash, the gold, was only there to the extent of perhaps ten percent. Without credit you will never get along, with all your beautiful schemes . . . Do not try to fool people by talking about 'Czarist obligations which do not concern the Soviet.' You know as well as I do that the money the Czarist Government borrowed here, in France and in Holland was used to build railways, provide rolling stock, waterways and the pipeline Baku-Batum. Why not admit that you are in possession of the proceeds of these debts in various ways, but that you want to keep the property, like a thief? . . . Why not admit that you share with me the faith that you are near, very near the end of your tether, and that, before many months, Russia will come back to civilization, but under a better government than the Czarist one? Be men, and admit, like Lenin did, that Bolshevism does not work, that you have made a mistake . . ."[15]

Following this diatribe, Deterding attempted the old tactic of price-cutting, but it didn't work against a Standard Oil Company with a tapline to the immense Russian reserves. He tried to persuade his old friend Walter C. Teagle, now president of Standard Oil of New Jersey, that trading with Russia was downright sinful, a crime against Christianity and capitalism, but Teagle would not be swayed.

A measure of Deterding's desperation at losing out in the contest for a Russian oil monopoly was suggested by the events of the night of May 11, 1927, which resulted in the breaking off of diplomatic relations between Britain and Russia.

Agents from the Home Office, responsible for British internal security and an agency with which Deterding was well connected, suddenly appeared at the offices of Arcos, Ltd., the British version of Amtorg, a Soviet trading organization. They seized files and documents, claiming that Arcos was in possession of "stolen" British military secrets. Neither the Foreign Office nor the Cabinet had been advised in advance of the raid, which occurred one day after the Soviet government obtained $50 million in credits from the Midland Bank of London. Pressure of course was immediately and successfully applied on the bank to cancel the loan, and the Baldwin government broke off relations with Russia to the visible pleasure of Sir Henri and the sizable anti-Communist sector of British public opinion. To Francis Delaisi, writing in *Foreign Affairs* shortly afterward, the Arcos raid had little or nothing to do with military secrets:

"The polemics carried on in the press between Mr. Stalin, the spokesman of the Soviet Government, and Sir Henri Deterding, Director-General of the Royal Dutch Petroleum Company, have made clear to all the world what a few of the initiated had suspected and declared from the outset: that the breaking-off of diplomatic relations between Great Britain and the Soviet Union was not the spontaneous action of the British Government, but was inspired, and perhaps commanded, by certain large-scale oil interests . . . The Petrol Napoleon has remarkable strategic abilities, but he is not a diplomat . . . He has not realized that, among democracies, feeble but suspicious, great trusts can succeed only if they are veiled in secrecy. Sir Henri Deterding talks too much . . ."[16]

Though it had long been American policy to support the British, Standard Oil, with private considerations and corporate profits uppermost, viewed such developments with satisfaction. It was not at all deterred from broadening its relations with the Soviet oil trust by Deterding's self-serving bleat that such practices were "against the interests of humanity and trade honesty." It merely stepped up its purchase of Russian oil until by 1928 it was buying $10 million worth annually. Regarding this program, Standard Oil of New York issued a statement at 26 Broadway defending the Russian contract: "The long distance between the United States and India makes the cost of the transport of oil from this country to the Indian markets a substantial item. If, therefore, Russian oil could be supplied to the Indian markets at a fair price, there was an obvious economy in shipping such oil from Black Sea ports by saving at least 5,000 miles." Defensively it added that "In July 1920, Secretary of State Hughes had announced that it would be proper for American businessmen, at their own risk, to trade with Russia."

Unmentioned was the fact that State Department policy toward Russia, during Hughes' four years as Secretary of State, was tailored exactly — coincidentally or not — to the specifications of Standard's current progress in obtaining Russian oil concessions. Nor did the statement mention the fact that Hughes had retired from the State Department to his cozy and profitable niche as Standard's general counsel.

The whole Standard Oil publicity operation, with Ivy Lee's skilled hand on the levers, had reversed itself. For years a constant fusillade of Standard Oil publicity handouts decrying Russian Communism had been directed at all media of public opinion. Now Standard was pro-Russian. Ivy Lee himself toured Russia and came back to write a book, *U.S.S.R.: A World Enigma* (1927), which all but echoed the glad cry of the muckraker Lincoln Steffens on his return from Russia that he had seen the future and it worked. In his self-proclaimed role of "Little Brother to Big Business," Lee sent out "confidential letters" to influential Americans sounding out the possibilities of Russian recognition.

Somewhat obsequiously, Standard's image-maker wrote Elihu Root, a former Secretary of State and Republican elder statesman, that "I would never want this country to recognize Russia if you yourself, after examining all the facts, should deem it unwise. What I would like to see, however, is a condition brought about under which you, and men like you, should think it wise to accord such recognition."[17]

Another Standard executive, G. P. Whaley, possibly with the assistance of one of Ivy Lee's ghost-writers, was also called upon to answer charges in the press that his company was "selling out" to the Bolsheviks. Standard, he wrote in a magazine article, "believes that trade contracts with Russia will make for wholesome reconstruction, and, further, that it is only common sense to recognize that Russia is the economic source of supply for certain markets. An opportunity given to Russia to dispose of some of its surplus in its natural markets will avoid such surplus being forced into competition with American products where transportation costs are in favour of the United States."[18] Put another way, it was more important for Standard to achieve a favorable position in the Indian kerosene market than for an American company to adhere to its government's economic policy toward Russia, partly guided as it was by retaliation for the Soviet Union's refusal to assume the obligations of the previous regime.

Turning away in disgust from such spectacles as Standard's sudden discovery of virtues in Marxism, turning eventually, in fact, to flirtation with the fascist movements soon to spring up all over Europe, Deterding commented, "The sordid intrigue and competition is a grim enough business; the attempts to explain it in terms of morality and ethics is sheer hypocrisy."[19]

A silent amen may well have been pronounced by Harry Sinclair brooding in his jail cell over the fate of those who vaingloriously set themselves up as serious rivals to Standard Oil.

12.

The Little Wars
of Calvin Coolidge

Anyone who imagines that the late 1920's were notable chiefly for revelry in the speakeasies, or that the administration of Calvin Coolidge was a happily somnolent interregnum between the World Wars, may be surprised to learn that we fought our first "Viet Nam" late in that decade. Officially it was termed the "intervention" in Nicaragua, but despite the circumlocutions applied in Washington it was a war in the jungle, complete with live bullets, dead marines, search-and-destroy missions, and dive-bomber attacks on native villages.

And deep in the background, much deeper than the newspaper headlines or the placards ("Wall Street Is the Real Bandit") carried by hundreds of persons picketing the White House suggested, was the pervasive influence of oil politics.

Nicaragua was practically an American protectorate, in which marine battalions had frequently landed from their base at Guantánamo. In 1927 more than five thousand marines were sent into the Central American republic when another rebellion broke out. A young mestizo named Augusto Sandino, who had been employed by an American oil company in Tampico, had been "radicalized" by the agitators then trying to unionize the oilfields. He returned to Nicaragua with a small library of works on socialism and syndicalism and took to the mountain jungles with his followers, who rarely numbered more than a few hundred. This force, led by the young partisan whose guerrilla techniques would be earnestly studied by all who hoped to bog down the American armed forces and sap their vitality in bamboo wars and rice-paddy "interventions," managed to tie up most of the combat battalions of the U.S. Marine Corps for several years. Perhaps destiny was trying to tell us something.

What impelled the United States to intervene in Nicaragua besides its traditional iron-handed benevolence toward the southern hemisphere? Oddly, indirectly, it was the counter-intervention of "Red Mexico," which then occupied about the same position of disesteem as Castro's Cuba today. America widely believed that Bolshevism was implanted below the border, and that Mexico City was the capital of a revolutionary movement which would spread throughout Central and South America if it wasn't halted. Mexico had proven that by taking a proprietary interest in its own oil resources and making it difficult, almost unprofitable for American companies to operate there.

"Keep Cool with Coolidge" had been a campaign slogan, but coolness was missing when the President sent a special message to Congress on January 10, 1927, explaining his Nicaragua policy: "I have the most conclusive evidence that arms and ammunition in large quantities have been on several occasions since August 1926 shipped to the revolutionists in Nicaragua. Boats carrying these munitions have been fitted out in Mexican ports, and some of the munitions bear evidence of having belonged to the Mexican government. It also appears that the ships were fitted out with the full knowledge of and, in some cases, with the encouragement of Mexican officials and were in one instance, at least, commanded by a Mexican naval reserve officer . . ."

In fact, despite her denials, Mexico had sent the arms and other munitions — four boatloads in all — which permitted Sandino to lead the marines on a long, frustrating chase through the jungles. (Like Pancho Villa, Sandino was never captured; he was assassinated in 1934 despite the official amnesty granted him.) The rifles carried by Sandino's guerrillas, ironically, were of American manufacture. They bore Russian markings, which provoked some American newspapers to charge they had been supplied by the Kremlin, but actually they had been manufactured for the Kerensky regime which preceded the Communist but which fell before the rifles could be shipped to Russia. The rifles were then sold to Mexico as army surplus, a classic case of false economy.

The State Department under Coolidge, despite the propaganda being churned out by Standard Oil headquarters, had reverted to an anti-Communist stance and, perhaps a trifle over-heatedly, raised the "spectre of a Mexican-fostered Bolshevistic hegemony intervening between the United States and the Panama Canal." All that hubbub was really caused, however, not by fears that Mexico was about to plant the red flag from the Arctic Circle to Patagonia but by its self-centered, nationalistic oil policy.[1]

The man who set himself up against the U.S. oil industry, and ultimately the U.S. government, was the son of a Syrian camel-driver. His name was Plutarco Elias Calles; Elias being his father's name, Calles his Mexican mother's. His father had migrated to Mexico during the 1870's after the Southern Pacific imported a camel corps from the Middle East to replace the horses and mules unable to work efficiently on the rail line being pushed across the Arizona and New Mexico deserts. When the work was finished, Elias crossed the line into Mexico, settled down on the parched mesas of Sonora, and raised a Mexican family.

His son Plutarco was a bright boy, who educated himself and became a schoolteacher. Later, studying the works of

Tom Paine and Karl Marx, he became a labor leader, agitating among the silver and copper miners of Sonora. Naturally this made him a marked man for the *rurales*, the security police of the Díaz regime. And naturally Calles became a revolutionary, joining the Sonora rebel general Alvaro Obregón in the northern Mexico campaigns in a loose alliance with President Carranza. Eventually Calles himself rose to be a power in Mexican politics. He was a "finger general," the Mexican equivalent of a battlefield promotion. When casualties were heavy, a commanding general would point to a promising subordinate and intone, "You are hereby appointed general." Thus Obregón appointed Calles, who quickly rose to be his political and military equal.

By 1920 Obregón and Calles decided Carranza would never carry through his promised land reforms or really crack down on the foreign oil companies through the provisions of Article 27 (by which only Mexicans could actually own the exploited oil lands, and the foreigners who leased them were required to pay taxes). Around Tampico, in fact, the Americans had established a sort of extraterritorial enclave with the muscle supplied by a General Pelaez, who collected a fortune from the Americans for protection. The British interests, headed by Lord Cowdray of Mexican Eagle, were not so fortunate and were constantly harassed by outlaw bands whom they suspected were in the pay of their American competitors. Cowdray got fed up and tried to sell out to his American rivals, but the British government stepped in and insisted that his interests be acquired by Shell and other British firms.

Lord Cowdray got out just in time, because a new upheaval was beginning. A "revindicating revolution" was proclaimed by Obregón, Calles, and a lawyer named Adolfo de la Huerta (no relation to the former President) to unseat Carranza and restore "revolutionary idealism." American oil interests, it was reported, came up with financial support for the revindicators because they believed Obregón could be "handled." Carranza was assassinated by one of his own staff officers, and the triumvirate of Obregón, Calles and Huerta established itself in the National Palace.

Triumvirates have been doomed ever since they were invented by the Romans. This one seemed less durable than most. Huerta was an idealist and a music-lover (he ended his career as a singing-teacher in Hollywood); Obregón a wily and supple political general, and Calles a Marxist radical obsessed with raising wages and redistributing the haciendas to the peasants.

Huerta served as provisional president until Obregón was elected, and it appeared for a time that there would be political stability. Obregón knew that he owed his election to promises that he would crack down on the American oil companies. The British were more popular in Mexico because they were incorporated there and operated through Mexican boards of directors while Americans made it plain that no "greasers" would rise to the management level. Both the British and the Americans were hit by a sixty percent oil export tax ordained by President Obregón to refill the empty treasury. And both were greatly alarmed by the imposition of the dreaded Article 27, with an estimated $618 million invested in their Mexican oil properties. Now came the first split in the triumvirate. Huerta wanted to let the British off the hook while soaking the Americans. But Obregón knew that if his treasury was ever to be replenished it would have to be through diplomatic recognition from Washington and financing from Wall Street.

Obregón in 1923 negotiated an agreement with the United States — the Warren-Payne Treaty — by which the provisions of Article 27 were watered down through adjudication of Mexican claims by a Mexican-American commission and the Obregón government would be recognized by Washington. The American oil industry was greatly reassured by this development, which correspondingly dismayed American liberals. As the latter saw it, American policy toward Mexico for the past decade had been governed by a delicate concern for the overweening privileges of the Dohenys, the Rockefellers and the Guggenheims in exploiting Mexican oil and minerals without seeing to it that their native work force was paid a decent wage, without any respect for Mexican sensibilities, without regard for Mexican property rights.

The attitude of Americans in Mexico was that of a haughty colonialism. They associated only with the Mexican upper classes, which were more Spanish than Indian in origin. As Walter Lippmann would observe after a Mexican visit: "It is a notorious fact that in the recent past the personal associations of the United States officials were not with the government to which they were accredited, but with that class of Mexicans, among whom are to be found the rich, cultivated and sometimes charming people, who are financing and provoking armed rebellion. It is no less a notorious fact that many of the lawyers and representatives of the oil companies were not satisfied to argue their claims under international law, but openly and persistently used all the influence they possessed to undermine the stability of the Mexican government."[2]

A counterrevolution led by Huerta broke out at the end of Obregón's term in 1924, when Obregón nominated Calles as his successor and Huerta thought the mantle should have fallen on his shoulders.

Now the British and American colonies had to choose between Huerta's insurgency and Calles' legitimacy as Obregón's chosen successor. The British oil interests made a wise choice and put their money — literally — on Huerta, who was moderate in his demands on foreign oil companies. The Americans in Mexico generally backed Calles, and one wonders what went wrong with the usually sensitive intelligence system which had been so adept at sorting out Mexican political figures according to their Tampico attitudes. It could hardly have been a secret that Calles had been soaked in Marxist doctrine since youth. It should hardly have escaped them that his following was composed in almost equal parts of the Obregón-dominated army, the Obregón-led peasants,

273

and most critically, perhaps, by the Calles-dominated labor unions which were formed into a strongly motivated if poorly armed militia. Possibly the Americans decided to back Calles only because the British supported Huerta, a perversity for which they would pay dearly.

Washington's strong-arm policy, now guided by President Coolidge, with Hughes still the Secretary of State, swung quickly into line with that of the American oilmen. Regarding the Huerta counterrevolution, Hughes issued a statement ringing with moral fervor: "It was not a revolution instinct with the aspirations of an oppressed people; it was a matter of personal politics. It was an effort to seize the Presidency; it meant a subversion of all constitutional and orderly procedure. The contestants, seeking to overthrow the established Government, had taken possession of certain portions of the Mexican territory, and either were claiming tribute from peaceful and legitimate American commerce or were attempting to obstruct and destroy it . . . The refusal to aid the established Government would have thrown out more influence on the side of those who were challenging the peace and order of Mexico, and we should have incurred a grave responsibility for the consequent disturbances."[3]

Hughes' statement, served up as a campaign document by the Republican National Committee for the 1924 national election, was the official explanation for the American intervention, by indirect means for the most part, in Mexican internal affairs. Later those words would ring with irony rather than righteousness and would help explain Washington's bitterness toward the protégé it selected, largely because he was the choice of the reasonable Obregón, without making a proper estimate of his intentions.

The Huerta uprising broke out in the south and along the Gulf, powered largely by venal generals and mercenaries. It was said to have the support of the British oilmen and some of the smaller American interests, but the cause was lost when Washington not only placed an embargo on the shipment of arms to the Huertistas but covertly sent weapons and ammunition from U.S. army arsenals to the Obregón-Calles forces. The latter, with their bigger and more earnestly motivated battalions, succeeded in putting down the Huerta revolt in short order. Yet they were not properly grateful, as Secretary Hughes explained in that Republican campaign document: "When the Mexican Government regained control of territory which had been temporarily occupied by rebels, Federal and state authorities attempted to force American citizens to repay taxes, duties and other charges previously paid to de facto [that is, Huerta] authorities . . . The State Department made representations . . . The outcome of the Department's action was gratifying, as the Mexican Government promptly issued definite instructions . . . that repayment of such duties and taxes should not be required . . . losses and damages suffered by the American interests were kept to a minimum."[4]

No sooner had Hughes turned his back on the Mexicans, and on retirement from the State Department had become more directly involved in defending the interests of the American Petroleum Institute, Standard Oil and other corporations, than anti-gringoism sprang up again south of the border and this time was given direction by Plutarco Elias Calles. He had been elected to succeed Obregón largely through support of CROM, the Mexican central labor organization, and CROM demanded that Article 27 be enforced. That, of course, coincided with Calles' own indoctrination; his program called for return of the subsoil rights in the oil regions to Mexican control, land reform, laws more favorable to labor, and severe restrictions on the temporal power of the Catholic Church.

Simultaneously, troubles erupted in the oilfields around Tampico and there were predictions that blood would streak the oil-slimed Pánuco River running through the forest of derricks and network of pipelines to the sea. Suddenly generals who had always been ready to take the oil companies'

275

money began to spout radical slogans and issue manifestos, others entered the service of the British or American oil companies as their protectors. Every producing field, tank farm and refinery was forced to increase its army of guards. You could buy off a general, no matter whether he quoted Marx or Bakunin at the top of his lungs. But the labor syndicates, blessed by both Obregón and Calles, had grown much more powerful and their agitators could not be bribed or suborned, nor could their saboteurs be detected in time to prevent huge fires. Setting fire to the oily surface of the Pánuco could start a chain-reaction combustion spreading for miles down the river. There were strikes, lockouts, sitdowns, pitched battles between the unions and the oil companies' private armies. The formerly ignorant and humble Indian, with a few years' experience in the oilfields behind him, knew where to put a dynamite stick to blow up the valve on a pipeline or do the most damage to a cracking plant.

Only a few months after he took office Calles was being pressured by such events and the arguments of one of his Cabinet ministers, Luis Morones, the corpulent leader of the labor syndicates who wore a ring on each finger, that the U.S. oil companies should be "twenty-sevened." President Calles then invoked Article 27, which the oilmen declared was close to expropriation.

Washington's reaction was swift and harsh, but for the time being verbal. It was difficult to tell from the State Department's declaration whether Frank B. Kellogg was Secretary of State or Secretary of Petroleum. He declared that Mexico, by taking that entirely constitutional action, had placed itself "on trial before the world." Ever since it has been quoted by Latin American revolutionaries as document No. 1 in the case against "Yankee imperialism"; it was the kind of diplomatic insult which is often followed by a declaration of war.

"A great deal of property of Americans," Kellogg recited, "has been taken under or in violation of the agrarian laws for which no compensation has been made, and other properties practically ruined and, in one instance, taken by the Mexican Government on account of unreasonable demands of labour. Mr. Sheffield [the U.S. ambassador] will have the full support of this Government and we will insist that adequate protection under the recognized rules of international law be afforded American citizens for property taken. So long as we are satisfied that this is the policy of the Mexican Government and this course of action is being carried out with a determination to meet its international obligations, that Government will have the support of the United States . . .

"I have seen the statement published in the press that another revolutionary movement may be impending in Mexico. I very much hope that this is not true . . . [That sentence was an example of what diplomatic correspondents like to call a "veiled threat." Kellogg's "veil" was strikingly transparent.] It is now the policy of this Government to use its influence and its support on behalf of stability and constitutional procedure, but it should be made clear that this Government will continue to support the Government in Mexico only so long as it protects American lives and American rights and complies with its international engagements and obligations. The Government of Mexico is now on trial before the world. We have the greatest interest in the stability, prosperity and independence of Mexico. We have been patient and realize, of course, that it takes time to bring about a stable Government but we cannot countenance violation of her obligations and failure to protect American citizens."[5]

In Mexico City the Kellogg note was received with outrage, it was an unforgivable offense against the local *machismo*, it made brothers out of peons and proprietors. Worst of all, it was condescending in tone and lecturing in manner. Day after day the Mexico City papers were full of Morones' fulminations against the "insolent Yanquis." Some American newspapers meanwhile were advising Washington to muster the National Guard and send troops across the border; the same ones, in many cases, which had howled for the invasion of Cuba in 1898 and the Pershing expeditionary force in 1916.

A war climate was being created out of diplomatic bluster and journalistic gasconade. Between November 1925 and March 1926 ten notes flew back and forth across the border, more like missiles than state communications. Kellogg's often iterated point, couched in his turgid style, was that the Mexican oil laws were "confiscatory," that confiscation was a violation of international law.

Calles' ripostes, it must be granted, were more pungent. At least one of them got under the American skin like a *banderilla*; it touched on the subject of Prohibition, which most Americans detested a lot more than any Mexican actions against rich Americans' property in Mexico. If Article 27 was "confiscatory," Calles needled Kellogg, so was the Eighteenth Amendment. "When the Prohibition law was enacted in the United States it paralyzed established businesses falling under its provisions . . . and completely to paralyze a business would seem to be tantamount to destroying lawfully acquired rights therein, but nevertheless the American Government was not deterred by that consideration." Kellogg starchily replied that "the liquor business in the United States has not been a property right, but a licensed occupation which was subject to the fullest extent at all times to the police powers of the States, to license by the United States, to the war powers of the Federal Government and now subject under the constitutional amendment to the police powers of the United States."

A final Mexican note, however, was more conciliatory and conceded that laws which the United States regarded as confiscatory would not be applied retroactively and renewable concessions would be granted Americans to confirm the old property titles. For a time the controversy quieted. Then came the Nicaragua intervention and the revelation that Mexico had shipped arms to the insurgents who were killing U.S. marines in Nicaragua.

About that time, too, Calles' ecclesiastical laws were causing a Catholic reaction. Calles had come down hard on the Church. He had closed convents and religious schools and forbidden the clergy to participate in any political activity. Mexican Catholicism, with its Aztec influences, has always been an exotic offshoot of the Mother Church, but its hold on the people was stronger, if subtler, than Calles and the radical labor leaders had suspected. The Catholics, under their "Christ the King" banners, fought back with boycotts and armed uprisings.

In some regions priests and nuns were mistreated and forced to go underground at the urgings from Mexico City that the Church was responsible for all the people's miseries. This was the period illuminated with a harsh brilliance in Graham Greene's novel about an alcoholic English priest, *The Power and the Glory*; the priest hears confessions in stables and preaches in huts. "Pray that you will suffer more and more and more. Never get tired of suffering," the fugitive priest implores. "The police watching you, the soldiers gathering taxes, the beating you always get from the jefe [chief] because you are too poor to pay, smallpox and fever, hunger . . . that is all part of heaven — the preparation. Perhaps without them — who can tell? — you wouldn't enjoy heaven so much. And heaven. What is heaven? . . . Heaven is where there is no jefe, no unjust laws, no taxes, no soldiers, and no hunger. Your children do not die in heaven . . ."

Some American bishops and the Knights of Columbus participated in an anti-Mexican crusade. The Ku Klux Klan, however, declared that the State Department in its anti-Calles pronouncements was being used as "the tool of Rome." Public opinion in the United States was further inflamed when Mexico accorded diplomatic recognition to the Soviet Union, and almost as soon as it was established the Russian embassy began circulating anti-American propaganda.

279

In October 1927 another counterrevolution broke out. It was led by generals Gómez and Serrano, both reportedly financed by oil companies, Gómez having announced that he would reverse Calles' oil policy and negate Article 27 if the revolt succeeded. Obligingly, the United States embargoed arms shipments to the Mexican government, but the Gómez-Serrano movement was quickly crushed and both of its leaders captured and executed.

Late in 1927 President Calles could congratulate himself on having survived — but little more. He was receiving a brutal education in the laws of economics. There was little he could do to improve the quality of Mexican life — redistributing parched mesas and sterile barrancas still wouldn't provide more food, nor could the urban masses long endure on a diet of Marxist slogans — unless he was able to win the support of outside capital. He needed hundreds of millions in loans for reconstruction. Meanwhile the treasury was as bare as it had been under any of the corrupt generals who sat in the National Palace. His restrictive program against the oil companies had only decreased tax revenues. The companies had lowered production from 193 million barrels in 1921 to 64 million in 1927; revenues correspondingly had dropped from $42 million to $14 million, and the national budget had always been based on a one-third contribution from oil revenue. The price of silver, the second most important export, had also fallen.

About the same time it occurred to the Coolidge Administration, and to the oil magnates whose interests it held in tender regard, that economic warfare, diplomatic assault, and covert support of armed uprisings might not be the answer to the Mexican problem. A hint of sweet reasonableness suddenly wafted into the Mexican-American atmosphere; Americans south of the border were no longer publicly assailed as gringos, while Americans tried to eliminate the word "greaser" from their vocabulary.

To replace the abrasive Sheffield, whose resignation was

encouraged, the radiantly charming Dwight Morrow, the embodiment of tact and understanding, was sent to the American embassy on the Avenida de los Insurgentes. Morrow, a Morgan partner, thoroughly understood the viewpoint of the New York bankers, who realized that the funded Mexican debt could never be collected until the country made an economic recovery. Even the hard-nosed U.S. oilmen had come to understand that oil production, their overriding concern, was not increased by a climate of unrest which they had helped to foment. Morrow's instructions were to cut through diplomatic folderol, slash red tape, forget ancient grudges, and arrange a compromise with Calles that would result in a new era of good feeling.

Morrow performed magnificently, demonstrating an understanding for Mexican sensibilities, for Mexican pride, hitherto absent from relations between the two countries. Ambassador Sheffield had made it a rule never to call at the National Palace; Morrow appeared there daily for a talk with President Calles. The new ambassador was interested in and knowledgeable about Mexican art, culture and history, and he never talked down to the Mexicans, a habit which they probably had resented more than all the economic injustices with which they had been visited.

Calles, formerly doctrinaire, likely to bristle at the sight of a silk hat and cutaway, thawed out completely under the genial ministrations of the new ambassador. The latter, on his part, was able to report that it was a mistake to consider Calles a ranting Bolshevik; that the Mexican President had cast off his Marxist indoctrination and become a political realist.

Some of this high-level amiability soon seeped down to the Mexican masses as the result of a masterful public relations job by the American embassy. It happened Will Rogers was a friend of Morrow's and was induced to come down to Mexico City as President Calles' guest, delighting the Mexicans by jesting at the expense of big business back in the States. Even more fortuitously, Charles A. Lindbergh, the No. 1 world hero for having flown the Atlantic solo from New York to Paris in the *Spirit of St. Louis*, was a family friend and Morrow's future son-in-law. Lindbergh's stature then was comparable to that of all the astronauts rolled into one.

Morrow persuaded Lindbergh, who would marry his daughter Anne two years hence, that a "goodwill flight" from Washington to Mexico City would symbolize the dove of peace to Mexican-American relations. It was a risky flight over desert and mountain in a monoplane, but Lindbergh agreed.[6] Some of the delirious prose that attended every Lindbergh activity was present in the *New York Times* account of his takeoff: "Intent, cool, clear-eyed and clear-headed, under conditions requiring supreme moral and physical courage and consummate skill, America's young Viking of the air lifted his gray plane from a hummocky, soggy, puddle-bespattered morass into an underhanging fringe of threatening mists just before noon today, pointed its nose south-westward, and was off again on a new, hazardous venture to a foreign land . . ."[7] It took him twenty-seven hours to complete the flight to Mexico City the afternoon of December 14, 1927. President Calles, Ambassador and Mrs. Morrow and 150,000 Mexicans were waiting to greet him at the mountaintop airport outside the capital.

"It was perfectly thrilling when the plane came to earth," his future mother-in-law wrote in her diary that night. "Dwight brought him to the President who welcomed him and gave him the keys of the city. Lindbergh only said 'thank you' very simply. The throng on the field shouting and screaming with joy was indescribable. As we went to the car our clothes were almost torn off. Oh! the crowds in the streets on the way to the Embassy! — on trees, on telegraph poles, tops of cars, roofs, even the towers of the Cathedral. Flowers and confetti were flung every moment."[8]

For six days Lindbergh enjoyed a triumph the Mexicans have never given another man. Thousands followed him and cheered him every time he appeared outside the embassy; the city's aldermen took him on a ride through the floating gardens of Xochimilco; José Ortiz, the leading matador, dedicated a bull to him, and even the anti-American labor unions turned out to stage a huge parade in his honor under banners reading "Welcome Lindy! Mexican People Is Great Comrade of the American People." It was extraordinary how the visit of one man accomplished a complete turnabout in Mexican feelings about the United States, Mexico City's *Excelsior* predicting that mistrust would be dispelled forever, Calles terming it a "priceless embassy of goodwill." The Democratic New York *World* was inclined to look upon the Coolidge Administration's well-spaced successes in foreign affairs with a sardonic eye, but on December 21 it commented editorially, "It is just eleven months since Secretary Kellogg appeared before a committee of the Senate and charged that a Bolshevist government in Mexico threatened the peace of the United States. The Mexican government which was a Bolshevist threat in June is the same with which a new Ambassador has succeeded in establishing unusually cordial relations, and all Mexico is cheering Lindbergh. The flight of Lindbergh follows a series of events which indicate a real shift in sentiment and a thoroughgoing change in policy . . ."

The Lindbergh visit may have been mere window-dressing; even Ambassador Morrow's diplomacy, its studied geniality, may have partaken more of Madison Avenue advertising methods than of the grand tradition of European chancelleries. Much as he admired the whole man, Harold Nicolson, his friend and biographer, observed that Morrow was insensitive to "the more subtle differences of human character."[9] Mark Twain might have been able to understand how Morrow's approach worked with the Mexicans, better than his English biographer. He even managed, after three years of the most delicate and patient negotiations, to bring about a reconciliation of Church and state in Mexico, a problem which had defeated the wiliest intermediaries sent over by the Vatican. The penetrating power of sheer goodwill is as incalculable as American faith in it is mysterious to the European mind.

Something of the Morrow personality shines through in an anecdote which his wife told Nicolson. Just after he had succeeded in making peace between the Mexican government and the Catholic Church, he and his wife were awakened one Sunday by the first church bells to ring in Mexico for three years. "Betty," Morrow boasted to his wife, "I have opened the churches of Mexico!" Other bells joined in. After a half-hour of increasing din, Morrow said plaintively, "Betty, would you now like me to close the churches of Mexico?"[10]

Along with the priests who could now come out of hiding, American oilmen had every reason to bless Morrow's name with whatever fervor they could summon. The Mexican Supreme Court, reflecting the changed temper of Mexican-American relations, handed down a decision it had long been nursing in its conference chambers, upholding an injunction sought by Pan-American, the old Doheny company now controlled by Standard Oil. The injunction would restrain the government from enforcing its denial of drilling permits to companies not complying with Mexico's petroleum laws. This included companies responsible for about seventy-five percent of the country's oil production.

Back in New York, where the headquarters of most of those companies were located, the executives and lawyers were less inclined to throw their hats in the air over the decision. Their opinion that the Mexican high court's decision was less sweeping than Ambassador Morrow and the State Department believed was echoed by the *Wall Street Journal*: "The only thing the Court decided was that the cancellation of the permits in this one case was wrong because a 50-year limitation could not be put on a title in fee simple. Owners of leaseholds that have less than 50 years to run must surrender their titles to the Government and accept a 'Concession.' The Court utterly failed to pass upon or even notice an oil company's complaint that the law deprives a foreign corporation of the right of ownership. The decision leaves the American oil companies sitting on a limb with the confiscatory saw at work between them and the trunk of the tree."[11]

With Article 27's enforcement nullified, at least for the time being, the United States pressed its case for the amendment or elimination of two other articles, the effects of which were discussed in the *Wall Street Journal* article just quoted. Instead of waiting for the Supreme Court to rule on the constitutionality of those articles, President Calles rammed sweeping amendments through an obedient Congress. He followed them up with executive orders further loosening the Mexican petroleum laws.

Calles, in fact, was in full retreat from his former radicalism. So was his old patron General Obregón who, like Calles, had acquired large land, industrial and financial holdings in the past several years. Apparently it was impossible for a Mexican President not to become rich — and therefore conservative — though an exception was to appear a half-dozen years hence. Calles and Obregón, the latter all set to return to the National Palace when Calles' term expired in 1928, now proclaimed that the only way to "rebuild Mexico" was to work in tandem with American capitalism. The final accolade was now bestowed on the camel-driver's son: he was referred to as Iron Man Calles.

At least one expert foresaw trouble ahead, when and if demands for more rigorous control of oil concessionaires rose again, over the fact that many of the earlier titles were fraudulently acquired. "Even the most anti-Mexican Administration in Washington," he wrote, "in the future is not apt to permit itself to be pushed by oil interests into the indefensible position of protecting illegal American titles in a foreign country. This will not prevent the United States Government, however, from being thrown directly into the dispute over the validity of titles, which is certain to develop . . . Fear of the consequences of this provision of the law is not limited to companies desiring to retain corrupt titles. Holders of titles acquired in good faith are also apprehensive. Their concern is shared by the Washington Government for two reasons. First, titles in Mexico, as in most countries which have gone through cycles of dictatorship, revolution and disorder, are notoriously shaky. In many cases Federal and local government records have been destroyed . . ."[12]

During the next several years, with Calles keeping a firm grip on the federal government in or out of the presidency, there was a deceptive lull in the controversy. Obregón succeeded Calles in the National Palace but was assassinated by a religious fanatic several months after taking office; the next three presidents, Gil, Rubio and Rodríguez, were kept under Calles' dictatorial control. Rubio, in fact, had to resign when he fell out with the Iron Man.

Meanwhile the Mexican government worked diligently to attract further investment by the oil companies. It was alarmed when British geologists, who were usually wrong about Mexico, reported that the Mexican fields were about played out. The government, through its publicity organ, declared that "there is no actual foundation" for such pessimism, that "the proven potential capacity of the existing wells was never so great as now . . . To those who do not understand the matter it should be explained that all Mexican oil wells are self-producing, no pumping being resorted to as in other fields . . ."[13]

Mexico appeared to be accepting, with an Aztec fatalism, that it could not endure as a modern state without being dependent on the United States. "American imperialism," as one leading Mexican journal brooded early in 1928, "is a fatal product of economic evolution. It is useless trying to persuade our northern neighbors not to be imperialistic; they cannot help being so, no matter how excellent their intentions . . . Let us study the natural laws, in the hope of finding some method by which, instead of blindly opposing them, we can mitigate their action and turn it to our advantage."[14] Another

Mexico City journal lamented the fact that European capital, formerly dominant, no longer dared to challenge the U.S. policy of "domination," and concluded, "We find ourselves, then, at the mercy — Mexico the same as other continent Republics — of American capitalists, reigned over by bankers."[15]

One commentator, however, correctly foresaw that if Mexico decided to nationalize her oil lands in the future there wouldn't be much that Washington could do about it, "For the handicap of belligerent Washington Administrations in the past has been the indifference of the American people toward troubles of the American oil men, and the positive opposition of a strong group in Congress to American intervention in the southern Republic." Anti-Mexican sentiment during the late 1920's had been grounded, in the United States, on Calles' anti-Catholic measures. "Mexican Governments," he continued, "shrewdly have counted upon this attitude of the American people to balance the Rockefeller-Doheny-Mellon pressure in Washington." Many Americans sympathized with Mexico because she had been "the underdog and Washington usually the aggressor," but they were wrong in believing, generally, that the United States had made large concessions to arrive at an understanding with Calles. "In this popular American misconception of the Morrow era as representing a change in policy, instead of a mere change in method, exists a danger for the future."[16]

That "danger" arose in 1932, when the Depression was tightening its grip on the world and venture capitalism was under attack on all fronts. That year the P.R.M. (National Revolutionary Party) decided on a six-year program calling for a "cooperative economic system tending toward socialism" and the nationalization of foreign-owned oil concessions. In 1934, when the dour and dedicated Marxist, Lázaro Cárdenas, was elected to the Mexican presidency, it was apparent that U.S. oil companies were in trouble. Cárdenas meant

287

what he said, was incorruptible, utterly determined to "twenty-seven" the American oilmen out of Mexico, and even after leaving the National Palace, with the lingering influence of Mexican presidents-emeritus, has down to the present exerted himself by remote control to keep the 1911 revolution on the tracks.

Shrewdly, Cárdenas avoided arousing American public opinion on the religious front and put little emphasis on the secularization program, but in 1937 the subsoil rights of foreign-owned oil companies were declared to be nationalized, and that was only the beginning.

The eruption of labor troubles in the oilfields was Cárdenas' entering wedge for more drastic action. The eighteen thousand Mexicans employed by oil companies received higher wages than most of their fellow workers, but he maneuvered to use their demands for increased pay as a weapon against the oilmen. As soon as Cárdenas took office the foreign concessionaires felt themselves under intense pressure. Roscoe B. Gaither, an American lawyer expert in Mexican jurisprudence and in the Cárdenas period, has written that "Constant threats of administrative cancellation of concessions were made, admittedly with no legal reason or basis. Drilling permits legally required to be issued were refused. Confirmatory concessions, pending since 1925 or before, were denied or unwarrantedly delayed."

Cárdenas plunged on with the nationalization of many mines and factories, but knew he had to move more cautiously where the oil interests were concerned. "Its confiscation required preparation," Gaither wrote, "the creation of an excuse that would at least sound plausible." President Cárdenas found his excuse on November 3, 1936, when the Oil Workers' Syndicate, undoubtedly with presidential sanction, made demands which Gaither declared were "so far-reaching and extravagant that obviously no company could accept them and continue to exist . . . As time progressed it was evident that labor did not intend the demands to be met."[17]

288

The oil workers went on strike when their employers refused to accede to demands which even the American Federation of Labor would have considered outlandish; undoubtedly they were designed to be rejected and allow Cárdenas to make his next moves. The labor syndicate insisted, among other things, that many executive posts (including the assistant general manager and the assistant general sales manager) be filled by workers selected by the syndicate. Workers were to be pensioned at the companies' expense after twenty years. The companies were required to furnish chauffeured limousines for the use of syndicate officials on their travels. Free medical service had been extended to employees for many years, but that was to be expanded, along with free hospitalization and dental care, to include all members of a worker's family, not only his wife and children but his grandparents, great-grandparents, brothers and sisters under the age of sixteen. The companies would also have to furnish first-class transportation to all workers on their vacations, no matter how far or to which country they planned to travel. Other demands included a work year of only 233 days, 56-hour pay for a 40-hour week, and double pay for working outside when it was raining, triple pay for those working in marshy areas.

The oil companies understandably choked up, refused the demands, and were hit by a ten-day general strike in May 1937, which ended when the government announced that the matter would be settled by the National Labor Board. "Over a period of many years," Gaither observed, "the books of the oil companies had been inspected annually, and often at more frequent intervals, by government tax inspectors. They had never found any serious fault with the general accounting system used by the companies. But the committee of experts, appointed by the Labor Board to ascertain the capacity of the oil companies to pay, now claimed that this accounting system, which was the same as that used by oil companies throughout the world, was inefficient! Asserting that many items entered as losses should have been entered as profits, the committee had no difficulty in arriving at the conclusion that the companies were able to pay what was demanded. The committee's highly technical report, containing some fifteen hundred pages and involving a complete study of the entire accounting of all the companies for several years, was made by the Government experts in the record time of thirty days."[18]

The Mexican Supreme Court, obedient as always to the executive power, upheld the decision that the oil companies would have to comply with the Oil Workers' Syndicate demands. When the companies refused, President Cárdenas issued a decree on March 18, 1938, declaring all their properties expropriated. The army seized everything it could lay hands on, from derricks and refineries to company records, cash on hand and personal property. The companies and their American personnel were briskly dispossessed and sent packing back to the States.

If expropriation turned out to be a mixed blessing to the Mexicans, it was an unmixed curse to the American oilmen. Mexico found it almost impossible to sell its oil in any area dominated by the British, Dutch, and American oil companies; a calamity like outright seizure always drew them together, a band of brothers defending their mutual interests in a free market. Mexico could sell its products only to three nations increasingly being outlawed in the late 1930's, those of the future Axis — Germany, Italy, Japan — and even that trade, conducted on a barter rather than a cash basis, was cut off by the ensuing war.

The Mexican attitude toward its oil resources gradually relaxed and became slightly more permissive on the subject of foreign influences, though there was no doubt about the Mexican people's determination never to allow direct exploitation again. The more conservative views of President Manuel Avila Camacho, Cárdenas' successor, resulted in

Mexico's payment of $24 million for the expropriated American properties, plus three percent interest since 1938; several years later it settled British and Dutch claims — totaling $250 million — for $21,250,000. And in 1949 two American companies were granted drilling permits under the supervision of Pemex, the Mexican government's oil agency. Eight years later Pemex made a profitable deal to sell natural gas to the United States after it tapped rich new fields in the state of Vera Cruz.

Americans learned a costly lesson in Mexico during almost three decades of exploitation made possible largely through the use of force and corruption; they made mistakes which they would not repeat elsewhere, being the first to suffer the blows of an outraged government. It was a different lesson from that impressed on the rest of the world, which according to the French oil historian Delaisi was that "Who attacks Standard attacks the Washington government directly."

In Mexico they learned the equation that oil plus nationalism equals exodus. From now on national sensibilities would have to be treated with the utmost tenderness; for a top executive diplomacy and knowledge of the country involved and respect for its pride and prejudices would be as important as a working acquaintance with geophysics. They also learned that to obtain the full support of their government they would have to stand on very firm ground with public opinion; it wasn't enough to run the American flag to the top of an oil derrick. They could only hope that another lesson derived from the Mexican experience was not ignored by other countries: a country seizing oilfields cannot profit from the gesture unless it has been assured of a market — and the marketplace remains where it has always been, New York, London and The Hague.

13.

Dad Joiner
Blows the Roof Off Texas

The stage was set for the East Texas discovery, and the discovery
was made. The crib door was open and the swill barrel full. Here
were inestimable riches that would go to the fastest, smartest
manipulator.
— George Sessions Perry, *Texas: A World in Itself*

To a nineteen-year-old tramp reporter, more tramp than reporter, crossing the Texas-Louisiana border in 1934 was like
entering a wild new world: boomtowns instead of hobo jungles. Back in Louisiana there were sheriffs to urge along what
the Roosevelt Administration delicately referred to as "tran-
sients," and a railroad detective said to have shot more than
twenty-five men off freight trains to save himself the trouble
of arresting them. At first glimpse from the door of a box-
car, East Texas didn't look like much and appeared to be
even more "depressed" than the rest of the country. That part
of Texas had once been covered by forests of loblolly pine, but
lumbermen had leveled the woodlands and left the countryside with a permanent five-o'clock shadow in which, among

the scrub growth, there were patches of red soil on which white and Negro sharecroppers tried to raise cotton. Razor-back hogs and ragged children wandered around, escorted by lean and hungry hounds. Most of the houses leaned into themselves and seemed on the verge of collapse.

Then, suddenly, the scrublands opened up on a vista of der-ricks. Booted off the freight by a brakeman, you found your-self in Tyler, Texas, overrun by boomers, oilfield roughnecks, drillers, gamblers, leasehounds, and the hard-bitten soldiers of what was called the Hot Oil War. In Tyler, every bed had three men claiming title to the unwashed linen and sleeping in eight-hour shifts. It must have been one of the few regions in the United States with a labor shortage. And down in Hous-ton, the capital of this new bonanza, there were even more splendid symptoms of prosperity. The Rice Hotel lobbies were filled with men smoking 50-cent cigars, their trouser pockets bulging with rolls of hundred-dollar bills secured by rubber bands. Down the street the Snappy Cafe, one of the few places in town where you could buy a bottle of whiskey and drink it on the premises, was thronged every night; a few blocks away the up-a-flight gambling houses were crowded around the clock by men playing poker for high stakes. You could overlook the fact that a few more blocks away from the Rice Hotel there was a ramshackle warehouse, a U.S. "transient camp," where it took influence to obtain a meal ticket and the night's use of a cot. The crust of East Texas had recently erupted with the greatest explosion of oil the world had seen thus far.

All because of an old Alabaman named Columbus M. Joiner, better known as Dad Joiner, the King of the Wild-catters. In 1930 he was seventy years old, had been rich a couple of times, and poor a lot oftener. In the best Southern po'-boy tradition, he had wandered all over the map and tried a number of occupations. Born in Lauderdale, Alabama, in 1860, he received a total formal schooling of seven weeks. Despite or because of his scant education, he acquired a fondness for reading; late in life he estimated that he had read ten thousand books, and among the unlettered boomers of the oilfields he was something of a legend for quoting long passages from Shakespeare or the Bible to the pounding rhythm of a drilling rig. For a time he tried storekeeping in Alabama, then migrated to Tennessee, where he qualified as a lawyer and served in the state legislature.

In 1913, at the age of fifty-three, he took up a new calling when he moved to Oklahoma, caught the oil fever, and became a wildcatter. That is, he obtained leases on promising ground, then persuaded other persons to bankroll the project of driving wells. A wildcatter who became rich and successful was an oilman. In his definitive study of the wildcatter breed, Samuel W. Tait, Jr., has observed that it has deep and ineradicable prejudice against outsiders, who are regarded as unable to understand the conventions of the game: "It was reflected in the remark of an oil man who found during the early boom in Illinois that he could secure a promising lease there only if he entered into partnership with a banker and several merchants. 'Nothing doing!' exclaimed the wildcatter. 'I know what I would be up against with those fellows. As long as I got big wells everything would be fine. But if we got a lot of little stinkers that pumped a few barrels a day, I'd be expected to stay around and look after them as long as they paid a measly five or six percent. And all the while fields would be blowing in all over the Southwest and I wouldn't be there. No, thanks!' An oil well, this man knew, is next to worthless if it can't pay back its original cost, or 'pay out,' in the oil game's own phrase . . . Another characteristic of the wildcatter which sets him apart from business in other fields is his view of credit. He may owe the butcher, baker and grocer, and give the matter no more attention than is required to tear up their duns. But two sorts of obligations a wise oil man will never attempt to avoid: he will meet all payrolls and he will keep his credit good with supply companies. The men who try to beat either are thereafter déclassé, and reputations travel fast and far throughout the oil country from Olean to Los Angeles."[1]

To a wildcatter a five or six percent return on his money was ridiculous. He was a gambler, first of all, then a promoter. Dad Joiner caught on early that you had to play for high stakes. In his first venture in Oklahoma, he bought an oil lease for $55, sold it for $255, and turned an overnight four hundred percent profit. From then on Joiner experienced all the joys and sorrows of a wildcatter's career. Bad luck dogged him most of the time, such as when he drilled a well near Earlsboro, Seminole County, and ran out of money when he reached 150 feet. With a few thousand dollars more he would have tapped the great Seminole field, which enriched Cities Service years later. His Oklahoma Star well near Cement, Oklahoma, brought up a "show" of oil months before the Fortuna Oil Company, with its greater resources, exploited the same pool.

In 1925, when he showed up in Dallas with a battered suitcase full of dirty shirts and a batch of leases on barren, unpromising East Texas acreage, he was sixty-five years old and just about at the end of his rope. His only assets were a homely, winning manner and a reputation for honesty. A small, spry, bright-eyed man in rundown boots, he went around town singing his wildcatter's song and trying to raise the money for his new scheme.

Geologists considered East Texas, actually the northeast corner in the basin west of the Sabine River, a hopeless case. "No salt domes," they muttered, "absence of the Woodbine formation." Joiner knew that geologists were not infallible, and with borrowed money secured more East Texas leases until he had the oil rights to an estimated ten thousand acres. Most of the acreage was planted with cotton, sweet potatoes, corn and peanuts by the impoverished farmers of the basin. One geologist, A. D. Lloyd, an Oklahoman whom Joiner had consulted on previous occasions, shared his optimism about the Sabine basin. Lloyd looked over the ground, then rec-

295

ommended the site for his first well. Joiner did not follow Lloyd's recommendation, however, because one of the property-owners, a widow named Mrs. Daisy Bradford, would not lease her 975-acre farm unless the first well was sunk there. So his first exploration took place two miles from the spot Lloyd had recommended.[2]

Somehow he scraped enough money together by selling shares in his venture to start drilling in August 1927. As the wiseacres in Dallas put it, he was "po'-boying" the Rusk County well; poor-boying being the term for an operator who puts together a well-drilling outfit out of a makeshift rig, battered old piping, a much-used bit and worn-out boilers, the faith of a few co-workers, and a line of credit at the nearest general store.

Dan Joiner started work on Daisy Bradford No. 1 — the old lady was so flattered by having the well named for her that she served free meals to his drillers — with the minimum in equipment even for a po'-boy operation. Timbers for his rig had to be cut on the land he had leased, and his two "mismated" boilers, which the crew called Big Joe and Little Joe, were fueled by wood chopped out of the scrub pine. His rotary drill, he admitted, was "nothing to brag about." And his financing was strictly hand to mouth, based on credit, goodwill, and Joiner's ability to sell pieces of the action whenever starvation threatened. The only favoring factor was geological; he was drilling through soft rock.

On his first well, the bit got stuck at the 1,098-foot level and could not be shaken loose. He had to abandon that hole and "skid" his rig downhill a hundred feet away and make a new start. Meanwhile, his money troubles increased. Members of the crew drifted away unpaid. Joiner was reduced to selling $25 certificates for a small interest in the new well. He journeyed to Houston and Dallas to peddle his certificates, stopped in diners, struck up conversations with strangers, and persuaded them to throw in with the venture.

Finally he raised enough cash to start drilling his second well. Bad luck again. The bit went down 2,518 feet; then it was learned that the pipe was hung wrong and drilling had to be suspended. He took off for Houston to hire a new chief driller and buy special equipment. The new driller, Ed Laster, signed on partly for cash and partly for an interest in the well. When he took a look at Daisy Bradford No. 2, he told Joiner the well would have to be abandoned and a third one started.

Again old man Joiner hit the road with his satchel full of stock certificates, and devised other methods of financing. "He disposed of some leases to nearby farmers in order to meet payrolls," one authority has written, "selling eight acres for $125 — the land later was divided into two four-acre plots and one of them sold for $10,000 and an interest carried in a well thereon. Finally he began exchanging stock for labor and supplies.[3] There were so many shutdowns on the operations at the Daisy Bradford farm that one scout for a major oil company who visited the site twenty times never once found the rig working.

Daisy Bradford No. 3 began drilling in May 1929. Work often had to be suspended while Dad scrounged more cash, or wood was cut for the boilers, or the wretched equipment was repaired on the spot. It took Joiner and his crew seven months, in fact, to reach the 1,530-foot level. By now his project was a communal effort. Practically everybody for miles around had a piece of Joiner's enterprise. Whenever Dad was shorthanded, nearby farmers would stop tilling their sweet potato patches and join the drilling crew. A banker in Overton ten miles away regularly put on overalls after his bank closed and lent a hand at the well while his wife cooked for the crew. Twice Joiner's lease on Mrs. Bradford's acreage ran out and the widow granted him extensions. In exchange for groceries and other supplies Joiner issued his own scrip, which began circulating around East Texas in lieu of currency. The whole economy of Rusk County, and much of the neighboring ones, was tied into the success of the old man's operation.

By the time Joiner had celebrated his seventieth birthday, early in September 1930, Daisy Bradford No. 3 had reached the 3,500-foot level. The bit began grinding through a layer of rock. On October 3 the hopeful sign of oily sand was brought to the surface. Two days later the drilling site was mobbed by more than five thousand persons, many of whom had camped out there overnight, most of them with certificates attesting to a tiny percentage of ownership in the enterprise.

It wasn't particularly dramatic watching the crew labor in the autumn sun. The drilling had to be halted frequently while mud was bailed out of the hole. Then a "swab," a steel and rubber device which created suction, had to be lowered to bring up gobs of oily sand.

Toward nightfall there was a gurgling noise coming up from the pipe, just what Joiner and chief driller Ed Laster had been waiting months to hear.

"Douse the boilers!" Laster shouted at the crew.

A stream of oil came welling up — not a gusher. But as it gathered force underground the oil began to spray over the crowd and gas came roaring out. Oil-soaked investors danced under the shower and congratulated each other on becoming oil-rich.

"I dreamed it would happen," Joiner said, "but I never really believed it."

He turned to Laster and asked, "How much will she produce?"

Laster's guess was fifty-six hundred barrels a day. Joiner, at his urging, then went back to Dallas to rest up after his three-year effort to prove out the Daisy Bradford lease. He had hardly started unwinding when all the uglier aspects of an oil strike made their hasty appearance. Lease-traders and other speculators showed up and within two weeks of discovery more than two thousand land transactions were recorded in the Tyler-Longview-Kilgore region. Hamburger stands and whorehouses sprang up; the town of Joinerville was laid out on the highway above the Bradford farm.

The rumor went around that all the certificate-holders, being small fry, would be cheated out of their $25 investments either by Joiner or by men to whom he had sold larger pieces of the enterprise. An indignant editorial in the Tyler *Courier-Times* defended Dad Joiner's integrity and demanded: "Is he to be a second Moses to be led to the promised land, permitted to gaze upon its 'milk and honey' and then be denied the privilege of entering by a crowd of slick lawyers who sit back in palatial offices cooling their heels and waiting while old 'Dad' worked in the slime, muck and mire of slush pits and sweated blood over his antiquated rig down in the pines near Henderson?"[4]

The Sabine basin soon was swarming with vulpine types out to grab what they could. It rapidly became obvious that East Texas was probably the world's richest oilfield of the moment: a 134,000-acre plot extending over parts of five counties and measuring about forty-two miles long and twelve miles wide. Other wildcatters, inspired by Joiner's effort in the basin, had begun drilling in recent months. Two weeks after Dad's well came in a trade journal was reporting: "Ed. W. Bateman and others are spudding No. 1 Della Crim in the Eldridge Sevier Survey, Rusk County, approximately four miles southwest of the town of Kilgore, and about ten miles due north of the Joiner discovery."[5] Before the end of the year Bateman's well came in with an explosion of fifteen thousand barrels daily. Others rapidly sunk around Longview also became big producers. Harry Sinclair, in between court appearances, came down and looked the East Texas field over and announced that he was buying in with everything he had. "I believe," he said, "this is the biggest oilfield I ever saw in the making, and it has not even been scratched."[6]

299

And now, while Dad Joiner found himself engulfed in lawsuits (150 in the four years after Daisy Bradford No. 3 came in, he later estimated), the sharks gathered in the pool he discovered. Just how they operated was described by a witness to the spectacle, George Sessions Perry, who provided a fairly comprehensive explanation by imagining himself to be one of the independent operators hoping to chisel out a profitable lease for himself: "I had to do selective leasing, and yet to me all land looked alike. It was common knowledge that certain big companies had seismograph crews working. These crews were working out subsurface geological structures by shooting dynamite vibrations into the earth and seeing how promptly they bounced back. If they bounced back much more quickly in one spot than others nearby, the presence of a salt dome was indicated. (A salt dome is, roughly, a cone-shaped pocket in which oil is frequently trapped.)

"First, to save trouble, I tried to bribe the man who tabulated the findings of the seismograph crew to give me the information I wanted. I did it subtly so that he could take it or leave it and not have an obvious right to be offended. If he didn't choose to be bribed, I then had his maps stolen. That failing, I bribed the map maker who struck off duplicates for the oil company. If that didn't work, I bribed the archivist in the oil company office. He didn't have to steal them for me. I would be satisfied with a photostatic copy. With this information, I took a lease, promoted a well, and, if I struck oil, I was rich . . . I was a success and a leader in the community.

"Suppose I were a lease-broker. The best person, then, to bribe was the head land man of one of the big companies. When his company was about to take a 12,000- or 15,000-acre block, he tipped me off. I leased land in the middle of the proposed block for fifty cents an acre. I didn't want to seem greedy, so I leased only a couple thousand acres. (If I took too much, they might abandon this block and leave me holding a bag full of leases.) I then held out on my confederate's company until, in order to complete its block, it bid fifteen dollars an acre for my lease. If I split even with the company land man, my net profit was $14,500. His half I delivered to him in cash, out of my suitcase, at a Houston hotel."

The East Texas oil strike raised a huge crop of new millionaires just when the rest of the country was sunk deep in the Depression. Mr. Perry was not saying, he made clear, that *all* of them were crooks and thimbleriggers. "There are, beyond question," he wrote in 1942, "some honest people who've made millions in oil, who never so much as paid or accepted a bribe." But, said Mr. Perry, "If I, as an oil operator, were a normal but impressionable young man who'd found myself in a business climate where I was constantly seeing commercial piracy, mixed in with a little shrewdness and some luck, being turned into huge, fast fortunes all around me, I might very well be tempted into playing the same game. If I were originally a honkytonk bouncer or an ordinary clever chiseller, the probability is I'd be hungry for power, and a display of power, and, if I could keep out of jail, I'd get it. For I very likely would have told a thousand lies, worked skin games, been bribed and have paid bribes, to have got quick millions in the first place. Because into its fold the oil business in Texas has invited and accepted some of the most talented, simon-pure thieves that ever perjured themselves in any of the spectacular expansion periods of any of the new American industries."[7]

From his eyewitness view, in fact, it seemed to Mr. Perry, an able journalist and talented novelist (*Hold Autumn in Your Hand* won the National Book Award in 1941), that the East Texas oil rush generated more knavery than any other comparable event. The western gold stampedes may have been more violent, and there may have been more corruption connected with the building of the railroads to the Pacific, but "surely none of these enterprises drew upon sharper talents or easier consciences than the oil business in Texas."

Within a few months after Dad Joiner's No. 3 well bubbled up, the dreary sandhill landscape of the Sabine basin was imprinted with oil derricks from one end of the horizon to the other. Kilgore at first was the center of the rush. Then the town of Longview, with an upsurge of civic jealousy, yearned to share in the boom. Its Chamber of Commerce offered $10,000 for the first operator to bring in a well within the Longview trading area. Just twenty-eight days later an Arkansas syndicate came through with a gusher only five miles from the center of Longview.[8]

The big companies, as it happened, were a bit slow in joining the competition, largely because four months elapsed between the Joiner and Longview discoveries and partly because of a lingering skepticism, possibly fostered by their own geological surveys showing East Texas to be a region of dry holes, that it was really a major strike. Before it became dead certain that the East Texas field covered about 240 square miles, in comparison with Oklahoma fields of 20, they allowed independent operators to snatch up most of the worthwhile leases. "Even after the field was a year old," Ruth Sheldon Knowles has written, "the major companies still owned less than a fifth of the producing wells and proven acreage." Thousands of small operators were able to secure leases before the bigger bankrolls were tossed into the game, and "East Texas was the genesis of more oil fortunes and independent oil companies than any other field in history. The field was so huge that even those who thought their leases were on the fringe or completely outside soon found they were in the fairway."[9]

Among the luckier entrepreneurs cited by Mrs. Knowles in her enlightening study of American oil exploration were the six Glasscock brothers, native East Texans, who had operated a small family circus. Before World War I, they had a headlining high-wire act. Afterward the family circus broke up and the brightly painted wagons were parked in the barnyard of their old homestead near Longview. Gus Glasscock and his brother Lonnie worked in the oilfields as drillers until they accumulated enough capital to buy two rigs and operate on their own. After Joiner's strike, the whole family was reunited and went into the oil business, using one rig for drilling under contract, the other for developing their own lease-holds. "This land," Gus Glasscock remarked, "ought to be good for something besides raising acrobats." Their first hit was on the grounds of a Negro school within the Kilgore town limits, a thundering 39,000-barrel producer. Next they drilled into their own barnyard and brought in a 20,000-barrel well where their father had scratched long and hard for a bare living.

Long before the East Texas frenzy reached its crest, Dad Joiner knew there would be no such rich and happy ending for him. The leases he had more or less reserved for himself covered only a few square miles — very rich in oil, to be sure, but acquired without much legal advice. His certificate-holders were clamoring for the courts to place him in receivership. Almost every day there was a new suit filed against him in the Dallas court. All he wanted, then, was a little peace of mind.

He bought time by going into voluntary receivership, time to consider making a deal by which someone with more financial weight could take on the job of defending his leases.

The best offer came from a hitherto obscure dealer named Haroldson Lafayette Hunt, who had formed a syndicate with several Dallas men. Hunt had parlayed a talent for poker, as a professional gambler in Arkansas, into a wildcatting career of his own. Under the circumstances — the clouded title to some of Joiner's leases, the swarm of those who held Dad's scrip, certificates and subleases, all the po'-boy paper — Hunt's offer was fairly generous. Joiner agreed to accept $30,000 in cash, $45,000 in short-term notes, and a guarantee of $1.2 million out of future profits.[10]

The lawyers got most of that, and Joiner retired to a small house appropriately located on Mockingbird Lane, in Dallas, to contemplate the rise of H. L. Hunt, who made a hundred million dollars out of the deal, which served as the seedling for Hunt's estimated fortune of more than a billion. Only God would know which of the men had the best of the bargain.

Hunt is regarded as possibly the richest man in America, and suffused by nostalgia for the America of his youth spends his time and energy in promoting old-fashioned patriotism, organizing homely singsongs in his Dallas mansion, publishing his own right-wing propaganda, and piling up more millions, though he confessed in a recent interview that he had only the vaguest idea of what he is worth. Dad Joiner died broke in 1947, at the age of eighty-seven, having made a local name for himself as the heaviest book-borrower at the Dallas Public Library.[11] From all accounts, he was satisfied with the hand he had been dealt; no one could take away from him the fact that he discovered a field which had produced more than 3.5 million barrels of crude oil and is still freely flowing.

That huge reservoir of oil discovered by Dad Joiner turned out to be something of an economic embarrassment at first. Mexican production had kept sinking despite the more favorable exploitive conditions dictated by Calles, and by 1930 conservationists were sounding the alarm about the depletion of the U.S. reserves. Then came the East Texas discovery and an enormous glut that threatened to ruin the American market. Overproduction had always been the great threat to the oil companies' financial position.

A thousand wells were draining the East Texas field within eight months after discovery. The price of oil dropped from $1.30 a barrel in 1930 to 10 cents, and finally plummeted to 5 cents. Up went the cry for "dollar oil." Somehow the state of Texas or the federal government had to find a way of stemming the overflow. By an oddity of the Texas laws, the Railroad Commission was in charge of the oil industry, and that was the agency empowered to deal with the situation, principally by an attempt to prorate the producers and establish a quota system. "The chief fruit of this action was the term 'hot oil,'" as George Sessions Perry noted, "a comprehensive phrase referring not only to oil flowed in excess of the official allowable but stolen oil as well."

It might have worked if human frailty had not entered the equation. The workings of the hot-oil graft were succinctly described by Mr. Perry, who observed that the main trouble was that the Railroad Commission's operations were "fraught with the most paralyzing temptations" and the distance between being tempted in the Texas of 1931 and succumbing was very short. "If I had a well under the scrutiny of one of the minions of the Railroad Commission, and I didn't care to broach certain delicate subjects to him, I just had a little plumbing done the first time he went to town. That is to say, I connected a pipe onto the well at a level below that at which inspection occurred, and then I let her flow.

"For that matter, if my neighbor had a lease superintendent who was drawing two hundred dollars a month, I might pay him five hundred dollars not to look while I also made an underground connection between my neighbor's well and my own storage tanks. If the owner caught me at it, I probably knew something on him that would keep him quiet. In any case, if a week or two passed before he caught me flowing his well, I'd made a very decent little fortune. On all of this hot oil, of course, the landowner did not receive a penny of his one-eighth royalty to which, under his lease contract, he was entitled. In many instances, he had already received a first-rate skinning when his land was leased. For example, after an agreement had been reached on the terms of the lease, I may have switched the papers on him while he put on his glasses . . ."[12]

Initially it was the conservation aspect, rather than the skulduggery involved in skirting the Texas laws, that concerned the federal government. Only a year before Dad Joiner's well came in, the Federal Oil Conservation Board reported there was an imminent danger that U.S. oil resources would be exhausted. "Neither the high rate of domestic consumption, nor the excess of exports over imports would be disquieting if the petroleum resources of the United States bore anything like the same ratio to the world's resources as the production ratio of 68 percent. According to the present opinion of our best petroleum geologists, our total resources, instead of being 68 percent of those of the world, are not more than 18 percent. If our petroleum reserves are not to be drawn upon at a faster rate than those of other countries, our resources should be several times larger.

"The obvious inference is that the United States is exhausting its petroleum reserves at a dangerous rate. If the international comparison is made, this country is depleting its supply several times faster than the rest of the world. How real is the danger expressed in this fact, and what remedy can be devised are questions confronting the American people as they plan for the future . . . The depletion rate of our own resources can be brought more into accord with that of foreign resources only in one way — *importing a greater quantity of crude petroleum.*"[13]

Despite the flood of Texas crude that ruined the market for the time being, Washington was concerned with the wastage involved in the East Texas field. Henry L. Doherty, a pioneer in the cause of oil conservation, warned the Federal Oil Conservation Board that there was a "shocking magnitude of waste," that the usual methods of extracting oil from the ground left ten barrels dribbling away as waste for every barrel taken out, that enormous quantities of natural gas were simply "blown off" as a waste product. He advocated that an oilfield be considered as a unit rather than allowing the "law of capture" to continue in effect. "A petroleum pool is by nature," he said, "incapable of being divided up and operated according to the surface divisions that have been arbitrarily created. It must be developed as a unit to prevent both the waste of petroleum and gas and economic waste as well. If

100 people own property on an oil structure and 99 wanted to defer the time when the oil should be produced, a single owner can either rob them of their oil or force them to drill at his will, and can carry out his operations in a manner that will sacrifice the greatest part of the value of the deposit."

If production were controlled by state or federal law, he added, "it is highly probable that we can recover 85 to 90 percent of all the oil the pool contains." Federal regulation was the only authority that could control the piratical conditions in the oilfields.

Charles Evans Hughes, as counsel for the American Petroleum Institute, placed himself in opposition to Doherty's argument for federal regulation. "It does not appear that there is any prospect of sudden disaster," he told the conservation board. "Oilfields do not play out in an instant. Such fields have their periods of flush production, followed by many years of gradual decline." Constitutionally, he held, the federal government was only "one of enumerated powers" and was not "at liberty to control the internal affairs of the states respectively, such as production within the states, through assertion by Congress of a desire either to provide for the common defense or to promote the general welfare."

To which Doherty replied, "I have no wish to stretch the powers of the Constitution one iota beyond their plain and manifest meaning, but if the oil lawyers and Judge Hughes are right in this matter then the agitation must be directed to the amendment of our Constitution to enable the Federal Government to do that which may from time to time become necessary for our national safety . . . To me it is inconceivable that Congress should have the power to sacrifice the lives of the citizens of the States in event of war if Congress sees fit to do so, and yet Congress, according to the great oil lawyers and Judge Hughes, is unable to conserve petroleum as a war resource to lessen the necessity for the need to sacrifice human life . . ."[14]

Overproduction in the East Texas field, with the attendant

gunplay and corruption, soon forced Congress to take cogni-
zance of the situation and consider the matter of regulation.
At least one congressional oil expert, Samuel B. Pettengill
(author of a 1936 paperback titled *Hot Oil*), was troubled
by doubts about the extent to which the government could go
in regulating a private enterprise without running the risk
of emulating German and Italian fascism. "If the price of
crude oil is 'stabilized' by law, at one dollar per barrel, are
we not also bound in time and in justice to stabilize all the
fractions that make up that dollar? How much shall we allow
the royalty owner? How much to invested capital? How much
to labor? How much to depletion and depreciation? Will not
all these elements clamor at Washington to increase their
fractions of the total? If so, the decision will be dictated
by political pressure, by pull, by lobbying, by favoritism, by
contributions to party war chests, by the 'invisible government.' Economic questions will receive political answers. If
that is not true, then we must breed bigger and bolder bureaucrats than earth has yet spawned, except in dictatorships.
Perhaps we want a dictator. Or do we only want a dictator
for the other fellow? Perhaps that is the biggest question
of all."

The Hot Oil War certainly proved that Texas by itself was
not equipped to handle the problem. The glut was almost
terrifying in its enormity. Every day 848,000 barrels were
gushing out of the East Texas wells.

A quota system was then established. In Oklahoma the
picturesque Governor Alfalfa Bill Murray simply proclaimed
martial law and shut down all his state's twenty-nine producing fields "until we get dollar oil." In Texas, however,
Governor Ross Sterling had to move more cautiously. At first
he tried to work out a quota system, by which each well was
prorated on how much oil it could produce daily. Texas individualism got in the way of that scheme, and some sort of
heavy-handed enforcement became necessary. Governor

Sterling finally called out the National Guard, the command-ing general of which, unsurprisingly, was the general coun-sel of the Texas Company (Texaco).

Militiamen patrolled the East Texas field and set up road-blocks, but truck convoys bearing "hot oil" often ran the blockade at night, undeterred by running gun battles. In Texas a bootlegger was one who ran oil instead of booze. All sorts of tricks were conceived to get around the state's regu-lations. At night the oilfield quietly bustled with clandestine activity. The producers posted lookouts on their derricks to keep a watch for the militia patrols, then ran their crude through unregistered pipes to bootleg refineries or pipelines whose owners did not trouble to record the unofficial intake.

Railroad Commissioner Ernest O. Thompson, charged with controlling the illegal outflow, made a survey of all the pro-ducing wells and thoroughly alarmed everyone but the boot-leggers with his report that the East Texas wells could pro-duce a total of 100 million barrels a day if unchecked. This, it was estimated, was twenty-six times the daily world con-sumption.[15]

Many of the independents, however, continued to evade the law. Their bootlegging methods could have been studied with respect by Al Capone and his associates. Whenever pos-sible, of course, they simply bribed the Railroad Commission's operatives to look the other way. (Occasionally, however, an oilman would balk at the cumshaw system. Perry cities a Houston oilman named Mooers who went to Austin to ask an increase in his "allowable," or quota, and was told by a Rail-road Commission employee that the price would be $5,000. Mooers agreed, but paid him in a hotel room with marked currency. The Commission man was arrested when he left.)

The East Texas highways for a time were almost as exciting as a Chicago street during the gang wars. Come nightfall and the bootleg convoys hit the road, often with state police or militia cars in hot pursuit, guns blazing on both sides. Road-side honky-tonks and hamburger stands served as lookouts for the hot-oil convoys. They would signal with their electric signs if the police or National Guard had recently been spotted in the vicinity. More subtle operators had their trucks rebuilt to contain a "reserve" tank with a few hundred gallons of bootleg oil compartmented from the legitimate load.

When it was impressed upon Texans that only interstate agreements or federal regulation would restore order and raise prices on the oil market, they replied with native brio that Texas was a special case, with an exalted status among her sisters in the federal union. As Representative Pettengill explained the Texas contention, "Texas did not come into, or join, the Union, like other states organized out of territory previously under the jurisdiction of the Union. It is her proud boast that she entered the Union by documents having the effect of an international treaty; that she was an independent sovereignty and joined the Union under her own terms and with her own reservations . . . the Texans argue that no 'law of the United States' (even though valid in other states) has any greater dignity than, or the power to override, the treaty by which Texas became one of the United States." That theory — part of the Texans' belief that theirs is a superstate — had never been tested, as Pettengill pointed out, and "it may present an absolute bar to the Federal control of Texas oil production."[16]

On behalf of the governor, Jack Blalock, a Marshall, Texas attorney, filed a brief maintaining that "Texas is the owner in her own sovereignty of millions of acres of its public domain. This public domain is in part underlain with vast deposits of petroleum. Texas is the lessor of thousands of oil leases and collects the royalty in its own sovereignty from more than 700 oil wells . . . These provisions were in the constitution of the State of Texas when it was laid before the Congress and before its annexation in 1845."[17]

Posed against Texas intransigence was the doughty figure of Harold L. Ickes, who became Secretary of the Interior in the Roosevelt Administration and administrator of the oil industry provisions of the National Recovery Act. A testy citizen, as bad-tempered as he was honest, Ickes had an old reformer's passion for the socially justified reorganization of anything that came under his jurisdiction; a zeal for tidiness, outraged by the near-anarchic competition of the East Texas field, that verged on regimentation. The fiercest paladin of the New Deal thus confronted the wildest partisans of utterly free enterprise.

Red-faced and close to ranting, he descended on a meeting of the American Petroleum Institute in Dallas and charged the assembled barons with waste, extravagance and profligacy. Unless the industry subscribed wholeheartedly to the Petroleum Code, he blustered, "the people of the United States one of these days will go into the court of public opinion and demand and receive a finding from that court that you are incompetent to manage this magnificent heritage."

He did not spare the feelings of the oil operators when he observed that they doubtless were unanimous in believing that the government had no business regulating private industry "no matter how badly managed" through the NRA. "Again if I were not as polite as I really am, I might remark that if private initiative is so wonderful and so self-efficient, how did it happen that the oil industry got into such a mess and why did it ever think of appealing to the Government for help?

"Texas has always had it within its power to stop the production of illegal oil within its own borders. It is all very well to insist upon 'state's rights,' to demand that it be left to the sovereign state to regulate what it is claimed is purely an intrastate matter . . . But it will not suffice merely to prevent the seepage of hot oil and its products into the channels of interstate commerce. No state will be doing its duty to itself or complying with its obligations to the Federal Government if it allows the production of a single barrel of hot oil even if that barrel is used within the producing state. Oil brought up in excess of the allowable is a constant pressure

311

upon the market and a menace to the price structure, even if it never leaves the state of its origin."

He also had a few unkind words for giveaway contests between competing filling-station chains, the 1934 forerunner of the 1968–1969 rash of jackpot offerings, for the consumer's dollar. "Who will be so bold," he demanded, "as to deny that it may come to pass that the tourist of the future will have to trade in his Chevrolet or his Plymouth for a huge truck in order to be able triumphantly to carry home the radios and kitchen stoves and baby grand pianos that he will be able to garner as premiums from competing filling stations as he tours the country?"

Ickes grandly closed his sermon by advising the oilmen to "set your house in order" and go along with the government, lovingly sheltered by the Blue Eagle (symbol of the National Recovery Administration), because "if we fail it will be at the cost of the whole oil industry. You will have to pay the price."[18]

The Texas oilmen sputtered into their bourbon and branch water for a week over that speech. A reasoned reply was made by their organ, the *Oil Weekly*, five days later: "In one part of his address, Mr. Ickes exhorted the people of Texas to rise up in their might and demand elimination of hot oil; so as to be assured, in effect, of receiving $1 or so a barrel, instead of 10 cents, for their crude oil; so as to recover a high instead of low percentage of their oil reserves. The important fact which the Administrator seemed to overlook was that most of the several million people in Texas are not sellers of oil, whether the price is $1 or 10 cents, and are therefore never seriously wrought up over hot oil. On the other hand, most of the several millions of Texas are motorists, buyers of oil. Why should they rise up against hot oil, when it puts gasoline down to bargain prices? If there is any rising of Texans in their might, it is more likely to be under the leadership of some astute politician, claiming that high oil prices benefit the oil companies and Wall Street, and that oil conservation laws are but generators of high prices."[19] Thus the specter of the demonic Rockefeller was raised again.

But Texas began to swing around when cooler heads reasoned that hot oil, like war, was hell. One of the leading peacemakers was Charles B. Ames, the board chairman of Texaco, who pointed out that neither industry nor government could "directly control production" but "cooperation between principal oil-producing states is necessary and can be achieved by agreement by some of these states with the approval of Congress." The resulting compromise was the Interstate Oil Compact Commission, to which the oil-producers submitted more or less gracefully for their ultimate good. The secret refineries closed down, the illegal underground pipes which snaked through East Texas and siphoned off hot oil were uprooted, the bootleggers reformed or took up some other pursuit. "The huge refineries' systems have the situation in their capable, metallic hands," observed George Sessions Perry, "and a strict economy of natural resources is being practiced."[20]

"To a shower of gold," wrote Thomas Carlyle, "most things are penetrable." The same goes for oil, sometimes known as black gold. The manifold material blessings conferred by the East Texas boom changed the state for better *and* worse, contributed mightily to the feeling that Texas was something special, a state unto itself, not only for its size but its favored position with Providence. With such a large target in the butts, it is easy to satirize the blowsier aspects of Texan culture, the quality of the parvenu raised to a previously unattainable degree, the barbecue-and-bourbon simplicities, the obsession with mink coats, Cadillacs and swimming pools, the conviction that the oil-depletion allowance was conceived by the Founding Fathers and sanctified by God.

The influence of oil wealth on Texas, and Texas' consequently disproportionate influence over the national government, has been studied and deplored and defended at length.

It contributed the careers of John Nance Garner and Sam Rayburn, and finally that of Lyndon B. Johnson, all of them New Dealers, more or less "liberal" Democrats, yet bearing allegiance to the totems of the oil industry. Johnson's rise to national consequence and ultimately the presidency was nurtured on Texas oil. So was the wheeler-dealer morality widely admired and emulated a few years ago. And so was the feeling among wheeling, dealing, oil-enriched Texans that they constituted a new breed which others called, and they did not deny, the Super-American.

In *The Super-Americans*, John Bainbridge has delivered the definitive analysis of Super-Americanism, its origins, its myths and beliefs, its loud and genial proclivities. It is epitomized, Mr. Bainbridge believes, by the ardent spirit of the wheeler-dealer. This is typified by "a canny, adventurous millionaire whose approach to business is strictly free-style. In what appears to be an unquenchably lighthearted and casual mood, he is constantly in the process of extending his enterprises by buying, selling, borrowing, merging, and trading. His transactions, always called deals, usually involve sums of at least seven digits; to save time in calculating, he customarily drops the last five. He keeps no regular hours . . . He shuns conferences, paperwork, consultations with lawyers, and other time-consuming activities that pass for accomplishment in the life of the ordinary businessman." Mr. Bainbridge cites as a typical wheeling-dealing triumph that of two Texans who swooped down on Hong Kong and bid against British, Japanese, and Wall Street interests for a 40,000-square-foot parcel of real estate. Less than three hours later they walked off with the prize, outbidding the others because, as one of the Texans explained, "the others had to spend so much time in conference."[21]

By some psychological or atmospheric oddity, that expansive spirit seems perfectly natural and unexceptional under the wide blue skies of Texas, but it does not travel well. What is merely extravagant, even rather charming in its naive and

314

hyperbolic aspects in Texas, becomes something of an excrescence when transplanted elsewhere. Its excesses may be noted in Manhattan nightclubs, in Beverly Hills mansions even more Xanadu-like than their neighbors, and in their most garish manifestations in Las Vegas gambling casinos and Palm Springs estates. One native Texan observed that California seemed to bring out the worst in the species, though certainly there is no culture clash between the tall Texan in hand-tooled boots and the sun-cured exuberant native Californian; or between their similarly minked and jeweled and tightly girdled wives. In and around Hollywood, this observer noted "the worst qualities we Texans possess carried to the point of absurdity. The touch of exhibitionism which in ourselves I'd always considered a rather pleasant, a lively manifestation of our healthiness and youth, I found not only distastefully exaggerated there, but unrelieved by our staying power and our genuine if naive beliefs."[22]

Oil caused a cleavage among those Texans who consider themselves top drawer or upper class. As John Bainbridge analyzed the social structure, the "Ante-Oil Group" constituted the upper crust; its money came from cotton, rice, cattle or timber, usually before the turn of the century. Then came Spindletop, Burkburnett, East Texas, and all the other providers of affluence.

"The second stratum of Texas society," Bainbridge wrote, "is the Post-Oil Group, whose wealth dates from around the turn of the century and stems in large part from oil. Some students have been tempted to subdivide this group into Old Oilers, who made their money before 1930, and New Oilers, who made it after that, and to declare that while Old Oilers are accepted by society, New Oilers are not. This is rank simplification, of course, but not without a certain rough validity . . . It still happens, too, that a hostess, in the course of issuing an invitation, will say, 'There are going to be a few oil people present — I hope you won't mind.' 'You have no idea how the Old Guard resents the oil people,' a Dallas Old

315

Guardsman once informed a dinner companion. 'You can be sure we do all we can to keep them out of everything worthwhile, especially our really top organizations, such as the Shakespeare Club. Why do we do it? I'll tell you why. We consider oil money the same as gambling money, and we just don't care to associate with gamblers. As for their wives, they're what I call the monkey-fur set. The Old Guard simply won't have anything to do with them, and, oh, how they would like to get into the inner sanctum!' . . . The fact that several public-spirited oilmen rank among the state's leading citizens does not detract from the essential accuracy of an offhand and not unkindly intended remark by a socially fortified San Antonio financier, who said simply, 'Oil people as a group are a little out of it.' "[23]

Texans of the Super-American variety, for all their extroverted manner and their boastful tendency (not so noticeable in the second generation, which has been refrigerated or Ivy Leagued by schooling in the North), are extremely sensitive now about the criticism of outsiders. They do not like to be studied with the sociological or even the objective eye, and they bellow with hostility at anyone who comes down to Texas openly displaying a journalistic or literary intention. (Yet the most telling inquiries into Texas politics and mores have been written by such natives as Larry King, William Brammer, and others.)

They pronounced anathema, for instance, on Edna Ferber's novel *Giant*, whose protagonists were a couple of cattle millionaires and whose heavy was Jett Rink, the ruthless oilman, and they continued to denounce its author even after a lushly sentimental film version was produced with the beauty and chivalry of Texas represented, respectively, by Elizabeth Taylor and Rock Hudson. With a certain feline acuity Miss Ferber did remark upon certain outré aspects of Texas high culture, a swarm of private planes converging on a house party "bearing nice little alligator jewel cases and fabulous gowns and overbred furs," against a background of "the grey dust-bitten shanties of the Mexican barrios." It did seem to her that Texas at times was a "vortex of airplanes and bourbon and Brahman cattle and millions and little white mink capes and Cadillac cars." She may have offended any Confederate recidivists by claiming that most Texans were still Northerners, unacclimated to the harsh steppes, who "lived against the climate in unconscious defiance of this tropical land. They built their houses with front porches on which they could never sit, with front yards forever grassless, they planted Northern trees that perished under the sun and drought . . . Arrogantly, in defiance of their Mexican compatriots, these good solid citizens, the men sweating in good cloth pants and coats, the women corseted, high-heeled, marcelled, hatted. We're the white Americans, the big men, we eat the beef and drink the bourbon . . . we're Texans. So they drank gallons of coffee and stayed awake while the Mexican Americans quietly rested in the shade, their hats pulled down over their eyes; and the Negroes vanished from the streets."[24]

What really outraged most Texans, of high or low degree, was the fact that Miss Ferber dared to compile her research on their vast and variegated community in a mere six weeks, when six years would be considered insufficient. A Houston *Post* columnist, George Fuermann, one of the state's cultural arbiters, provided one anecdote on that theme: "Frank Wardlaw of the University of Texas Press has just heard how Edna Ferber managed to get material for her novel *Giant*. As Mr. W. heard it, Miss Ferber, while flying across the Southwest in an airliner, sent a note to the pilot: 'Please fly a little lower. I want to write a book about Texas.' "[25]

Yet, with the fascination all Americans have about themselves, particularly under criticism, they helped make *Giant* a huge success both as a novel and a film. Another Houston *Post* commentator, bemused by the fact that Texas bookstores alone accounted for eight percent of the book's sales, noted that when the film was first released in 1957 Texans "flocked out for their beating in the guise of entertainment. They even laughed as the knife operated." Four years later the film was revived especially for Texas and again they flocked to the theaters, possibly, thought the Houston *Post* man, because of a "facet of character peculiar to Texas: an almost masochistic interest in that which slashes deep." To Mr. Bainbridge, it seemed more likely that "Texans delight in looking in the mirror, regardless of whether they are pleased by what they see there."

Generalizing about any large group of people is impudent, if not dangerous, and this holds true, no more and no less, for those specimens under the top-drawer category of Texas Oil Millionaire. There may be generic similarities visible to the casual beholder, the billowing self-confidence, the cracker-barrel conservatism, the gaudy and uninhibited personal behavior, never more on display than when the vaunted "eyes of Texas" are *not* upon it; but there is no stereotype. H. L. Hunt, carrying his lunch in a brown paper bag, bears little resemblance to the high-flying Murchisons or Sid Richardson or the late Mike Benedum; even less, except in some political facets, to William F. Buckley, Jr., the scion of a Texas oil millionaire and the Scaramouche who publishes the *National Review*.

Nor could three less similar types be assembled than Everette Lee DeGolyer, Glenn McCarthy and Hugh Roy Cullen, the first a scientific oil-finder, the other two wildcatters of the old tradition.

Cullen was one of the few Texans who had a kind word for Standard Oil. At the beginning of his career he was closely associated with the Rockefellers and Mellons. As founder of an oil-finding firm, the Quintana Petroleum Corporation, he generally operated by getting Standard or Gulf to back his hunches and share the proceeds. Through this method he eventually accumulated about $200 million. Some of it went into right-wing, anti–New Deal movements and the Liberty Network, a chain of radio stations in thirty-eight states which

broadcast his appeals for a return to political fundamental-
ism. Most of it, an estimated ninety-three percent, he gave
away to schools and hospitals. With a modesty quite rare
among his peers, he explained his giveaway program: "Most
of it came out of the ground — and while I found the oil in
the ground, I didn't put it there. I've got a lot more than Lillie
and I and our children and grandchildren can use. It's easier
for me to give a million dollars now than it was to give $5 to
the Salvation Army twenty-five years ago." The reason he
remembered that $5 donation: his check to the Salvation
Army had bounced.[26]

The earthy, ready-fisted, free-spending Glenn McCarthy,
who made and lost several sizable fortunes as a wildcatter,
was closer to the norm established in outsiders' minds —
not least, that of the late Edna Ferber, who was generally
considered to have McCarthy in mind as the heavy of *Giant*,
incidentally the novel's most believable character. At the
height of his wildcatting glory McCarthy owned a $2 million
Boeing Stratocruiser, in which, accompanied by a squadron
of smaller planes, he would whisk a house party off to Canada
or Mexico. He built the Shamrock Hotel in Houston, possibly
to satisfy the whim of riding into the lobby on horseback.
Finally he was whittled down by the larger operators, and all
but wiped out, simply because he was determined to stay an
independent. "He could have saved just about everything if he
had been willing to incorporate," an oilman said. "Or he could
have made a deal with Sinclair. They offered him a hundred
million for his holdings and another fifty million to pay off all
his debts. He could have paid his taxes and put seventy-five
million cash in the bank. But that's not the way independents
operate."[27] McCarthy, still independent, is now the proprietor
of an expensive nightclub in Houston.

And then there was the gentlemanly, cultured Everette
Lee DeGolyer, who had made a fortune in his youth in the
Mexican oilfields. "Sheer luck" was the way he later explained
it. "I was just a kid at the time and it seemed to me there was

319

nothing left in the world to accomplish." Instead of spoiling away, he went on to make other oil strikes, become the fore-most oil geologist and pioneer in the field of geophysics, per-haps the most avid book-collector in the United States (and the greatest book-reader in Texas, next to Dad Joiner). Part of his fortune went into reviving the *Saturday Review* when it was about to go under. Of his fellow oilmen, DeGolyer more than once remarked that "the talent for making money can imply a lack of talent for leading a useful life." His own life was the best argument you could find in Texas that the opposite could be true.

But it was the forgotten Dad Joiner, living out his long years not much more than a diamond bracelet's throw from Nei-man-Marcus, where his successors spent a large part of their fortunes, who started it all with his broken-down rig and what he called his "dream," the dream that produced the Super-Americans.

V.

Imperial Realities

14.

The New Arabian Nights, Revised American Edition

Oil is for the Arabs! Why do you not exploit your lost wealth, which is being plundered by aliens? Remember that the oil which flows under your land is seized by your enemy! Remember oil, your lost wealth! Oil is for the Arabs!

— Radio Cairo slogan

In the simpler days of warfare, the spoils were within reach of the foot soldier and regarded as part of his pay. He could break into the houses of an enemy town, rape the females, slaughter the males, and walk off with anything that was portable and valuable. Ever since the First World War, plunder has been conducted on a more dignified and impersonal scale; even the spoils have been industrialized and bureaucratized. The jackpot is oil, even though it may not be located on any of the territory fought over.

It is tempting for anyone writing about oil history to view history as a whole through oil-coated binoculars, which can produce distortions and overemphasis. But it is even more dangerous, as various national leaders learned, to underestimate the crucial importance of oil; to ignore the dictum of Ralph K. Davies: "Modern warfare depends on armament and armament depends on oil."

Modern strategy and geopolitics must take into account several factors of chrome-plated, steel-cored consistency. Eighty percent of the *proven* oil reserves lie in the eastern hemisphere. Strategically, the Middle East, with most of those reserves, is the fulcrum of world power. The critical campaigns of the Second World War were fought on the Stalingrad-Alexandria axis, with the oil riches of the world behind that barrier to the east. Can anyone doubt that if the Nazi armies had broken through that barrier in Russia and Egypt, they would have won the war?

The oil domes of the Middle East are the first prize and prime consideration of grand strategy, the dynamite to which is attached the Arab-Israeli fuse.

Buried deep beneath more emotional considerations surrounding the Viet Nam struggle is the fact that the coasts of Southeast Asia command one of the great oceanic bottlenecks, the Strait of Malacca, and therefore the passage of the tanker fleets.

Ever since 1918, the Middle East's resources have been apportioned with a nice exactitude according to the military weight of the oil companies' respective nations. After World War I, when the oil reserves of the northern tier of the Middle East were the most important, Great Britain not only took over the greatest share, with France as a junior partner, but was the adjudicator which grudgingly, after lengthy bargaining, granted the United States a foothold. Just before World War II, the American share of oil produced in the Arab world was only thirteen percent, compared to Britain's sixty percent. In 1956, taking into consideration the supremacy of American military, air and naval power, the shareout was radically altered: United States sixty-five percent, Britain thirty percent. By that time, of course, the southern tier of the Arab world was pumping out the most oil.

324

In the past twenty years the attention of the American oil industry, and therefore of the State Department and the Pentagon, has been focused on one of the most desolate and forbidding sections of the world. Judeo-Christian America must squat in the marketplace with peoples who detest everything we are supposed to stand for; an American President, in wartime, drops everything to take a cruise with the King of Saudi Arabia; air-conditioned American enclaves spring up on the Persian Gulf and the Arabian peninsula as encapsulated from the native world around them as if they had been established on the dark side of the moon; all the time millions of tons of crude are pumped out of the deserts and drained away by pipelines and tankers, within hailing distance of the U.S. Sixth Fleet and U.S. air force bases, and all the time the Arab-Israeli fuse, delicately held in place by the Russians, grows shorter . . . and shorter . . .

The Second World War only confirmed and reinforced the lesson of the First, that a ready supply of oil was essential to victory. Germany, Japan and Italy formed an axis of have-nots while their opponents were the leading haves and could win the war eventually by simply denying the Axis powers any hope of lubricating their war machines from the wells of the Caucasus, the Middle East, the Dutch East Indies.

From beginning to end, the German campaigns were based on the necessity of obtaining the necessary oil. Blitzkrieg warfare was designed principally to break through to the oilfields and secure a supply that would keep the field armies going. The German General Staff was acutely aware of the fact that oil shortage had been a principal factor in the earlier war, but thought the handicap could be overcome by lightning flashes of movement toward the resources of the Middle East and southern Russia. The equation confronting the Nazi planners was grim. In 1938 Germany imported 41 million barrels of oil, produced only 4 million barrels inside her own borders (through synthetic processes). Most of the 50 million barrels stockpiled at the beginning of the war had, in fact, been supplied by Standard Oil of New Jersey, Shell, and Anglo-Iranian.[1]

How could Hitler and his generals have hoped to conduct a major war with such slender petroleum resources? They would depend on their chemical genius to provide substitutes, meanwhile pouring everything they had into the drives toward Baku and Kirkuk. And during the uneasy alliance with Russia at the beginning of the war, they would persuade or bulldoze Stalin into selling them oil for their stockpiles. The expensive process of making synthetic oil and gasoline within the borders of the Reich was forwarded in 1939 and within two years the new industry was reported to be producing 30 million barrels. "Germany," wrote Harold L. Ickes from a gleaning of intelligence reports, "has put approximately one million transported laborers to work on the construction of huge coal-oil plants in West Prussia and Silesia, and is said to be obtaining about one-third of its petroleum supply from coal resources."[2]

Yet the operations of every Luftwaffe squadron and panzer column, as the memoirs of their commanders attest, had to be governed by the necessity to conserve fuel. Time after time blitzkrieging panzers literally ran out of gas and came grinding to a halt. It might be inferred from the reports and memoirs of Guderian and Rommel that they worried almost as much about their fuel supply as the activities of the enemy. Thus they had to stake everything on "lightning" war. Synthetic fuel at best was a risky improvisation. During the aerial Battle of Britain, Spitfires using 100-octane had the advantage over German aircraft powered by synthetic fuel which provided less speed and maneuverability.

Ickes, as the U.S. oil czar during wartime, was understandably obsessed by oil's role in defeating the Axis powers but he believed that the catalytic cracking plants which produced high-octane "come close to being the last nail in the coffin of the Axis. The new superfuel that they produce has quality factors which make it even better than the 100-octane of a year ago, and the use of it gives the American-made plane the advantage of greatly superior speed and maneuverability. Fueled with it, one of our bombers can carry a 25 percent greater bomb load. In other words, on a long-range offensive to the Axis capitals, 1,000 American-made four-engine bombers with an aggregate bomb capacity of 8,000,000 pounds would be able to transport 2,000,000 more pounds of explosives on every visit than if fueled by yesterday's 100-octane gasoline. A two-engine bomber with a 4,000-pound bomb capacity can carry another 1,000 pounds."[3]

The German war machine was benefited, it was revealed after the war, by having obtained Standard Oil's ethyl (or anti-knock) patents in an exchange with I. G. Farben, which attracted much indignant attention.* This advantage accrued to the Nazis largely because Germany was one of Standard's best prewar customers.[4]

During the earlier years of the war the Germans overcame their petroleum handicap through the forceful use of diplomacy, trade concessions and territorial acquisition. Against the British navy's blockade they threw in their U-boats, which concentrated on British oil tankers, more than half of which had been sunk by mid-1941. When they sneaked over the Molotov-Ribbentrop agreement, by which Stalin bought time at the expense of the Allies, they forced Russia to deliver 16 million barrels of oil from the beginning of 1940 until the Nazi armies invaded Russia. That invasion was partly dictated, in fact, by Stalin's rejection of Hitler's demand that the Germans and the Russians jointly exploit the Russian oil resources. Stalin, whose revolutionary career started in the oilfields, could watch the Nazi occupation of western Europe without wincing, but he drew the line at allowing a German jackboot any purchase on the door to Baku's oil. So a considerable share of German military power was diverted to an

* For a fuller account see Appendix A.

attempt to take the Caucasian oilfields. With their 1938 production of 213 million barrels kept at that level, or more likely increased through German engineering efficiency, Baku could have supplied all the oil needs for Hitler's New Order. The Nazi legions did manage to encompass the Maikop field, accounting for seven percent of Russia's total production, but were soon driven out by the Red armies.

The Asian flank of the Axis was equally desperate for oil, as well as other raw materials. The Japanese, particularly, were driven to extreme measures, even developing a process for making aviation fuel out of the roots of pine trees, which were also unplentiful.

Their thirst for oil became acute in mid-1941 when the United States, the Netherlands and Britain stopped all trade with the Japanese Empire. Until then much of Japan's oil had come from the East Indian fields tapped by Royal Dutch. The situation in Tokyo was so bad that all the gasoline-burning taxis had to be taken off the streets. It seemed to the men in the war ministries that only an explosion of naval and military force would break the blockade — the alternative was a surrender of its objectives on the Chinese mainland and a withdrawal to the home islands — and according to Harold Macmillan, in *The Blast of War*, the Japanese navy was persuaded to cast its vote for war, though previously it had adopted a conservative policy toward the dream of an East Asia Co-Prosperity Sphere, because the oil embargo would soon keep its battle fleets at their bases.

Thus Japan plunged into the war, largely if not entirely motivated by the need for oil resources. The U.S. commander in the Pacific, Admiral Nimitz, later said that when he took command of the Pacific Fleet in 1941 he believed victory would depend on beans, bullets and oil in that order, but that four years later he reordered those priorities to oil, bullets and beans.

For some time before Pearl Harbor the Japanese through their intelligence apparatus eagerly studied the possibility of

328

either seizing or destroying the American oil facilities in California. In several instances cited by Ickes, the Mitsubishi Company tried to obtain precise information on alkylation and octane plants, with their capacity and construction date, in California by writing the editors of U.S. trade journals. From the information they tried to gather the Japanese had in mind a forcible takeover bid. Ickes related that he was reminded of another painful occasion when, for the mere asking, the Japanese government was permitted to purchase a gigantic relief map of the San Francisco Bay area showing in scrupulous detail the locations, the kinds of, and the distances between the industrial plants and oil refineries of that section. "The map had been on exhibition at the San Francisco Exposition and, therefore, everybody, including the Japs, had had plenty of opportunity to study it. But the Japs are a painstaking race, and here was an opportunity to acquire a key map on the sniveling pretext that they 'admired' it so much that they wished to own it as an unusually fine specimen of map-making!"

The Japanese, however, were passionately secretive about their own oil facilities. "As far back as 1923," Ickes recalled, "an American petroleum engineer paid a visit to the Island of Sakhalin, the whole of which was at that time occupied by the Japanese. His purpose was 'just to look about.' He was promptly slapped in jail where he was allowed to languish for a few weeks before the Japs blindfolded him, whirled him around a few hundred times, and started him for home."[5] Ickes may have been referring, in his hyperbolic style, to the undercover mission of the two Sinclair engineers, who were treated hospitably before being deported.

Even before Pearl Harbor, Ickes had been laboring to bring about a more perfect cooperation between the government and the oil industry. In the summer of 1941, following his appointment as petroleum coordinator for national defense, he invited oilmen from all over the country to Washington. They approached the conference table with trepidation. Ickes conceded that "it was not to be wondered at that the oilmen had their fingers crossed when the meeting was called to order. Wasn't I one of the more toxic New Dealers? Didn't I look with suspicion on anyone who made a profit? Didn't I believe that Government should rule business with a black-snake? Wasn't I the so-and-so who had tried to take over the oil industry back in 1934? And, finally, hadn't I aspired to be an Oil Czar?"

Ickes quieted such inner doubts by appointing Ralph K. Davies, the ranking vice-president of Standard Oil of California, as his deputy, and bluntly telling the assembled oilmen: "If we can't work this out cooperatively, there is something wrong with us." Through the Petroleum Industry Council, Ickes and the industry carried out its primary purpose, as he put it, to "furnish simple direction to the oil industry during the war period." The cooperative system established under emergency conditions even took over such outside activities as a scrap rubber drive, in which the four hundred thousand filling stations were used as collection points for 454,155 tons of rubber.[6]

As with Germany, Japan's desperate lunge for oil resources turned out badly. The Japanese achieved the capture of the fields in the Dutch East Indies and in Burma which had long been exploited by the Dutch and the British. The Dutch, however, destroyed an estimated eighty-eight percent of their production facilities, while the British blew up as much of the old Burmah Oil Company installations as possible before retreating toward India.[7] The Japanese restored some of the wrecked facilities to production, but the toll taken of their tankers by American submarines forced them to rely increasingly on synthetics. And when the Americans began their Flying Fortress raids on the home islands, the situation became even more critical. By 1945 Japan was reduced to pleading with Soviet Russia to supply oil in exchange for several of their remaining cruisers.

Late in the war some American operations in the European theater were constricted by fuel shortages which were particularly hard on Patton's offensives toward the German border. That was due largely to the success of German U-boat operations, but despite such losses American ship-yards built up the U.S. tanker fleet to eight hundred ships, more than the whole world's tanker fleet before the war. By mid-war the United States had raised its oil production to 4 million barrels a day. And it was needed. A World War I division had a total horsepower of 4,000, mostly in supply trucks; a World War II mechanized division, 187,000 horse-power.

The most striking privation, as it turned out, was on the home front, where U-boat successes meant the rationing not only of gasoline for cars but fuel oil for heating homes. New England was particularly hard hit, because it had come to depend on oil heating to a greater degree than the rest of the country. Tankers carrying oil from Venezuela and the Gulf of Mexico to New York were sunk with alarming regularity. During the hard winter of 1942–1943 there were demonstrations and riots, and oil trucks were overturned by mobs when oil-burning furnaces suddenly went dry. By mid-1943 the near-miraculous construction of the Big Inch pipeline from the Gulf Coast to the northeastern states was completed in slightly less than a year's time. The Big Inch poured three hundred thousand barrels of oil into the eastern terminals every day.

Oil, once again, had proved to be the vulnerable plate in the armor of Germany and her allies. They carried on to the bitter end on synthetics extracted from coal and lignite, but the result might have been different if their air and ground forces had been able to operate with greater efficiency on products refined from petroleum.

America's share of the victory in World War II, along with certain seismic vibrations in the international oil situation resulting from it, enabled American oilmen to join in the competition for the oil resources south-of-Suez with advantages they had never possessed when Iran and Iraq were thrown open to exploitation. (Not that their foreign rivals suspected the Americans of lacking enthusiasm. As evidence to the contrary, there was the mysterious death of King Faisal of Iraq and the accusations that followed. Faisal, the British favorite since World War I, when he was Colonel Lawrence's protégé, had been defeated when he sent his army against French-mandated Syria. On September 7, 1933, King Faisal died suddenly in his hotel room in Berne, Switzerland, after returning from an automobile ride; the hotel manager died later the same day. In the international oil world, it was rumored that his death may have been connected with his reported negotiations with American oilmen.)

The American target, at the end of World War II, was the Arabian peninsula and its offshore islands, all floating on a sea of rich crude. The major companies got the biggest bite, but a number of independents moved in to nibble around the edges. Hitherto the latter, feeling themselves unable to cope with the intricate political and social problems involved in venturing into an underdeveloped country, had mostly stayed at home. Then J. Paul Getty made his big strikes in the Arab world, and other independents acquired concessions in the same area, including Edwin Pauley, the Californian who became a political power in the Truman Administration.

A familiar specter — depletion — arose in the American oil industry following World War II, during which the industry concentrated on production rather than exploration of new sources. As in the years following World War I, there was now a fear that American reserves were running low or would in the foreseeable future. The geological researches of Wallace Pratt and Lewis Weeks determined that while the United States had within its borders only about one-sixth of the world's supply, it had produced two-thirds of all the oil consumed thus far. A hundred times more exploratory wells have been drilled on American soil than on foreign lands where oil might be discovered. This ratio is accounted for, as Ruth Sheldon Knowles, a petroleum specialist for the government during World War II, has noted, by the fact that "in America whoever owns the surface owns the sub-surface, and thousands of men are free to contract with each other to explore. In other countries, governments own the subsoil and either explore it themselves as a monopoly or grant exploration rights to a relatively small number of companies."[8] Thus independents as well as majors were impelled to venture abroad.

The trouble was, they had to penetrate a world almost as much a *terra incognita* as it had been for centuries, a vast desert peninsula ruled by petty tyrants and largely peopled by nomadic tribesmen, many of them bitterly hostile to all Christians and Westerners. How could anyone know the political structure, the religious differences between the Wahabites and other Moslems, the personal traits of sheikhs and dervishes and imams, the extent of feudalism, the polygamous system by which an Arab king might fill a whole palace with his direct descendants? Who knew the sociology of Saudi Arabia, let alone such vaguely defined enclaves around its edges as Yemen, the Aden Protectorate, the Sultanate of Oman, Trucial Oman, Qatar, Bahrein, the Neutral Zone, and Kuwait?

Not many, perhaps, but there had been a greater penetration of the southern part of the Middle East than was generally known. We'd had an eye on the place, it seems, for a long time, almost as though we extrasensorily perceived the future importance of the peninsula. For generations American missionaries had been trying to convert the Arabs to Christianity with a signal lack of success. Washington and the tiny, barren Sultanate of Muscat first established diplomatic relations in 1834. A Confederate general, Braxton Bragg, was commanding general of the Egyptian armed forces for a time. But Arabia, of course, had always been a

British sphere of influence: Lawrence of Arabia and all that. The American opportunity lay in the fact that, following World War I, there had been a split in British policy. Lawrence and his fellow Arabist Gertrude Bell supported the aspirations of King Faisal of Iraq when fighting broke out between the Iraqis and the Saudi Arabians. King Ibn Saud of Saudi Arabia had his British supporter in St. John Philby, who lived in Djeddah and cultivated Ibn Saud's friendship. During the Iraqi–Saudi Arabian war, it was reported that American ships brought arms, bought by oil interests, to the Arabian ports; this was in defiance of the policy of the British Colonial Office, which was responsible for relations with the Arabs, to "keep out unscrupulous concession hunters."[9]

By "unscrupulous" they meant American. Under the Red Line Agreement, of course, the whole Middle East outside Persia was staked out for the benefit of the international consortium. It did not seem to have occurred to its participants that if oil possibilities appeared south of the Iraq border outsiders might bore their way in, that the sheikhs and princelings of the Arabian peninsula might not consider themselves bound by the consortium's rules.

A small, determined New Zealander upset all their calculations. Major Frank Holmes had served with the British forces in the Mespot during World War I as a commissary officer. Those duties required him to range far and wide in search of supplies, down along the Persian Gulf (as the Iranians call it, the Arabian Gulf as the Arabs insist it is). Holmes was a self-educated mining engineer who acquired a smattering of knowledge about oil exploration. In Kuwait, on Bahrein, and elsewhere he sighted oil seepages.

Frank Holmes was cut to a familiar pattern — another Patillo Higgins or William Knox D'Arcy, a loner with an obsession. After he was demobilized, he journeyed to London and persuaded several men who, as part of a mining syndicate, had formerly employed him, to organize the Eastern and General Syndicate to obtain concessions along the Persian

Gulf. This must have taken all his powers of persuasion; it was well known that the major companies had made geological surveys in the area and concluded it promised little.

Holmes was stymied at the outset by the opposition of the British government's representatives in the sheikhdoms and of Anglo-Persian, which used the Colonial Office as an instrument of policy. Anglo-Persian took the spoiler's attitude toward Holmes and all other interlopers. Its board chairman, Sir Charles Greenway, wrote a memorandum stating that his company did not consider it likely that oil would be found in Kuwait, at the head of the Persian Gulf less than fifty miles from the great Anglo-Persian facilities at Abadan, or on Bahrein, but that he and his executives were "agreed that even if the chance be 100 to 1 we should pursue it rather than let others come into the Persian Gulf, and cause difficulties of one kind and another for us."[10] The intervention of the British High Commissioner kept Holmes out of Kuwait. And the sheikhs themselves were generally uninterested in oil exploration, some of them being fearful of the political complications oil brought with it. The ruling sheikh of Kuwait was opposed to a concession, initially, because an oilfield would take workers away from the pearling industry, which he considered more valuable.

Finally Holmes, after several years of wandering around the deserts, managed to get his foot in the Arabian door. A concession at El Hasa, in what is now Saudi Arabia, seemed promising. He put in his bid with Ibn Saud, and once again the British Colonial Office intervened on behalf of Anglo-Persian. But since the British had always supported Faisal of Iraq against him, Ibn Saud decided to go against their wishes on the theory that whatever was bad for Britain must be good for Saudi Arabia. He granted the El Hasa concession to Holmes and his Eastern and General Syndicate.

While the syndicate undertook geological surveys on the El Hasa concession, which provided for an annual rental of $10,000 and for immediate exploration, Holmes went off to Bahrein to stake out another claim. The ruling sheikh of the island was more interested in water than oil. Holmes suggested that artesian wells be driven, and when they produced water from underground springs, the sheikh was so grateful he gave Holmes an oil concession.

Holmes and his backers now held title to two of the most valuable concessions in the world, but they needed financing from the major companies. A Birmingham University professor, George Madgwick, assembled all the geological surveys and announced that he was certain there were large quantities of oil to be found in the concessions. Shell, Burmah Oil and Anglo-Persian all inspected Professor Madgwick's findings but reported that they were still unimpressed. The Holmes group then turned to the American majors. Standard Oil of New Jersey and Gulf were approached, but neither was enthusiastic. Gulf finally agreed to undertake exploration, but first they had to obtain permission from their partners in the Iraq consortium. The latter sternly told Gulf to drop the project; the Iraq group neither wanted to explore the Holmes concessions nor to have anyone else do so. So Gulf had to pull out of Bahrein or give up its share of the Iraq deal, exchange a sure thing for a gamble, and the Mellon company was too conservative for that kind of risk-taking.

"At that fateful moment," wrote an unofficial historian of Aramco's beginnings, "emissaries of the Standard Oil Company of California appeared on the scene and the wary king's [Ibn Saud] gaze softened. SOCAL was ripe not only for new foreign fields but for a revolutionary approach to the principles and methods to be used in developing the oil resources of 'underdeveloped' foreign lands. Innocent of government backing or political motives, sincerely interested only in oil and a fair division of its monetary rewards, the American firm convinced the king of the purity of its intentions. In 1933 it accepted from him, on behalf of the infant subsidiary then known as California Arabian Standard Oil Company, a concession giving it the most restricted and underprivileged position then enjoyed by any Western enterprise in an Eastern country."[11]

Standard of California obtained its leasehold largely through the intervention of King Ibn Saud's most trusted adviser, St. John Philby, a strange and fierce man utterly devoted to Arab interests, who was at the opposite end of the political scale from his neglected son Kim, who much later made the family's name notorious by defecting to the Soviet Union and gleefully unmasking himself as a long-time Russian agent planted in the Foreign Office. Philby urged an American deal simply because he was convinced that ultimately it would be more advantageous for the Arabs than any arrangement with the supremely arrogant British-dominated companies.[12]

The main provisions of the Standard of California contract, as published by Ibn Saud's official organ in Mecca, included "(1) The concession was granted for a period of sixty years beginning with the date exploration started. The Company was given the absolute right to explore, drill, produce, transport, handle and export oil and oil products and all other carbonic substances. (2) The Company was to advance the Government an initial loan . . . (3) The Company was to start operation of the concession not later than September, 1933 . . . (4) The Company was to pay a royalty of four gold shillings per ton of crude produce . . ."[13] Since the contract was signed in May 1933 and drilling operations were supposed to start by September, it was obvious that King Ibn Saud's demand for haste was impelled by a need for funds greater than the $2 million brought in by pilgrims to Mecca and Medina, which supplied most of the Saudi Arabian budget. A population explosion within the royal family was the main cause of his financial stringency. He had sired forty-four sons by then, and they in turn were producing a dismayingly large crop of grandsons, and all had to be maintained in a princely state.

Several years of exploratory drilling began under the toughest conditions, even for oilfield workers experienced in other hostile climates. The temperature was often 130°, and there was no natural shade. No liquor was permitted, nor smoking in public, under the harsh dictates of the Wahabite Moslem faith. Friday, the Moslem Sabbath, was the day off. Even more difficult, in a different way, was the problem of adjusting Arabian-American relations, of making Americans tolerated in a land utterly alien to their outlook, of corporate survival in a medieval kingdom whose national life had been unchanged for a thousand years. "It had to grow experts as it went along," Michael Sheldon Cheney has written from his own experiences as an Aramco public relations man. "Its executives had to become sociologists, its welders diplomats, its roustabouts educators, in a situation that had no precedent in practice or theory . . . Intending only to run a technical operation with equal profit to Arabs and Americans, dedicated to a strict minding of their own business, they ended by setting off, if only through their very presence in that unsophisticated world, a chain reaction of developments that has reached into every aspect of Arabian life and culture." Cheney, writing after he left the company's service, believed that invaluable lessons have been learned in dealing with such nations, that "no earth-satellite project, no search for an intercontinental missile [he was writing in 1958] is of more urgent concern than the results of such experiments as Aramco's in the basic field of human relations."[14]

California Standard also took up Holmes' option on drilling rights on Bahrein Island, where oil was discovered in 1932. The scramble was on throughout the southern tier of the Middle East. Iraq Petroleum, trying to recoup on past mistakes, bid against California Standard for Holmes' El Hasa concession in Saudi Arabia, but King Ibn Saud and his adviser Philby again favored the Americans. Gulf Oil was infuriated by the Bahrein discovery, which it had left to others because its partners in the Iraq consortium frowned upon the venture.

Gulf, without consulting those bullheaded partners, engaged Frank Holmes to try to obtain a concession in Kuwait.

He soon found a rival in the field, Archie Chisholm, the representative of Anglo-Persian, who had the edge by virtue of the local sheikh's treaty obligations to deal only with a British company. The contest was finally settled in London by the governments of the companies involved. Happily for Gulf, its head man, Andrew Mellon, was now U.S. ambassador to London. Combining national and personal concerns, more the latter than the former, Mellon persuaded the British government to accept an agreement highly favorable to Gulf, considering that Britain exercised virtual suzerainty over the disputed territory. Thus the immense resources of Kuwait — with one-sixth of the world's oil as of a few years ago, and the fifth biggest producer after the United States, the Soviet Union, Venezuela and Saudi Arabia — were scooped up by an Anglo-American combine. The Kuwait Oil Company is owned fifty-fifty by Gulf and British Petroleum (successor to Anglo-Persian).

The real discoverer of the Kuwait oil billions, Frank Holmes, inevitably, was ill rewarded. There must be some operative law, not susceptible to human perception, governing such things. Holmes' syndicate sold its claim to a fractional royalty, something like Gulbenkian's eternal five percent bite out of Iraq, for several thousand pounds to Gulf. It would have been worth about £5 million a year by the estimate of Christopher Tugendhat (*Oil: The Biggest Business*).

The workings of Kismet were discernible, too, in a final cracking of the Red Line barrier.

During the years leading up to World War II, it became apparent that Arabia and its sheikhdoms would be extremely important to any giant of the petroleum industry hoping to maintain its world standing, not only because of the quantities of crude involved, nor its rich low-sulfur content, but because of its central geographic location in regard to marketing, plunk on the dividing line between Europe and Asia. By the time the war started the oil was beginning to flow. In the fall of 1939, the California Standard-Arabian (later Aramco, or Arabian American Oil Company) field at El Hasa had completed drilling eight wells. The company had already sold a half-interest in its concessions to the Texas Company which, unlike California Standard, had set up a distributing system in the eastern hemisphere.

In consideration of the future and increasing importance of King Ibn Saud's land, Saudi Arabia was treated with tender loving care during the lean war years, when his pilgrim income evaporated and oil exploration had to be suspended. Somewhat brazenly, the American oilmen tried to obtain funds for the King and his horde of dependents through Lend-Lease. When that effort failed, California Standard arranged loans to tide the regime over. At the same time Ibn Saud was receiving financial assistance from the British.

To prevent a British takeover bid, President Roosevelt in 1943 declared "the defense of Saudi Arabia" — from whom was not stated — "is vital to the defense of the United States" and made that country eligible for Lend-Lease aid. As one oil historian has commented, with scholarly understatement, "This was the crowning achievement of almost three years of effort on the part of the Texas Company and the Standard Oil Company of California to obtain direct aid for Saudi Arabia from the United States government. It relieved them of the burden of financing the King; it enhanced the American company's prestige and importance; it committed the United States to the protection of the American concession in Saudi Arabia and removed the possibility of British penetration."[15]

Put more bluntly, the U.S. Treasury, not to mention the armed forces, were placed at the service of an Arab despot, with the bills being paid by the American taxpayer.

The government as well as the oil industry continued to focus its extramilitary attention on Middle Eastern oil during the remainder of the war years, particularly after a government mission headed by Everette Lee DeGolyer and W. E.

Wrather, director of the U.S. Geological Survey, made an inspection tour of the Middle East and gravely reported that that area would be the "center of gravity" in the foreseeable future. Through the government's Petroleum Reserves Corporation, Oil Administrator Ickes, now rather fondly regarded by the industry, proposed that the United States build a pipeline from the Persian Gulf to the eastern Mediterranean. This caused an eruption of protest from the other oil companies that such a pipeline would benefit only California Standard, Texaco, and Gulf while placing their competitors in an unfavorable position because Middle Eastern oil was so much cheaper to produce than American.

The influential DeGolyer, however, backed the pipeline proposal. "It seems fair to assume that the Government is under no greater obligation to go to war to protect its own investment in what is essentially a commercial enterprise than it is to protect the investment of its nationals in similar enterprises," he said. "To leave the American companies in a weak position is to invite disaster to the American position in oil. It is difficult for our people to realize the degree to which the chancellories of the great European nations are willing to interfere particularly in support of the business interests of their nationals or the degree of economic vassalage accepted by the smaller states of the Persian Gulf in the treaties by which they are allied to Britain. Able as American business may be, it cannot support itself against such inequal competition."[16] Hotly attacked from all sides, the idea was eventually dropped, and the facility known as Trans-Arabian Pipeline Company (Tapline) was built by the companies which would profit from its existence.

King Ibn Saud, a reactionary of the most ferocious type, was made the pet of the Roosevelt Administration, though some of its more doctrinaire liberals had to bite the bullet in going along with that program. Among them, of course, there was no great rejoicing when the hook-nosed old warrior chief of the Hejaz was singled out for a personal buttering-up by President Roosevelt and taken on a cruise of the Suez Canal in February 1945.

Among the lesser upheavals caused by World War II was that which shook the position of Calouste Gulbenkian and Compagnie Française as partners in the Iraq consortium. Eventually it caused a Middle Eastern realignment immensely beneficial to U.S. oil companies.

For once the crafty old Levantine out-smarted himself and almost lost his grip on that five percent share of Iraq Petroleum. As a Francophile, as a connoisseur of French womanhood, cuisine, art and customs, he decided to stay in France when the war broke out. He was comfortable in his suite at the Ritz, his villa at Deauville. And there were no German bombs raining on Paris as there were on London. When the French collapsed, he followed his favorite government on the dreary, disgraceful road to Bordeaux, Biarritz and finally that most ambiguous of capitals, Vichy. Thereby he technically became an "Enemy under the Act" as defined by wartime legislation enacted by Britain. "This not only wounded him — after half a century of service to British oil interests — it also led to the confiscation of his five percent in the Iraq Petroleum Company by the British custodian for enemy property," as his son Nubar recalled with a certain bitter humor, having long been kept in his domineering father's shadow. "He could not — or would not — follow the argument that the British authorities declared him to be 'an enemy' in order to protect him from actions he might be compelled to take under duress while he remained at Vichy.

"He was convinced that the Anglo-American-Dutch groups of the Iraq Petroleum Company seized the opportunity to prevail on the British Government to squeeze him (and the French) out of the Company and steal his oil, which was sold at a price fixed by an American oil-broker, without his or

342

French consent. None of the profits were marked up to him or the French. The Royal Navy was refueling with his oil and facilities in Iraq. Yet he was treated in this way! He could not understand it . . .

"Another consequence was that he decided to make use of Persian citizenship. He had been a Commercial Counsellor for the Persian Diplomatic Service (keeping an eye on his bugbear, the Anglo-Persian Oil Company). So long as Persia remained neutral, Persian status somewhat improved his position at Vichy."[17]

Iran, however, subsequently joined the Allies and Gulbenkian had to leave Vichy with the Iranian legation. He settled in Lisbon for the rest of his life.

Immediately after the war the Americans moved to nullify the Red Line Agreement. Publicly, it was stigmatized as the protective device of an international cartel; the Federal Trade Commissioner's report condemned it as a "sad case of wrongful cartelization." Privately, it was understood that the United States could not expand freely in the southern regions of the Middle East if the agreement remained operative.

The wartime sanctions against Gulbenkian and the Compagnie Française provided the Americans with the weapon they needed. Standard of New Jersey and Socony Vacuum (formerly Standard of New York) wanted to buy into the Arabian concessions, but Gulbenkian and the French vetoed the move. The two American companies claimed that the Red Line Agreement was dissolved when Gulbenkian and the French were declared enemy aliens.

Acting on that assumption, reinforced by an aggressive American policy toward the Middle Eastern oil shareout, further bolstered by American military and economic force used to maintain Iran and Turkey against the postwar threat of Russian expansion, the two American companies went ahead and bought into the Saudi Arabian concessions. Gulbenkian threatened action in the British courts, and had to be bought off with a settlement which gave him 3.8 million tons of oil annually for fourteen years in addition to his sacred five percent. But the Red Line had finally been erased.

In the new alignment, all-American, Saudi Arabia would be exploited by Standard of California, retaining a thirty percent share of the new company, Aramco; Standard of New Jersey, thirty percent; Texaco, thirty percent; and Mobil, ten percent.

With greatly increased exploration and production, with the construction of Tapline (requiring 265,000 tons of steel pipe and 1,500 vehicles of all kinds to be sea-lifted into the area), Aramco opened up the throttle in Saudi Arabia. It was confronted with the delicate task of operating in a feudal kingdom, of getting out the oil while keeping itself at a safe remove from all native affairs, but in the slightly jaundiced view of British oil historian Stephen H. Longrigg, the atmosphere was just right for an Aramco-style operation. "Aramco, operating under enlightened leadership in a territory which, with all its rigours and backwardness, was without the fervid politicians of the Fertile Crescent and Persia and enjoyed the only form of government suited to it, a patriarchal benevolent despotism . . ."

Enlightened self-interest, as exemplified by Aramco's policy toward its host, a policy which eventually made it the biggest and most lucrative American enterprise abroad, operated so well on the whole that Aramco served as the pilot model for all U.S. companies exploiting the resources of underdeveloped countries. Hands off politics, religion and native customs. Fair share of the proceeds. Never say no. Compromise on everything. Keep away from the local populace . . . No more Tampicos, in other words.

There were and are problems, of course, connected with dumping huge royalties in an impoverished country and with the differences in the Arab and American mentalities. When President Roosevelt took King Ibn Saud for a ride on the cruiser *Quincy* in early 1945, for instance, casually, without any great interest, Roosevelt asked the King how many miles

344

of railroad his country had. (The old Turkish-built Hejaz Railroad, from Medina to Damascus, had been mostly destroyed in World War I and never rebuilt.) The King confessed that he had never been on a train, and apparently wondered why Roosevelt brought it up if he didn't intend to do something about it. Two years later Ibn Saud began clamoring for Washington to finance a rail line from his capital to the Persian Gulf, taking Roosevelt's idle inquiry as a kind of promise. The result was that Aramco had to lay out $160 million to build the King's railroad.

No one was more Arabophile, no one had done more in Saudi Arabia to bring about the entry of Aramco than St. John Philby, the King's chief Western adviser, but even he confessed dismay in one of his memoirs at the extravagance of the newly rich royal family, "leading off with a despatch of a dozen princes to the New World to inaugurate the new era of the United Nations, and to ransack America for motorcars and other aids to the enjoyment of life. Other such expeditions followed, one led by the Crown Prince and another by [Finance Minister] Abdullah Sulaiman himself: each bringing back to Arabia substantial mementoes of its invasion of the richest country in the world." Sitting down to dinner in the gardens of the crown prince's estate at Riyad, he noted that all the food served had been flown from America on refrigerated planes. Saudi Arabia, or rather its rulers, could not be said to be using its oil revenues wisely or with any measure of social justice, Philby wrote. "There has unquestionably been a great deal of leakage," he added, "of a far from creditable nature, and there has been gross extravagance, while many of the undoubtedly useful development works that have been undertaken have been contracted for on an unnecessarily expensive basis."[18]

Professor Benjamin Shwadran, writing in 1959, after a dozen years of heavy dollar inflow, saw trouble ahead in the increasing Westernization of the Saudi Arabians, particularly those who worked for Aramco, and their abandonment of the philosophy that men were helpless pawns of fate. The tribes were making more urgent demands for a share in the revenues. There was a growing dissatisfaction with the status quo, with the traditions of a thousand years. "As long as the world demand for oil is great and prices are high and income constantly mounts," Shwadran wrote, "no serious disturbances might be expected. However, should production drop or prices go down, the King could no longer meet the ever-expanding demands of the royal house and the subsidized tribes, and the workers in the oil industry would be thrown out of work. The desert kingdom might then be rocked by serious political and social convulsions . . ."[19] Since then, of course, a more enlightened program aimed at spreading around the benefits of exploitation has been instituted.

For the thousands of Americans who have contracted to work in and around the El Hasa field and others for the past quarter-century, Arabia has been a mind-bending experience. In such company towns as Dhahran they adopt the style of all Americans living and working abroad on large projects, insulated against the native swarm and even the native climate in their air-conditioned, landscaped, sealed-off communities patterned as closely as possible after a decent American suburb. In Saudi Arabia, however, there are startling differences. "If your hostess wishes to buy you a camel saddle," the British journalist James Morris observed on a visit to America-in-Arabia, "you must drive the Plymouth; for no American woman may drive a car in Saudi Arabia, except in the company compounds. If she belongs to a Great Books Discussion Group, she will find herself handicapped when she returns to Ohio; for no books may be imported into Saudi Arabia. If she wants a highball, she must build her own still in the kitchen; liquor is forbidden in Saudi Arabia. If she gets a letter from a friend in Israel, she is instantly deported; a Tel Aviv postmark will be sufficient grounds. She cannot go to church, for Christian services are forbidden in Saudi Arabia; the priest who sometimes flies in from Bahrein, in the manner of an early Christian evangelist, describes himself to the Saudi authorities as a teacher. 'Oh, sure,' says your hostess, 'they'll have us all veiled before long — over my dead body!' "[20]

The American working in Saudi Arabia, in fact, submits himself to living under a virtual dictatorship. No one of the Jewish faith may be employed by Aramco. Even the practice of Christianity, in its outward forms, must be suspended for the duration of an Aramco contract. It is a bigot's paradise, provided you are both anti-Semitic and anti-Christian.

Michael Sheldon Cheney, looking back objectively on his own service with Aramco, pitied the executives who had to deal with more than twenty thousand Americans, plus the Arab nation and its headstrong rulers, who had a "brief life expectancy." They were always conscious that Aramco was "a guinea pig whose fate was watched with interest by industrialists and statesmen all over the world . . . Set against the popular picture of a big bad oil industry, our little band of altruistic executives clinging to their shining doctrine amid the Stygian night of Middle Eastern politics suggested a troop of boy scouts set adrift in a brothel . . . Striving to please everyone in a complicated and potentially explosive situation, they seldom pleased anyone. The interests of many diverse groups of employees had to be reconciled with those of four competing owner companies. Worse, these in turn had to be brought in line with the interests of the Saudi government, which also conflicted with those of the Saudi people, and notably of Aramco's own indigenous employees . . . Aramco was, in effect, the neurotic child of four parents, subject to the whims, qualms and jealousies of each. The simplest of policy decisions had to be referred back to the States . . ."

Cheney left the country just as it was caught up in "the tide-rip of pressures and tensions, nationalist, Communist, pan-Arab, anti-Israel, anti-Western and what have you," fearing that Aramco and all its works "may end by being swept away, almost accidentally, in some future upheaval that has nothing to do with itself."[21]

347

Such fears, of course, have remained constant and unremitting. The approximately $300 million of oil revenue channeled yearly into the Saudi Arabian economy is as much a stimulant of social revolution as it is a sedative against social unrest. The late, madly extravagant King Ibn Saud was unseated by his younger brother, the present King Faisal, who has sternly cut back on royal spending and instituted a program of social and political reform in hopes of maintaining Saudi Arabia as a bastion against Arab socialism. But there is always the threat of nationalization, now or in the future when concessions lapse. And there are such voices as those of the representative of Qatar, an oil shiekhdom on the coast of Trucial Oman, speaking before the sixth Arab Petroleum Congress in Baghdad in March 1967:

"In the past we were victims of military imperialism; now it is economic imperialism. Under the concessions system the companies are like vampires sucking our blood. We must try and establish new political and economic conditions, so as to use our resources for the benefit of present and future generations."

Or they can read the words of President Nasser of Egypt: "Oil is the vital nerve of civilization, without which its great works, its weapons, its communications, would be motionless. We can consider ourselves powerful, powerful in our thorough understanding of the strength of this bond which links us and makes our territory one."

Or the slogan endlessly shrieked over Radio Cairo: "Oil is for the Arabs! Why do you not exploit your lost wealth, which is being plundered by aliens? Remember that the oil which flows under your land is seized by your enemy! Remember oil, your lost wealth! Oil is for the Arabs!"

The long-range goal of Arab socialism obviously is to encompass a large share of the oil income of various states on the peninsula and spread it around the overpopulated countries, such as Egypt and Jordan, with lesser resources. An object lesson in Marxist realism has recently been supplied by the

348

tiny sheikhdom of Abu Dhabi, a principality the size of Connecticut and part of Trucial Oman at the lower end of the Persian Gulf. In 1966, after Sheikh Zaid deposed his backward predecessor, the country was opened up to exploitation and within three years its income shot up from nothing to $200 million a year, two-thirds that of Saudi Arabia. The capital, also named Abu Dhabi, a mud-flat village on the gulf only four years ago, now has six banks, fifteen new palaces, a thousand new businesses and a $4 million sports stadium. Much of the income has been spread around the population of twenty thousand and the sheikhdom contributes $20 million to the Arab cause; Sheikh Zaid himself receives one-fourth of all revenues but gives most of it away.

Yet Abu Dhabi has no port facilities, and supplies are lightered in from ships offshore, often to lie and rot on the beach. The labor force is imported from Iran and Pakistan and is resented by the natives. And with all that money pouring in, Sheikh Zaid managed to spend it even faster. In 1969 he journeyed to London in an attempt to raise loans on the following year's revenue, but the city bankers turned him down.

Oil is for the Arabs, but the "vital nerve of civilization" runs through London, The Hague and New York.

15.

Portraits in Oil: Wendell Phillips and J. Paul Getty

It might seem that the whole Arabian peninsula was conquered by the major American oil companies before and after World War II, but more than one American independent has found it a happy hunting ground provided he was lucky, daring, diligent, and able to empathize with the Arab mentality.

J. Paul Getty, whom the British newspapers invariably refer to with proprietary pride as the "world's richest man," snowballed his holdings above the billion-dollar level through his intrepid invasion of the Neutral Zone, a 1,500-square-mile no man's land lying in all its arid desolation between Saudi Arabia and Kuwait on the Persian Gulf. Getty, of course, was an entrepreneur of long experience who had started his career as a twenty-one-year-old wildcatter in Oklahoma.

A much less likely entry in the Arabian sweepstakes, one who less than twenty years ago knew little more about the oil business than he had learned from driving into a service station, was Wendell Phillips, explorer of southern Arabia, archeologist, paleontologist, author, and presently proprietor of the oil concession of Dhofar, the Incense Coast of antiquity.

"As a hobby," Phillips has been quoted as saying, "I also dabble in oil." He does indeed, as the owner of oil rights to more than a hundred million acres and of a fortune he estimates at approaching the half-billion mark. A forty-eight-year-old Californian who now lives in a penthouse overlooking Waikiki Beach near Honolulu when he isn't keeping an eye on Dhofar, he worked his way through the University of California at Berkeley by playing the drums in a jazz band.

At twenty-six he conceived, organized, and headed the largest scientific party ever to leave the United States — the University of California Cairo-to-Capetown African Expedition — and in 1950 was invited by the Imam of Yemen to excavate the Circular Moon Temple at Marib, the Queen of Sheba's capital. Phillips and his companions, unaware of the unrest around them, were preoccupied by archeological problems when they were suddenly attacked by Yemenite bandits. They fled across the desert until they reached safety, even hospitality, in the Sultanate of Oman on the western shoulder of the peninsula commanding the entrance to the Persian Gulf.

Literally, for young Dr. Phillips, it was a flight into fortune, a modern Arabian Nights. He was befriended by the King of Oman, Sultan Said Bin Taimur, became the Sultan's economic adviser, published the widely praised *Qataban and Sheba*, and was awarded eleven honorary doctorates. The Sultan encouraged him to undertake various archeological explorations of Oman, including the ancient Incense Coast, where the aromatic shrubs frankincense and myrrh grow, and a search for the lost city of Ubar, which was one of his few failures. It was a sizable disappointment because Ubar was known in legend as the Atlantis of Arabia, "a many-castled marble city of fabulous riches that possessed a fort of red silver encrusted with rubies," whose sinful inhabitants were turned into one-eyed, one-armed monkeys.[1]

351

This thoroughgoing romantic, with his dream of lost cities, was recruited by Sultan Said Bin Taimur as his economic adviser one day early in 1951. The Sultan was hopeful that oil could be found for the benefit, largely, of his people; he was one of the several Arab rulers with a well-developed social conscience. But he was depressed because a subsidiary of Iraq Petroleum had just dropped its option on a concession in the Dhofar province. Iraq Petroleum had held the concession for fourteen years and done nothing to develop it, hadn't even drilled a test well. Furthermore an Iraq Petroleum geologist had recently conducted a survey of the Dhofar possibilities and concluded that "the absence of sufficient thickness of source and cover rocks and of suitable structure precludes the possibility of finding any commercial accumulation in Dhofar."

The Sultan explained all this, adding that he didn't want any more concessions of that sort because "we need oil in Dhofar, not yearly payments."

"And by the Will of God," he continued, "we shall have oil, for I am granting *you* the oil concession for Dhofar."

Phillips was taken completely by surprise. Was it possible that the oil rights to a province the size of the state of Indiana could be granted so casually? "It gradually dawned on me," Phillips recorded, "that the Sultan was actually offering the oil rights on this huge piece of the earth's surface to me! As though in a dream, I thanked His Majesty for his gracious gesture and for his continued kindness to me, but, as I hastened to add, I know absolutely nothing about concessions in general, and Arabian oil concessions in particular. The Sultan nodded and replied that he was certain I would learn fast enough if I tried very hard."[2]

The Sultan, who spoke flawless English and was expert in international law, himself typed the terms of the concession. Phillips was granted the right to explore for and extract oil, bitumen and ozokerite (a waxlike mineral composed of hydrocarbons) throughout the province of Dhofar with the exception of cultivated land, shrines, burial grounds, the vicinity of mosques, areas reserved by the Sultan for possible military installations or airdromes. The Sultan's royalties were to be paid mostly in Maria Theresa dollars, the huge silver coins which are still the most acceptable currency in parts of the Middle East.

Phillips hurried to New York to arrange financing for exploration. It would be difficult because "This area of Arabia was remote from American thinking which was, in the main, oriented by Aramco toward Saudi Arabia. No oil had ever been produced within hundreds of miles of Dhofar. The cost of preliminary exploration alone would be millions of dollars — there was no place for ships to dock, no ports, no facilities. Everything must either be flown in or unloaded offshore and floated in by dhow, lighter or Arab swimmer. There were no roads into the interior and only a handful of us from the outside world had ever been into the Qara Mountains, much less across them where the oil, if any, would probably be." The one great advantage of a Dhofar concession, he believed, was the cooperative attitude of the Sultan, otherwise "my concession remained merely an interesting historical document destined for an eventual place of honor in my mother's scrapbook."

Phillips did proceed with a businesslike dispatch, however. The concession would be exploited through the Philpryor Corporation, which he had established with his friend Sam Pryor, the vice-president of Pan American World Airways. Phillips and Pryor met at the Twenty-one Club in Manhattan with Alton Jones, the president of Cities Service, a holding company with many subsidiary oil corporations, and got him interested.

The result, eventually, was that the Dhofar concession was assigned to a new Cities Service subsidiary, in which Richfield Oil of California would hold a fifty percent interest. The next issue to be resolved was the amount of royalty Phillips would receive. He knew all about Gulbenkian's famous five percent, but "With Dhofar I couldn't ask for too much be-

353

cause Cities and Richfield would have to spend many millions in exploration and even if they should finally prove I.P.C. (Iraq Petroleum) to be wrong and find oil, many more millions in drilling and development would have to be spent." So Phillips halved Gulbenkian's famous five percent and took a two and one-half percent share of all the oil produced and sold at Dhofar. Cities Service and Richfield stoutly resisted, Phillips recalled, but he stood fast and they finally gave in.[3]

Headquarters for the exploration outfit were set up first at the airfield outside Salalah, the provincial capital, then in a palm grove near the beach. Phillips and his experts flew scores of aerial missions over the territory, up to the vast and hostile barrens known as the Empty Quarter. At the Sultan's orders Arab engineers and workmen from the local tribes built a road over the Qara Mountains, which rise to four thousand feet above the Arabian Sea. They worked night and day on the thirty-mile road and managed to finish it before the arrival of the monsoon, which made the mountains impassable for any wheeled vehicle and treacherous even for camels. A miraculous transformation was taking shape. Small airconditioned towns were built on land where camels had grazed. Huge Kenworth trucks roared up the mountain highway, hauling giant collapsible derricks while the primitive Qara tribesmen stared in wonder. Hundreds of Arab workmen were recruited from Dhofar, Aden and Yemen and for the first time in their lives were given steady employment and medical services for themselves and their families.

Actual exploration began only after millions had been spent in laying the groundwork, building quarters for hundreds of workers, moving in thousands of tons of equipment, constructing port facilities — all pointing up the fact that modern oil exploration, particularly in a remote and inaccessible land, can be undertaken only with heavy corporate investment.

The first test drilling began in the spring of 1955, and at first it appeared that they were on the verge of success. They

354

were drilling, they found, into a "marmul structure," or surface anticline, eleven miles long and five miles wide. The first two wells brought up low-gravity crude, the third nothing but water.

Phillips and the Sultan were learning what a long, disheartening process the development of an oilfield often is, even when an all-out effort is being made. "Wendell," the Sultan wistfully remarked to Phillips on many occasions, as the latter recalled, "just think what I can do for my people when we have oil."[4]

Though Phillips does not mention them, Stephen Longrigg, the definitive historian of Middle Eastern oil, recorded that the project was slowed from time to time by "some political embarrassments" — evidently jealousy and suspicion on the part of neighboring sheikhdoms, and resentment over the fact the Sultan of Oman, long before the presence of oil was suspected, had always reserved Dhofar as a separately governed province, a sort of royal preserve.[5]

Six years went by after the first wells were drilled, and only enough oil was extracted to show there were deposits of some kind. The question was how much and whether it was present in commercial quantities.

In 1961 Cities Service and Richfield had a thousand men working the field and had spent, Phillips estimates, between $30 and $40 million. They had drilled twenty-three wells, six of them more than ten thousand feet deep. It looked like the greatest string of dry holes, or nearly dry ones, in petroleum history.

The last hope was to attract the interest of an independent, one with large resources, who wasn't answerable to stockholders and could risk a long shot.

The man who decided to gamble on Dhofar was John W. Mecom of the Pure Oil Company, one of the "big five" of the world's independent oil-producers. Then still in his forties, Mecom had opened fields in Texas and Louisiana and also held concessions in three of the Trucial Oman states and in

355

Yemen, Jordan and Colombia. One mark of his determination: he had drilled the world's deepest producing well in Louisiana, twenty-five thousand feet down.

Early in 1962 Mecom made a deal with the Cities Service–Richfield combine. He would drill one well at his own expense, after which the combine would decide whether to continue drilling in Dhofar. That fall Mecom took over the concession. In the next several years Mecom drilled five wells ranging in depth from 3,000 to 11,600 feet and brought up "oil shows" in three of them. Then the whole field began spouting oil and Phillips' fortune — not to mention the Sultan's and Mecom's — was made. Continental Oil entered the concession as a third partner; then Union Oil of California bought out Mecom's financial interest but the Texan stayed on as operator of the field. Nearby, in east-central Oman, Shell discovered another field and began building a pipeline through the Jabal Akhdhar Pass to the Gulf of Oman just north of Muscat.

The Sultan was so overjoyed that he more than suitably rewarded his chief adviser. "On October 12, 1965," Phillips related, "His Majesty gave the writer, in his own name, an offshore concession extending from the high-water mark out to a depth of one thousand feet covering approximately 300 miles of coastline at the entrance to the Persian Gulf from Khatmat Milahah to Ras al-Hadd. On December 12, 1965, the writer assigned the major interest in this offshore concession to one of the leading West German oil companies, Wintershall Aktiengesellschaft of Kassel, with the writer retaining a five percent interest in the concession following in the footsteps of the late great Gulbenkian.*

* This was one of the several indications that West Germany is hopeful of edging its way into the Middle Eastern oil picture. It has always enjoyed as much, or more, prestige in the Middle East as any Western nation, and perhaps the old Berlin-to-Baghdad dream has never really lost its grip. In 1969, however, West German aspirations in the area suffered a setback when, under Russian influence, a number of Middle Eastern countries announced they were extending diplomatic recognition to Communist East Germany.

"On December 12, 1965, His Majesty bestowed upon the writer a second offshore area covering approximately 450 miles from Ras al-Hadd to Ras Minji facing the Indian Ocean."[6]

Wendell Phillips must be the champion royal favorite of all time, the new Gulbenkian, though a less crafty and pretentious one. He still spends most of his time traveling around the world and lecturing on archeology and the Middle East. Certainly he is the only Arabist who got rich at the trade, and the only archeologist who went looking for a lost city and found an immense personal fortune.

J. Paul Getty, close to Phillips' opposite in temperament and background, conducted his Arabian foray in the most deliberate and longheaded style. Despite a flamboyant marital record — seven marriages and divorces — and regardless of a casually acquired journalistic fame, Getty has always been renowned as a very quiet, cat-footed operator as a businessman. If his personal life has attracted much attention, his business career is conducted along the most conservative and cautious lines.

Getty's conservatism as an independent operator, in fact, cost him a chance at huge stakes in the Middle East long before he made his successful sortie on the Arabian peninsula. In 1932 he sent his own representative to Baghdad to investigate the possibilities of acquiring an Iraqi concession. His agent soon reported back from the Iraqi capital that a very promising concession could be obtained for "a price that could be tallied in a few tens of thousands of dollars," he recalled in his autobiography. Just then, however, East Texas crude was selling for 10 cents a barrel and most of his capital was tied up; he was afraid of venturing large capital outlays in a politically troubled and already highly competitive area, and after several weeks of debating with himself he decided against the Iraqi proposition.

A "classic boner," he later called it, because "I had allowed

357

a fantastically valuable concession to slip out of my hands even though it was being offered at a comparatively negligible price."

He had to wait seventeen years to recoup on that "boner," but Paul Getty, in his business life, had learned patience.

Jay Paul Getty was a second generation oilman. His father was a millionaire by the time Getty finished his education at Oxford in 1914. Instead of enjoying the position of a prospective oil-fortune heir, he plunged into the business, more or less on his own, driving around the back-country roads of Oklahoma in a battered Model-T Ford. Except for the presence of the automobile — and it was present in large numbers around Tulsa, with newly rich Cherokee chiefs buying them a dozen at a time — the new state was "very much like Bret Harte's California or Jack London's Klondike," he recalled in his autobiography. Finally he acquired a lease and spudded his first well, near Tulsa, in 1916. That first essay as a wildcatter produced a well flowing seven hundred barrels a day.

The senior Getty was so pleased that he took his son into partnership, seventy-thirty, of the Getty Oil Company. Later Paul Getty was appointed vice-president and general manager of the family firm. As his father's junior partner, he quickly subscribed to the oilman's motto, "Get it before it's all gone." In his autobiography he explains this credo as resulting from the oilman's complex about the commodity in which he deals. Although oil company propaganda constantly assures the public that resources are all but "inexhaustible," the oilman knows better. Getty is one of the few — being an independent in every sense of the word — who openly admits his fears of depletion. In *My Life and Fortunes*, he predicted that *all* crude oil sources, at the present rate of consumption, would be exhausted "sometime in the twenty-first century."[7]

On his father's death, he inherited $500,000 as his share of the estate and with the thirty percent interest he owned in

358

Getty Oil began expanding in several directions. He bought control of Pacific Western for $1,120,000. Then he moved in on the Tidewater Associated Oil Company, stock in which was selling for $2.50 a share during the early part of the Depression. Tidewater interested him because it had organized an efficient marketing system which could dispose of the Getty Oil Company's crude. Standard Oil of New Jersey was competing for control of the same company, but Getty outmaneuvered the Rockefellers and walked off with Tidewater. At the bargain prices prevailing during the Depression he also acquired the Hotel Pierre in New York, the Skelly Oil Company and its subsidiary Spartan Aircraft. He managed all those takeovers without going to the banks, for which he has the westerner's enormous distrust.

After a profitable World War II, he realized that it was "essential" to get into the Middle East but watched the scramble for concessions on the Arabian peninsula with a "detached" interest and "waited for the smoke to clear." His caution was dictated, he later wrote, by what had happened to other oil companies which had grabbed for concessions in North Africa shortly after the British Eighth Army and the Afrika Korps left the arena. "By some incredible oversight, these firms failed to realize that the areas covered by their concessions were thickly sown with land-mines. These had to be cleared at staggering cost before prospecting operations could commence. To make matters worse, when the mines had been cleared and oil exploration got under way, the territories covered by the concessions failed to show any signs of bearing oil."[8]

Wary of political as well as military mine fields, Getty finally settled on the Neutral Zone, jointly ruled by Kuwait and Saudi Arabia, and with the oil rights indivisible, as his area of operations. The rich crude that poured out of the Kuwait fields suggested that the trackless deserts of the Neutral Zone might be more valuable than they appeared. Sheikh Ahmad of Kuwait sold his share of the rights to the concession to Aminoil,

359

an American consortium. Aminoil could not begin operations, however, until King Ibn Saud of Saudi Arabia sold his half of the rights.

Getty learned that the State Department was "especially desirous" that the Neutral Zone exploitation be shared by another American company. He engaged a geologist, Dr. Paul Walton, to make aerial surveys of the terrain. He was ready to make his first moves only after receiving a cable from Dr. Walton stating, without a wasted word: "Structures Indicate Oil."[9]

Getty had always been known as a hard bargainer, but he was no match for the Arabian traders trained in the *souks* to wrangle half a day over the price of a goat. In return for a sixty-year concession to share the Neutral Zone with Aminoil, he had to agree to terms which most other oilmen considered ruinous.

Saudi Arabia required a down payment of $12.5 million, plus an annual advance of $1 million on anticipated royalties of 55 cents per barrel. That government also would receive twenty-five percent of the net profits. Getty had to promise to build a 12,000-barrel refinery and 150,000-barrel storage tanks in Saudi Arabia, and to deliver a hundred thousand gallons of gasoline and fifty thousand gallons of kerosene to the government as a bonus. Saudi Arabian government representatives were to be allowed to attend Getty board meetings. Fringe benefits, including pensions, retirement plans and insurance, along with free medical care and hospital facilities, were to be given all Arabian employees. The education of the employees' children was to be provided for. In the zone itself the company was to build a mosque, a post office, telephone and telegraph communications, and a water-supply system.

Getty agreed to those stringent terms, he has indicated, largely because of the possibilities of entering the Asian market with oil from the Neutral Zone, the "natural" outlet for Middle Eastern oil, as he called it.[10]

He realized that it might be difficult working in tandem

with the Aminoil combine, which was the senior partner in the sense that it was on the scene first and already had its advance party there. Aminoil suggested that Getty send only a skeleton staff to the Neutral Zone and avoid waste and duplication of effort by allowing Aminoil to handle the exploration, though Getty would have to share equally in the costs. He reluctantly agreed.

A year went by, and Aminoil's drillers still hadn't produced oil. Getty, becoming restive, sent his elder son George out to make a survey of the progress. When he returned, George Getty recommended that the Getty subsidiary operating there, Pacific Western, begin its own exploration. His father finally accepted the idea, and that was the beginning of a four-year struggle in the Arabian desert requiring the expenditure of $18 million.

Getty found that Pacific Western would "not only have to construct an entire new city but, literally, build a modern civilization where there was nothing." His drillers had to contend with 135° heat in the summer, lack of water (except for violent rainstorms and flash floods, occasionally, in the winter months), scorpions and vipers. Well-insulated housing with heavy-duty air-conditioning had to be provided, and before that port facilities had to be built and trucks and other construction equipment had to be imported.

In 1950, 1951, and 1952 Getty received nothing but bills from his share of the Neutral Zone enterprise. He kept the faith, he recalled in his autobiography, despite a feedback of rumors in the oil world that the Neutral Zone operations were ruining him. "Geologists' reports, the considered opinions of veteran oilmen in whose judgment I had confidence, and my own strong feelings — my hunch, if you wish to call it that — all supported the belief that the area would prove immensely rich in petroleum . . . Exploration and drilling crews reported finding encouraging signs and indications during the course of their prospecting operations. The men on the crews and my field supervisory representatives on the scene continued to have high hopes. But that was about all . . ." Aminoil, similarly, had failed in its efforts thus far.

The first strike was made in 1953 when the drills chewed through "Burghan sand" and opened up a strong flow of crude at the 3,500-foot level. Eighteen months later another large producer was brought in nearby, at a depth of seven thousand feet, just beneath the "Ratawai limestone." There were two oil "horizons" in the field, as geologists explained. One was beneath the Burghan sand formation at thirty-five hundred feet, another beneath the Ratawai limestone shelf at seven thousand feet. As Getty put it, continued drilling showed that the Neutral Zone was "like an enormous layer cake, with numerous separate and great reservoirs of petroleum sandwiched between strata of rock and soil at various depths beneath the surface of the ground." Subsequent surveys showed there were three additional limestone reservoirs in which oil was trapped at various levels. The reserves there were estimated, conservatively, at 11 billion barrels.

The operational base at Mina Saud was rapidly expanded to handle the outflow from the Wafra field and its 150 producing wells. Two pipelines were built between the port and the field, along with a submarine pipeline that allows the larger tankers to lay well offshore and take on their cargoes of crude or refined oil.

Getty began expanding in all directions with the fifty percent share of Neutral Zone production as his new financial base. He bought or built a fleet of nine tankers, including four in the 53,000-ton class. He also began construction of a huge new Tidewater refinery on the Delaware River near Wilmington, Delaware.

He finally took a personal look at his Arabian concession in 1956, living in a company bungalow at Mina Saud for two months, and was understandably gratified when King Ibn Saud came sailing up on his yacht and invited him to a feast aboard. A year later Getty was intensely dismayed when *Fortune* published an article on the great new American fortunes and Getty's name led all the rest, including H. L. Hunt, Arthur Vining Davis, Joseph P. Kennedy, Daniel K. Ludwig, Sid Richardson, Alfred P. Sloan, Jr., etc., in that order.[11] Getty was, in fact, winkled out of the mass of new money as a probable billionaire and possibly the world's richest man. "To my acute discomfort, the press had 'discovered' me, and I had become a curiosity, a sort of financial freak," though "I for one have no conceivable way of gauging the validity of either of those grandiloquent titles."

To insulate himself against the consequent invasion of privacy, the onset of swarming journalists, crackpots, beggars and would-be borrowers, he established himself in well-guarded manorial style at Sutton Place, the seat of the Duke of Sutherland, outside London. That is now the center of the worldwide Getty oil interests, into which the profits come rolling by the millions, the tens of millions, as the great entrepreneur approaches his eightieth year.

The most recent estimate of his wealth was published in the Securities and Exchange Commission's official summary for September 1965, when his holdings in the Getty Oil Company were listed as having a market value of $1.2 billion — and they have greatly increased since then. But all those figures are meaningless, as Getty stoutly maintains, because there is "no such thing as a billionaire among active businessmen . . . little of his rated wealth is available to him in ready cash . . ."

There is no present need for the lord of Sutton Place to be wistful about that.

16.

Fifty-Fifty or Fight

During the past score of years the competition for Middle Eastern oil resources has repeatedly increased international tensions in that volatile and strategically crucial part of the world where Russian and American, Arab and Israeli ambitions converge. If eastern Europe was the epicenter of conflicting imperial systems before and during the first two world wars, the Middle East may well provide the explosive charge for the third.

The causes for international resentment and suspicion seem to multiply with every passing year. Additional irritants abound, but as the 1970's begin it is apparent that one of the most inflammatory is the fact that oil produced in Moslem lands goes to exploiting Western nations whose governments support their Israeli enemies. The situation could be reversed, and Western oil supplies critically reduced, as they were briefly during the Suez crisis, if only the Moslems' friend, ally and arms-supplier, Soviet Russia, was financially able to absorb their oil production. That would produce a critical state of affairs for the West, particularly western Europe, which continues to rely heavily on Middle Eastern production.

Some indication of Russian capacity for troublemaking in that area was provided late in 1969 when oil company headquarters and Western foreign offices alike were electrified by the announcement that Russia — for the first time in her history — would begin buying up part of the Iraqi production. The one reassuring factor in Western calculations had always been Russia's inability to pay out foreign exchange to absorb Arab oil. If that bulwark crumbles, the Western nations could find themselves in a critical situation; not all the new discoveries, such as that on the North Slope of Alaska, could make up for the loss or diminution of supply from the Middle East. Nor could such a transaction, resembling the cutoff of Japanese oil supplies in 1941, which persuaded Japan that she must go to war, be halted by the naval power the United States now parades in the eastern Mediterranean.

At the same time the revenue which the Arab nations receive from the West in exchange for their oil has gone, in part, to bolstering the Egyptian and Jordanian economies and refitting their armed forces for their front-line role in the struggle against Israel. This results in a curious ambivalence, a schizoid tendency which, perhaps necessarily, characterizes American and British policy toward Israel. One hand pushes military and economic assistance toward Israel, the other pays out funds which help to keep Israel's enemies in the fight.

Even the French, for so long relegated to a rear-rank position in the contest for Middle Eastern oil, were influenced by the four-cornered struggle to make an abortive power play during the last phase of the De Gaulle regime. One reason he cut off the supply of *Mirage* fighter-bombers to the Israeli air force, despite a contract to deliver fifty of the planes which had formed the backbone of Israeli airpower, was the vain hope that he would be able to persuade Saudi Arabia and Kuwait, both sluicing part of their immense oil royalties into the Arab cause, to grant the Compagnie Française oil concessions beside those of the British and American companies. That

365

ploy was a miserable failure, and undoubtedly was one of the causes of De Gaulle's ultimate rejection by the electorate.

An incalculable factor is the increasing weight of Arab socialism and the demand for social reform. How long can socialism and Western capitalism work in harness to exploit the resources of the Middle Eastern countries? How long will they tolerate an inevitable inequity in the profits of that exploitation? The rich crude from the Middle East, produced largely by cheap native labor under the supervision of highly paid Western technicians, is a bargain for the oil companies under the present arrangements. If the Arab nations ever learned to cooperate, to forget their mutual suspicions, they might form some regional system to produce, refine, and transport their own oil products. Every year their citizens learn more about the technique of oil production, many of them studying the necessary sciences in Western universities.

The rapid and continuing growth of Russian naval strength in the area, the Soviets' apparent determination to bring the whole area under their direct influence indicate the possibility of a Russian hegemony that would exclude the West. The Russian movement south, of course, has been facilitated by the British withdrawal "east of Suez," the American preoccupation with the war in South Viet Nam, and the Arab nations' need for military supplies and economic assistance in their war against Israel. In the last several years, through trade and industrial arrangements, Russia has succeeded in wooing Iran away from the United States, has its military missions in Iraq and Syria, and has acquired a controlling interest in Egypt. The Arabian peninsula may be next.

For the last twenty years the oil companies have been under constant pressure to increase the share of revenue going to the exploited nations. Thus the attention of the Middle Eastern oil-producing nations was riveted on Venezuela, halfway around the world, late in the 1940's. Venezuela is the largest producer after the United States and the Soviet Union and supplies about ten percent of the world's total oil production. For many years it had endured the dictatorship of General Gómez, whose arrangements with the oil companies were exceedingly profitable to them, to him and to his collaborators, but not the nation as a whole. His death in 1936 was welcomed with riotous celebrations. During the next dozen years the country alternated between military regimes and more liberal civilian rule, but in 1948 the first free elections in Venezuelan history were held. The popularly elected government, though later overthrown, managed to persuade the oil companies to grant the country a fifty-fifty split in oil revenue.

In Iran, particularly, that new arrangement was studied with interest. She had been exploited by the largely British consortium for forty years, was one of the oldest civilizations, with a once-glorious history and a proud culture of her own, and the Persians like the Chinese felt intensely humiliated by a virtual Western hegemony. "It was always more likely that a showdown would occur in Iran or Venezuela than anywhere else," oil historian Christopher Tugendhat has written. "In the Arab countries the industry was too much of a recent arrival, with the result that economic and political development was correspondingly less advanced." Iran's relations with her exploiters were somewhat different, less diffuse, more focused on long-standing grievances, than Venezuela's. "In Venezuela the industry was made up of several companies of different nationality whose interests and relations with the government were never entirely the same. In Iraq there was only Anglo-Iranian."[1] (Anglo-Iranian formerly was Anglo-Persian.) And since the Anglo-Iranian consortium was mainly British, it carried the handicap of Britain's former imperialism, the same handicap which caused King Ibn Saud of Saudi Arabia to favor American over British interests.

Stephen Longrigg, who generally stresses the benefits of exploitation over its wrongdoings, as befits a former official of Iraq Petroleum, maintains that Anglo-Iranian substantially bettered the Iranian standard of living, particularly among

367

its native labor force. He lists the housing estates built for the natives, the clinics, the medical and dental services made available, the educational facilities, wages comparing "more than favourably with those offered by any other employer in Persia." The paternalistic bounty of Anglo-Iranian, Longrigg notes, "being habitual and widely scattered and in part unperceived" was "accepted by the Persian workers and public rather with nonchalance or criticism than with gratitude."

On the whole he considers the Anglo-Iranian treatment of Iran and the Iranians "generous and enlightened," and suggests the subsequent assault on the company was an act of ingratitude. He does not believe that the company could have promoted greater social or economic evolution in the country because it would be taken amiss, perhaps as a form of imperialism. "Such a policy can appear attractive; but the suspicions of local publicists, the jealousy of threatened local interests, and the inevitable accusations of 'interference,' would probably invalidate such a programme and perhaps, paradoxically, harm the country itself."[2] It is only fair to say that most Western companies operating in the less developed countries also believe their efforts to uplift, to improve the living conditions of the natives must be limited to those actually employed by the foreign enterprise. Yet the standards thus raised become visible, and a cause of unrest, to the rest of the population; and just how to confront the phenomenon of "rising expectations" has not been worked out by the problem-solvers in corporate headquarters any more than it has in governments.*

In 1948, Anglo-Iranian, foreseeing trouble, opened negotiations with the Iranian government to liberalize the terms of the concession, which provided that Iran received a royalty of 4 shillings per ton of crude, plus twenty percent of the company's net profits above £671,250 a year. Iran was then

---

* The paradox is that the demand has not been met successfully by either socialism or capitalism. The former sometimes offers nationalistic fervor as a substitute. The latter, in the richer countries, offers a surfeit of material things to all but the bottom layer of society.

restive under British dominance. During the war both British and Russian forces had invaded the country to protect the supply lines from the west to the Russian armies of the south. Reza Shah had abdicated and been replaced by his son, the present Shah. The Russian occupation had been terminated only after hard bargaining at Yalta and elsewhere. During the postwar years, as Foreign Secretary Anthony Eden observed, "the country suffered from a succession of weak Governments, temporarily sustained by wayward deputies. Their programmes were admirable, their performance pitiable." The British were losing their hold on the Middle East while the Americans became the dominant power, and all over Asia the former imperialists of the West were being forced to surrender the East Indies, India, eventually Indochina.

A strongman-type Prime Minister, General Razmara, headed the government when a "supplemental agreement" was signed with Anglo-Iranian in July 1949. The royalty was increased by 2 shillings a ton and the government was guaranteed that its annual revenue would never fall below £4 million. In addition, the company undertook to advance the government £5 million to replenish an empty treasury.

Then it became known that Aramco had granted Saudi Arabia the same fifty-fifty split as Venezuela had achieved two years before. A current of outspoken discontent with Anglo-Iranian ran through the Parliament of Iran, which was raucous with the contending voices of the government party, the Tudeh (Communists), and the National Front headed by the elderly Dr. Mohammed Mossadegh. In the background was the sinister, rising murmur of the Teheran mob which, in an outbreak of fury, could temporarily make itself more powerful than any parliamentary political party.

As the dispute over ratifying Anglo-Iranian's offer grew more and more rancorous, and talk of nationalization of the oil industry grew in volume and enthusiasm, the political situation in Teheran became more unstable by the day. Greatly alarmed by reports from its representatives on the scene,

369

Anglo-Iranian hastily suggested renewed negotiations on the basis of a fifty-fifty split, but it was already too late for that. The right-wing government of General Razmara obviously couldn't hold out much longer.

All the febrile emotions of the native populace were now centered on the oil issue, with the aged but hyperactive Mossadegh as their hero. "How could anyone be against Mossadegh?" asked the present Shah in his memoir *Mission for My Country.* "He would enrich everyone, he would fight the foreigner, he would secure our rights. No wonder students, intellectuals, people from all walks of life flocked to his banner."

To the outside world Mossadegh was a rather ridiculous figure with his banana-like nose, his copious weeping or fainting publicly when overcome by emotion. The world's press made sport of him, front-paged photographs of him toppling or blubbering on the platform. But just as the hysterical Hitler did not appear comic to the Germans, Mossadegh was viewed as the national savior by the Iranian masses. They fervently believed that if Iran could produce and market its own oil all its economic and social problems would be solved overnight.

Mossadegh attained demagogic heights not only late in life — he was seventy — but came from the landowning aristocracy. Early in his political career he had opposed building railroads because they would, he believed, increase foreign influence. A member of the ruling family displaced by the present Shah's father, he had always been a rather misty nationalist who advocated that Iran achieve a total independence, economic as well as political. The parliamentary chaos, reflecting that of the Teheran streets, allowed him to become the dominant figure in the National Assembly and chairman of its oil committee. He was fond of a metaphor, which appealed equally to the street mobs, likening the oil industry to "a hidden treasure upon which lies a dragon." The man to slay that dragon, he indicated, was himself.

When the crunch came early in 1951, Mossadegh had succeeded in fusing the issues of oil, nationalism and social reform, though as a minister in previous governments he had never shown himself greatly interested in improving the conditions of peasants and workers. On February 19, as chairman of the National Assembly oil committee, he proposed that Iran nationalize her oil resources from well to refinery, from north Persia to Abadan. Prime Minister Razmara submitted the proposal to a panel of advisers who, grasping the fact that Iran might be able to run her oilfields but might not be able to find a market for their output, decided it was impracticable. On March 3, Razmara reported their findings to Mossadegh's committee. Four days later the Prime Minister was assassinated on his way to the mosque by a member of the fanatic Fidaiyin-i-Islam sect, and Teheran was thrown into turmoil. The Shah tried to quiet the country by naming the moderate Hussein Ala as Prime Minister, but the clamor for a quick solution only grew.

Mossadegh was willing to reap the whirlwind. Though his was numerically a splinter party, he rammed through Parliament a measure calling for nationalization and reading, "For the happiness and prosperity of the Iranian nation and for the purpose of securing world peace, it is hereby resolved that the oil industry throughout all parts of the country, without exception, be nationalized, that is to say, all operations of exploration, extraction and exploitation shall be carried out by the Government." Strikes, disorders and rioting spread from the capital to the huge British-built refinery complex at Abadan. By May 1, the Shah had signed the nationalization decree and named Mossadegh Prime Minister.

The British, of course, could no longer whistle up a gunboat to deal with the wogs. Their response was measured, legalistic. In 1933, the British pointed out, the concession agreement had been amended to include a provision for arbitration of any major grievances. The British named their representative, but Iran refused, upon which Britain asked the International Court at The Hague to intervene. Such recourse to The Hague is almost inevitably a lot of solemn nonsense, at best a sop to inflamed public opinion. How many bailiffs, to paraphrase Stalin, has the International Court? Meanwhile, pending arbitration, the British were willing to compromise. Anglo-Iranian's deputy chairman, Basil Jackson, was sent to Teheran with an offer to pay the Iranian government £3 million a month, with £10 million to be handed over in advance, until the dispute was settled; the company would continue to run the industry as surrogate for the new government-owned National Iranian Oil Company. Jackson's proposal was abruptly dismissed by the Iranian representatives after only a half-hour consideration. Another mission was sent out from London to suggest that Anglo-Iranian run National Iranian with the profits equally divided. That offer was also rejected.

Down at Abadan the situation was even more touchy. British technicians and other personnel had stayed on the job but were being pressed to say whether or not they would be willing to work for National Iranian, which they refused to do. British tankers were still loading in the Persian Gulf, but their captains were refusing to sign receipts stating that their cargo belonged to the National Iranian Oil Company. In some cases, the tankers had to unload. By the end of June 1951, all oil shipments from Abadan had stopped.

Mossadegh, riding the crest of his popularity, ordered all British personnel in the oilfields to get out within a week. Britain dispatched the cruiser *Mauritius* to protect the evacuation, and Anglo-Iranian decamped with more haste than dignity.

The Conservatives, headed by Churchill, with Anthony Eden as his Foreign Secretary, recaptured Whitehall and took up the responsibility of recouping in Iran in a mood of calm confidence. Other Middle Eastern sources were supplying the oil Britain needed. Eden believed that Britain could regain her position in Iran, if on less juicy terms, through patient diplomacy, and that it wasn't true that "Mossadegh or Communism" were the only alternatives. The British, as he later explained, were not enraged by Iran and "had difficulty in taking Mossadegh seriously. He was the first real bit of meat to come the way of the cartoonists since the war. 'Old Mossy' with his pyjamas and iron bedstead became a familiar figure." He piously insisted that Britain was interested in Iran's well-being as well as its oil. "If Mossadegh's policies were to prevail, the oil industry would be ruined and with it any possibility of material progress in Iran. A backward and corrupt agricultural state would move deeper into poverty, with calculable consequences."[3]

At the same time Eden was disturbed by the fact that the United States was taking a neutral stance, which was beneficial to Mossadegh. The suspicion may have been growing in Whitehall that the United States was viewing the Iranian turmoil as an opportunity, when the dust settled, for an American takeover. Eden met in Paris with Secretary of State Dean Acheson, whom he apparently regarded as sort of an honorary Briton because his mother was Canadian, who comfortingly did not "look like a typical citizen of the United States" and was "scrupulously fair-minded." The burden of Eden's message for Acheson was that Mossadegh must go, that there could be no thought of "excluding British technicians from Iran and handing over a very valuable British asset." Nor could Britain accept the idea of "confiscation without compensation."

American diplomacy was on the spot, trying on the role of honest broker and finding it uncomfortable. "The Iranians thought the disinterested Americans should take their part against imperialistic Britain," as one commentator wrote, "and American diplomatic representatives made statements which could be so interpreted. Every time the Americans asked the Iranians to make sacrifices, the cry of protest was loud. The British felt that in fact they were also fighting the American battle, for should they lose in Iran all American oil interests in the Middle East would be jeopardized . . . Ultimately, the basic differences in method and approach of the British and Iranians drove the Americans into the British corner . . . Not only did Americans understand the validity of the sanctity of contract and the cry against expropriation or confiscation, but they also understood the technical, financial, commercial and managerial problems . . . The Iranians only exasperated the Americans."[4]

The British were playing for keeps; they could give up India, Kenya and all the rest, but the Iranian oilfields were one of the foundation stones of the financial empire underlying the profitless physical one they were abandoning. They had raised Abadan from the desert floor, supplied it with a refinery capacity of 24 million tons, sixteen oil jetties, housing for a fourth of its forty thousand employees; and elsewhere there were six major producing fields. The loss of that capital investment would have been disastrous.

The day after the last Briton left Abadan, on October 3, 1951, the British announced they would do everything possible to prevent Iran from selling any of its "stolen" oil. Several Japanese and Italian companies bought small amounts of oil from National Iranian, but were immediately slapped with lawsuits by Anglo-Iranian. A virtual embargo on Iranian oil ensued.

Mossadegh was finding that expropriation had only raised a new crop of dragons to slay. His response, mainly, was more anguished speech-making. He made a dramatic appearance before the United Nations to plead against outside intervention, against allowing the International Court at The Hague to arbitrate. When he returned to Iran in December 1951, there was rioting in Teheran in which many were killed. In July 1952 he quit the prime ministership for four days. His replacement announced that he would try to arrange a settlement with Anglo-Iranian on more "realistic" lines, but he was quickly swept out of office when the Teheran mobs demonstrated against him. Order returned with the restora-

374

tion of Mossadegh, though in more than a year he had found no way out of the impasse.

Iran was strangling on its oil. It had exported 54 million tons in the two years before nationalization, only 132,000 tons since then. And while losing almost its entire revenue, the government had to assume responsibilities for the seventy thousand idle oilfield workers, for the road and pipeline net previously maintained by Anglo-Iranian. Mossadegh had hoped, of course, that the British would be forced to buy oil from Iran on his terms, but they had taken up the slack by increasing their imports from Iraq and Kuwait.

The more threatening the consequences to Iran's economy, the more unstable the political situation became with the Teheran mob and the Communists causing near-anarchy in the capital and the oilfields, the more intransigent was Mossadegh's stance. All attempts to reach a compromise, one based on some form of recompense to Anglo-Iranian, were rejected by the Iranian Prime Minister. Stephen Longrigg wonders how Mossadegh, without the technological or marketing setup necessary to operate a nationalized oil industry, could have hoped to prevail, what motives he had for persisting in his refusal to compromise. "Differently assessed by different observers, they certainly included a childlike, but politically exploited, belief that if the industry became 'our own' all must be well: the feeling that it was unworthy of a great nation (or was even a derogation of sovereignty) that an important foreign corporation should work and prosper on such a scale in its midst: the suspicion that the Company must be 'interfering' in State affairs, corrupting politicians, and perverting loyalty: the allegation that the Company's workers were ill-treated and dissatisfied . . ."[5]

In mid-1952 there was a joint Anglo-American proposal bearing the signatures of President Truman and Prime Minister Churchill which provided that the International Court would decide the amount Anglo-Iranian was to be recom-

375

pensed, that negotiations would settle how Iranian oil would again be absorbed by the world market, that the United States would loan Iran $10 million immediately to tide her over.

According to reports Foreign Secretary Anthony Eden was receiving from Teheran, there seemed little hope that Mossadegh would adopt a civil tone toward the proposals. The British agents described Mossadegh's condition as megalomaniacal and reported that he had to be treated like a fractious child. His hatred of the British and Americans was boundlessly irrational; he was reportedly considering an alliance with the Russians as a means of striking back at the West. Mossadegh's first interview with the British and American ambassadors did nothing to quiet Eden's fears. Eden recalled in his memoirs that Mossadegh demanded more money in threatening terms and gave the British one week in which to reply to a note he had dispatched on August 7, 1952, in which he had asked for £50 million. In Eden's opinion, any further attempts to conciliate Mossadegh would only offer him "further opportunities for blackmail."[6]

Conditions only worsened in Iran early in 1953. There was widespread unemployment, uncontrollable inflation, near anarchy in the streets of Teheran and at the oil centers. It appeared that the Mossadegh regime was merely the prelude to a Communist takeover. Mossadegh had dissolved the Iranian Senate, suspended the National Assembly, dismantled the Supreme Court, bullied the Shah into going into temporary exile, and he had made his wayward whims Iran's law. A coalition of nationalists and conservatives led by the Speaker of the National Assembly took to the streets of the capital in a royalist demonstration that almost got out of hand. Mossadegh was flushed out of his house by the mob and was forced to flee in his pajamas, hiding until his security forces restored order. The Shah barricaded himself in his palace while Mossadegh held onto power by forbidding all demonstrations and patrolling the Teheran streets with tanks and troops.

In the United States, meanwhile, there had been a change of administration. Foreign Secretary Eden journeyed to Washington to make certain that President Eisenhower and Secretary of State Dulles understood the British position on Iran and would continue American support. In his subsequent report to Churchill, Eden indicated that he was not entirely satisfied by the attitude of the Eisenhower Administration. The President seemed more determined to avoid a rupture of relations between the United States and Iran than in demonstrating sympathy for the British dilemma. Eisenhower conceded that it was necessary to avoid making any agreement with Iran that would cause other oil-producing nations to demand a greater share of the revenue, but he was convinced that there was no tolerable alternative to Mossadegh. Americans, as Eisenhower told Eden, would never be able to understand the necessity of armed intervention in the Middle East. If Russian control of Iran was extended, the West risked the loss of its Middle Eastern oil sources and, worse yet, the threat of another world war.

Eden tried to persuade Eisenhower, he recorded, that even if Russia moved into Iran in force it could not benefit from Iranian oil but would only deny it to Britain and the United States. The President demurred, quoting experts who had informed him that a pipeline could be built from the Caucasus to Abadan in a few years, and there was no firm agreement on how Mossadegh should be handled.[7]

The United States was still engaged in the Korean War, and it seemed to Eden that President Eisenhower was "obsessed by the fear of a Communist Iran" — just the argument Mossadegh had used on his own behalf, "me or the Russians" — and that Mossadegh had "evidently again scared the Americans."

On later reflection it may have occurred to some of the parties involved that the United States might have been expressing fears of a Communist Iran as a smokescreen for more selfish reasons than those trotted out for Eden. During his conversations in Washington, the British Foreign Secretary learned that Dulles planned to take certain actions designed to bolster Mossadegh against the Communists (though Mossadegh and the Iranian Communists were allied against the Shah's supporters and other conservative factions), and alarm bells rang in Eden's mind. Dulles proposed that American technicians be sent to Abadan, along with a "small amount of machinery which the Iranians needed," to keep the installation from falling into disrepair.

Eden's reply was forceful: "I said at once that I must emphasize in the strongest possible terms the deplorable effect on Anglo-American relations which the presence of Americans working in stolen British property would cause."[8]

Meanwhile Iran was racked by continuing disorder. The masses still supported Mossadegh, but the Persian elite regarded him as a madman, an impression reinforced for the rest of the world by photographs of Mossadegh fainting, weeping, ranting, being carried off unconscious by his followers after one of his emotional harangues. In mid-August a royalist coup d'état attempted to unseat Mossadegh, but it was clumsily executed and misfired. A combination of royalist and military factions had attempted to replace Mossadegh with General Zahedi as Prime Minister. Instead the Shah had to flee the country. On his way to exile in Rome, his plane touched down in Baghdad, where the Iranian ambassador tried to have the Shah arrested and returned to Teheran, but Iraq was still ruled by a pro-Western government and the Shah went on his way to Rome.

A few days later the royalists regrouped and organized street demonstrations against Mossadegh. The latter could probably have broken them up if he had been willing to allow the Communists to send their mobs into the streets, but Mossadegh was a patriot, if a curious and unstable one, and he couldn't take a chance on turning his country over to them in return for their temporary support. Instead he used the police to disperse the demonstrators. By that measure he

378

doomed himself; the army was against him and the Communists were no longer for him. On August 19 the royalists took over the streets again, there was no one to oppose them, and Mossadegh and his ministers went into hiding. Later Mossadegh was arrested and sent to prison for three years. General Zahedi took over the government, and the Shah returned from Rome in a triumph which must have been qualified by reflections on the fickleness of his people.

The royalist coup, it was widely reported, was financed and possibly organized by the U.S. Central Intelligence Agency, probably with the cooperation of the British Secret Service, which had a sizable and effective organization in Iran. In his memoirs the Shah, candid on many other subjects, avoids discussing just how the royalist minority succeeded in its coup against Mossadegh's mass following. Allen Dulles, then head of the CIA, dealt obliquely with the question in *The Craft of Intelligence*. In his opinion, Communist "stooges took over power in Iran in 1953." Admittedly Mossadegh had "come to power through the usual processes of government and not by any Communist coup as in Czechoslovakia." Mossadegh had concealed his purpose of "creating a Communist state." When this purpose became clear — to Dulles, at least — "support from outside was given to loyal anti-Communist elements . . . to the Shah's supporters."[9] Presumably this may be taken as a discreet admission that the "support from outside" was supplied by the CIA, since the chapter as a whole is titled "The Role of Intelligence in the Cold War" and deals with other CIA interventions.

To the authors of an unofficial history of the CIA, there is "no doubt at all" that the American "spooks" were responsible for Mossadegh's overthrow. They credit the coup to Kermit "Kim" Roosevelt, a grandson of President Theodore Roosevelt, and quote a fellow agent who said it was "a real James Bond operation."

As David Wise and Thomas B. Ross gathered the inside story from sources within the CIA, Kim Roosevelt, a Middle

East specialist for the OSS during World War II who later graduated to the CIA, arrived in Teheran some weeks before the uprising. He worked with several CIA men stationed at the U.S. embassy, seven Iranian agents including two men in the army's intelligence service, and Brigadier General H. Norman Schwartzkopf, who had organized the Iranian police some years before. After the Iranian army demonstrated its loyalty to the Shah, Roosevelt from his hideout "gave orders to his Iranian agents to get everyone they could find into the streets. The agents went into the athletic clubs of Teheran and rounded up a strange assortment of weight-lifters, muscle-men and gymnasts. The odd procession made its way through the bazaars shouting pro-Shah slogans. The crowd grew rapidly in size. By mid-morning it was clear the tide had turned against Mossadegh and nothing could stop it."[10]

It makes a nice cloak-and-dagger legend, but surely it must have taken more than a few shouting body-builders to overturn a Prime Minister with a fanatic following. The whole story undoubtedly has not been told and probably never will be.

On the surface, it appears to have been a tidy operation which disposed of an unstable government in a strategic borderland, restored the oilfields to British management, and not so incidentally resulted in bringing American oil companies into Iran for a large slice of the profits. For oil, a triumph. For the American taxpayer, something else again. More than a billion U.S. dollars have been poured into Iran in various aid projects, at least partly to defend that stake of the oil companies in Abadan's output. Much of that aid, supposed to help the peasantry out of their grinding poverty, was intercepted by the corrupt upper-class cliques in Teheran. A House investigating committee concluded that it was "impossible to tell what became of these funds."

The new government under General Zahedi was amenable to negotiating with the British for a new arrangement. Foreign Secretary Eden was delighted with the way things were going until he received reports from Washington that the

Eisenhower Administration, always tenderly susceptible to the oil companies' interests, was maneuvering to have American companies replace Anglo-Iranian. Eden lost a bit of his famous urbanity when "reports reached the Foreign Office that the State Department had been holding meetings with the American oil companies. At these, it was alleged, the State Department pressed for the formation of an all-American company to buy out the Anglo-Iranian. This idea was not to the liking of the American oil companies . . ." Oil is thicker than blood, it appears, and poaching is prohibited.

In the long negotiations that followed, Eden said, "It was a political necessity to meet Iran's requirements in respect of sovereignty, while giving the consortium the control they considered essential for their operations."[11] Another overriding factor was rewarding American interests; their government had just advanced $22 million to revive the Iranian economy. The happy sequel for the major U.S. companies was that, in return for overt and covert operations by their government, they were awarded a large piece of the action.

In the final settlement, National Iranian retained ownership of the concession, with approximately fifty percent of the revenue, which in 1955 amounted to £31.6 million. Anglo-Iranian remained top dog in the new international consortium formed, with forty percent. Shell got fourteen percent, Compagnie Française six percent, and five of the largest American companies — Standard of New Jersey, Socony-Mobil, Gulf, Standard of California, and the Texas Company — each seven percent. Another five percent was awarded the Iricon Agency consisting of nine other American companies, including Getty Oil, Richfield, Aminoil, Standard of Ohio, Signal Oil, Atlantic Refining, Hancock, Tidewater, and San Jacinto.

And there were two significant footnotes to the Iranian episode. Kim Roosevelt left the CIA and joined Gulf, one of the consortium's members, as government relations director, and in 1960 became a vice-president. Anglo-Iranian itself was so shaken by the affair, by the knowledge that it could be ruined if it depended solely on Iranian oil, that it was briskly reorganized, reoriented, and renamed. It is now British Petroleum, sixth among the world's producers with the largest reserves, still mostly in the Middle East. It is second only to Shell as a foreign competitor in the U.S. market, and under its aggressive new policy is expanding at a faster rate than any other major. British Petroleum, or BP as it advertises itself on service stations throughout the world, is also one of the several companies which made a major strike on Alaska's North Slope. Without the scare thrown by Mossadegh, it might still be pottering about, growing old and fat on too-easy profits from Abadan.

There was reason for gleeful hand-rubbing in many of the world's oil headquarters over the solution to the Iranian problem. From their standpoint, it served as a sharp lesson to the oil-producing companies that they couldn't go it alone. The indelible impression made by the Iranian experience was worth the fifty-fifty principle firmly established. (Or was it? In 1969, Iran, now friendly with the Soviet Union, announced that its share must be increased to help pay for the country's five-year, $11 billion development program. Jealousy of Kuwait, whose five hundred thousand citizens receive almost as much in oil revenue as Iran's 27 million, was evidently another factor.)

Hand-rubbing over Iran. But hardly a year had passed with Abadan going full blast again, when there was cause for hand-wringing in the West. The anguish was caused by President Nasser of Egypt who, partly in retaliation for the cutoff of American assistance in building the high dam at Aswan, a burden eagerly assumed by the Russians, nationalized, then closed the Suez Canal, the main tanker route for oil from the Arabian peninsula and the interchange between Asia and Europe. When that happened on July 26, 1956, a crisis arose in western Europe, which itself was forced to absorb a lesson in the exigencies of depending on Middle Eastern oil. Politics could also shut off the supply, just as markets could be closed as a counter to nationalization; extortion worked both ways.

Britain was caught with a six weeks' supply, the countries of western Europe with stocks that would last about a month. "The continuing supply of fuel, which was a vital source of power to the economy of Britain, was not subject to Colonel Nasser's whim," as Anthony Eden, then Prime Minister, summed up the situation. "The oilfields of the Middle East were then producing about 145 million tons a year. Nearly 70 million tons of oil had passed through the Suez Canal in 1955, almost all of it destined for Western Europe. Another 40 million tons of oil reached the ports of the Levant by pipelines running through the territories of Egypt's then allies, Syria and Saudi Arabia. More than half of Britain's annual imports came through the canal. At any time the Egyptians might decide to interfere with its passage. They might also prompt their allies to cut the pipelines. We had to gauge the implications of bringing oil from the Persian Gulf by the long haul around the Cape of Good Hope."[12]

Western enterprise and technology, however, already had made a start on solving the problem of the Suez bottleneck. The canal closure for several months in 1956, while Britain, France and Israel conducted their abortive military operations against the United Arab Republic, and the subsequent blocking of the canal after the six day war of 1967, only proved that Suez could be bypassed by the new super-tankers which, in any case, couldn't negotiate the canal.

For the time being, however, the 1956 crisis was very real.* It was brought on by Secretary of State Dulles' indelicate and abrupt termination of assistance to the Aswan project on which Nasser depended for feeding his nation. American

* It was hard on Saudi Arabia, too, when its production sank from 4.4 million tons a month to 2.7 million. King Saud, a reluctant captive of Egyptian policy and Arab nationalism, stopped all shipments to the British protectorate of Bahrein and forbade British tankers to load Arabian oil.

policy was then being formulated in a high-minded, and often high-handed, fashion which Nasser found insulting and U.S. allies regarded as equally repugnant. It was a matter not only of substance but of manner. In his most priggish mood, for instance, Secretary Dulles would state: "The United States cannot be expected to identify itself 100 percent either with the colonial powers or the powers uniquely concerned with the problem of getting independence as rapidly and as fully as possible . . . For while we stand together, and I hope shall always stand together in treaty relations covering the North Atlantic, any areas encroaching in some form or manner on the problem of so-called colonialism find the United States playing a somewhat independent role." The interposition of American naval power in the Mediterranean to force the British, French and Israelis to withdraw from their pounce on Egypt only enraged those nations and did not pacify President Nasser.

The Suez affair, however, immensely benefited the world's tanker fleets, whose operations have been called the biggest floating crap game in the world.

The Greek triumvirate of Onassis, Niarchos and Livanos, and the tanker fleets of other nationalities, made a killing and went ahead full speed on construction of a fleet of super-tankers which would allow the rest of the world to make itself independent of the Suez Canal route. And what a killing it was, when western Europe was critically short of oil and it was presumed that the shortage would last a half-dozen years (based on the fallacy that the Egyptians would never be able to operate the canal on their own). Profiteering was rampant. One instance cited by Christopher Tugendhat, the young British oil historian: before the Suez crisis the rate for transportation from the Persian Gulf to a northwest European port was 20 shillings a ton; after, it was 134 shillings a ton, almost a seven hundred percent increase.

384

It was also possible in the crap game of tanker operation to be wiped out, but the gamble apparently is worth the risk. The oil companies themselves operate only about one-third of the world's tanker fleet. The rest are operated on charter by Messrs. Livanos, his two ex-sons-in-law Onassis and Niarchos, and their fellow fleet-owners. The most spectacular figure in this dicy game, of course, is Aristotle Socrates Onassis, whose ambitions appear limitless and even encompassed marriage with America's First Widow. His is a Horatio Alger fable with a Levantine accent, like that of Gulbenkian or Zaharoff, a spinoff of the Christian minorities' adventure in the old Ottoman Empire. The Christian in Turkey, Greek or Armenian or Copt or Circassian, had to be a sharp-witted, nimble-footed fellow to survive and prosper. Onassis himself was born in Smyrna (now Izmir), the Greek enclave in Anatolia; he was fourteen when the Greeks and Turks massacred each other, and he demonstrated a high survival-quotient during the military occupation by cornering a supply of raki and bootlegging it in the U.S. Marine Zone. His subsequent flight to Argentina, where he prospered in the tobacco business; his marriage to the daughter of Stavros Livanos, the Greek shipping magnate; his acquisition of a whaling and merchant shipping fleet partly through rather dubious Liberty Ship deals; and his beneficial rivalry with his ex-brother-in-law Niarchos, all are part of one of the more romantic, or piratical, legends of the modern business world.[13]

When the Suez crisis broke, Onassis was being blacklisted by the oil companies for trying to put over a pipeline running from Suez City to Port Said, one end of the canal to the other, which would have permitted him to bypass the canal when his huge new tankers — one 65,000-ton class being built at Kiel and an even larger one under way in a Japanese shipyard — were placed in operation. They would be too large to use the canal, but a pipeline would allow their cargoes to be transferred. "Because I was in the doghouse with the oil companies," he told his biographer Willi Frischauer, "and could get no new charters, I had a great number of ships on my hands."

Onassis and his fellow magnates were riding high during the period of the canal's closure, but the boom was short-lived. "During the Suez crisis," Onassis explained, "the Defense Department, the U.S. government as a whole, were deeply concerned about the alarming situation and considering how to keep the oil flowing because the closure of the Suez Canal meant twice the tonnage was required — not ten, twenty, or thirty percent more but double the tonnage ordinarily needed while the Canal was open. There was even talk of the government putting up a fund of five hundred million dollars to promote the building of tankers . . . Unexpectedly and to the surprise of the highest authorities, it took only a few months to clear the Canal. This had the effect of suddenly turning the whole subject upside down. Suddenly, like all governments, the U.S. administration found that there was enough oil coming through in enough tankers and the situation was back to normal."[14]

But not for long. As bigger tankers were built, the Suez Canal more and more becomes what Nasser has made it, a malarial ditch, now far outside the calculation of the world's oil-transporters. At the close of the 1960's, Onassis and his peers were planning tankers in the 250,000-ton class and even larger. Onassis himself is said to have ten such ships on order. The problems of docking and offloading the mammoth vessels are still to be solved. One solution is to ruin one of the world's remaining unspoiled natural beauties, Bantry Bay on the southwest coast of Ireland, where Gulf has built a huge depot on Whiddy Island for the reception of such monster tankers and the redistribution of their cargoes to western Europe. Other super-plus-tankers of the future may invade the similarly unspoiled, deep-water fiords of the Maine coast. This may be a rather large price for the rest of us to pay for the enrichment of the oil-tanker division of international society and its glamorous creatures.

And things may get worse under the banner of industrial progress, unless progress is hurled back or redefined. There is no reason, says one authority, why a million-ton tanker shouldn't be built, at least not from the technical standpoint. Tankers of eight hundred thousand tons are now on the drawing board. What would happen if a million-tonner went aground and spewed out its cargo is not part of the naval architects' calculations.

The plans of Onassis and his fellow magnates are economically sound. "The big ships are cheaper to operate because a high proportion of the costs in shipbuilding and marine transportation are fixed," one authority states; "whatever the size of a vessel, expensive tools and equipment are needed to build and outfit it, and the bigger the hull, the easier it becomes for the shipyard to apply mass-production techniques for the steel shapes used in the cargo tanks. Once at sea, the super-tankers also have decisive advantages. If it is properly designed a long vessel moves through the water more easily than a short one, so that the engine size increases only slightly with the size of the tanker . . . So far as manpower is concerned there is no need for any increase; the 200,000-tonners have a crew of about thirty, which is the same as the 50,000-tonners built in the 1950's."[15]

All these colossal visions depend on a continuation of the booming oil market, of course, and that in turn on a surging prosperity. Once the demand drops, the tanker fleets lose equally colossal amounts of money because they have to be kept in perpetual motion to turn a profit. And the navigation of super-ships is not always the certainty it is claimed to be. R.M.S. *Titanic*, after all, was said to be unsinkable.

The Iranian and Suez crises demonstrated just how delicately balanced the oil supply situation is. By a historic irony most oil is located in the have-not countries — and concessions do not run forever. The Iranian consortium's expires in 1979, and if the world's reserves are greatly lowered by then, the matter will not be settled by sending in a CIA action squad and hiring a mob in the Teheran bazaars.

Meanwhile, in Iran or elsewhere, there is always the possibility of the maverick interloper who refuses to honor the major companies' arrangements. Until his death in a plane crash October 27, 1962, a swashbuckling Italian, who learned guerrilla tactics as a leader of the anti-Fascist resistance movement, presented such a challenge.

Enrico Mattei was head of the Italian goverment-owned Ente Nazionali Idrocarburi (ENI), and with his revolutionary mentality saw no reason why Italy should be frozen out of the oil game merely because it lacked military power and diplomatic thrust. A handsome, energetic fellow, he set about remedying Italy's lack of oil resources in the manner of a young Deterding — by first throwing the rule book out the window. Iranian concessions were his first concern. ENI had cooperated in the British-ordained boycott during the Mossadegh troubles, and when they were over he asked that Italy be allowed to participate in the consortium. No outsiders allowed, he was informed. The five percent share given the Iricon Agency, which was composed of American outsiders, enraged him.

Islamic nationalism was the weak point in the elaborate defenses the major oil-producers had built around their Middle Eastern holdings. Another was the fact that the fifty-fifty split, which the majors proclaim as Sacred Writ, isn't as equitable as it may seem. Mattei said so, in 1957, in tones that rang throughout the Middle East.

"The people of Islam are weary of being exploited by foreigners," he trumpeted to the consternation of the majors. "The big oil companies must offer them more for their oil than they are getting. I not only intend to give them a more generous share of the profits but to make them my partners in the business of finding and exploiting petroleum resources."[16]

The idea of full partnership, he shrewdly anticipated, appealed as much to countries like Iran, with their bruised national pride, as a larger share of the profits. Despite efforts by the American ambassador in Teheran to block any deal with the Italians, "to discourage us from entering into this new kind of agreement" (as the Shah revealed in *Mission for My Country*), the National Iranian Oil Company delightedly came to terms with Mattei. Under the contract National Iranian and ENI shared responsibility for management and the former received what amounted to seventy-five percent of the total profits. (The majors claimed it wasn't as good a deal as it seemed, pointed out that under earlier concessions the Iranians would have received a down payment and that they hadn't shared the expense of exploration and development as the ENI contract required.) From the viewpoint of London and New York, it set a dangerous precedent, which was exactly why the Iranians valued it. ENI found little new oil, but its concession served as the model for more generous terms in the area, including a Japanese concession for offshore rights in the Persian Gulf between Kuwait and Saudi Arabia and a Standard Oil of Indiana partnership arrangement with National Iranian.*

Although Iran's contract with the consortium does not ex-

* ENI, evidently, also served as the model for the announced formation of a British government–owned British Hydrocarbons Company. The announcement, in the summer of 1969, understandably sent a thrill of apprehension through BP and Shell. Proposed by a study group of the ruling Labour Party, the company would be "a major national oil company operating independently in its own right, exactly like the international oil companies, both in Britain and abroad." Dr. Colin B. Phipps, a geologist and a member of the Labour study group, wrote that the international majors have been preparing for such nationalized developments for some time. The majors have been expanding into petrochemicals and "will tend more and more to become processing and marketing bodies, with their exploration and exploitation activities . . . reduced to contractual functions carried out for a national company. The overall effect of this change of function will be for the oil companies to lose their role as international oil brokers . . ." ["Britain Joins the Oil Rush," *New Statesman*, August 1, 1969].

pire until 1979, it is already pushing for new terms. National Iranian demands that the consortium expand production and thereby increase Iran's royalties, pointing out that in 1968 Iran's production totaled 2,840,000 barrels a day, only slightly more than tiny Kuwait's 2,640,000 a day. If Iran does not receive increased income, a government source disclosed, it plans to seize half of the consortium's reserves and parcel them out under the new partnership contracts with other oil companies.[17] Under the present arrangement, Iran receives about $900 million a year on a twelve and one-half percent royalty plus a tax of fifty percent on all profits, but it demands $1 billion to fund its development programs.

Islamic independence of the international oil companies was first to assert itself in Syria despite her unstable government. Syria was the first Middle Eastern nation to market her own oil, income from which had risen to $20 million annually at last report. New discoveries reportedly will boost that income considerably. Despite general hostility to the West, Syria has made deals for her crude to finance the Euphrates development program and to pay for an oil pipeline being built by the Italians, a telecommunications network with West German technical supervision, and a new airport being constructed by the French. All these Western helpers, significantly, are have-not nations in terms of oil resources.

Elsewhere in the Middle East and Africa, the politics of international oil have brought war and revolution, with consequences not yet calculable. Young Nasserite officers toppled the regime of King Idris of Libya in the summer of 1969 just as Libya was moving up to the front rank of the world's oil-producers. Anglo-American companies were just bringing the desert wells to full production when Arab socialism displaced a somewhat corrupt monarchy. However, the radical new rulers did not appear to be considering nationalization of the oilfields. Nor did the oil companies hasten to promote a counterrevolution. Coexistence, uneasy though it may be for both parties, seems to be the only solution.

390

With the forced U.S. abandonment of Wheelus, its huge air base, the American companies were increasingly discomfited by their hosts' policies. Occidental, a major participant in the field, was particularly hard hit by a decree from the Libyan government requiring it to cut back production more than a hundred thousand barrels a day in mid-1970. Until then Occidental had been a favored company, and King Idris himself had attended the ceremonies inaugurating its $150 million pipeline and terminal on the Gulf of Sirte. Occidental's rise to major status, in fact, had largely been accomplished through its share of Libyan oil. In 1957, it was taken over by Dr. Armand Hammer, son of a Russian-born physician and a spectacular entrepreneur who had made several fortunes in operating trade concessions in the Soviet Union, establishing the famous Hammer Galleries in New York, and distilling whiskey, among other ventures. When he took over Occidental, it was an obscure California oil and gas producer with total operating revenues of less than $800,000. Ten years later it was earning $45,548,000 on a gross of $825,000,000. Dr. Hammer got into the Libyan field by wheeling and dealing in an atmosphere *Fortune* (July 1968) described as "redolent of buying and selling, winning and losing, bribery, and the transfer of money to Swiss banks." No doubt that background made him an Occidental especially distasteful to King Idris' successors.

The Libyan revolt proved, among other things, that internal unrest and subversion cannot be entirely pacified by oil wealth, even if the wealth is spread around to some extent. Just before the overthrow of King Idris, Libya's per capita income was $1,000 a year. Libyans, however, were inflamed by Egyptian propaganda, which unceasingly pointed out that King Idris refused to join the holy crusade against Israel. Islamic nationalism reinforced by resentment of a corrupt government propelled the revolution and sent King Idris into exile. Those ministers, courtiers, and bureaucrats who fled with him apparently would not suffer many privations abroad.

391

The King's favorites often became millionaires after holding office for a year or two, according to Western journalists. Oil companies seeking to join in the exploitation of the desert oilfields reportedly had to pay $1 million in bribes just to have their applications passed up to the Council of Ministers. Another million or two changed hands before that body approved of the applications. The Shelhi family piled up vast fortunes as royal advisers, one of them supposedly having collected $125 million during his four years in the government.[18]

Further to the south on the African continent the supranational oil game was being played under the old self-made, possibly self-destructive rules. The Nigerian civil war, the course of which was heavily influenced by the discovery of oil in what once promised to be a model African republic, continued at the cost of thousands of lives and endless suffering. It was bitterly epitomized in a British periodical by a cartoon titled "Nigerian Sacrifice" and showing a Nigerian officer placing the body of a child on the altar formed by a filling station pump.[19] Behind the lines of the Nigerian and rebelling Biafran forces, veteran exploiters such as Shell, British Petroleum, Gulf, Mobil, Texaco, and Standard Oil of California were draining the rich crude out of the country while uncounted millions of Biafrans starved or were slaughtered.

While Biafra's aspirations were slowly strangled by a Nigerian army and air force largely supplied by Russia and Britain, the oil companies hastened to complete a pipeline to the sea, "upon which," it was cheerily reported, "oil shipments will rise to some twenty percent above the 1966 figure."[20]

By the time the struggle finally ended early in 1970, the African nations realized what the Biafran secession was all about. "Nigeria has just gone through an oil war, not a civil war," a spokesman for the African bloc at the United Nations stated. The Biafran province included large quantities of high-grade, sulfur-free petroleum, production of which had reached 550,000 barrels a day before the secession in the summer of 1967.[21] Because the British group was so heavily involved in Nigerian oil exploitation, the former Labour government, despite a backlash from its backbenchers in Parliament, backed the central government to the hilt. And France, so long a have-not, provided arms for Biafra and thereby prolonged the fighting and the almost incredible suffering of the Biafran people. It had obtained the promise of concessions which would have allowed French companies to supersede the American and British. The outcome as usual: victory for the oil companies, death and horror for a segment of humanity.

For the international consortiums the crunch in the Middle East will come later in the 1970's when the first of the big concessions expires in Iran. Or sooner, if the Arab-Israeli conflict draws the United States into closer support of Israel and makes intolerable the presence of her oilmen in the various Arab countries.

If the Soviet Union in either case decides she can provide a major market for Middle Eastern oil, particularly if her military and political influence over the area continues to grow, there will be anxious hours in the oil company boardrooms.

Two new finds, as widely separated as the North Sea and the Siberian hinterland, may influence the decision-makers in the Kremlin. They also are an indication of how delicately balanced are the supply and demand factors which decide the social and economic fate of the Middle Eastern oil countries.

A consortium including Phillips Petroleum, Petrofina of Belgium, and French and Italian partners announced a major strike in the North Sea 185 miles southwest of Norway. One estimate was that it would produce 7.5 billion barrels of oil, four times the known European reserves. Jersey Standard subsequently drilled a high-producing well in Norwegian waters, and another exploration company, the Tennaco group, came up with a 2,000-barrels-a-day gusher in Dutch waters 115 miles north of Amsterdam. To geologists these

393

finds suggested an oil-bearing basin under the North Sea beneath British, Norwegian, Dutch, Danish and West German waters. If their optimism is justified, Europe would become increasingly independent of crude imported from the Middle East and North Africa.[22]

Possibly of greater significance in the relation between international oil and power politics was the announcement that a huge new oil and natural gas field had been discovered in western Siberia. Soviet officials predicted the discoveries near Samotlar, south of Vorkuta and near the Ob River, would produce 14 billion barrels of oil, which places the find in a class with the North Slope of Alaska. Russia already exports 600 million barrels of crude and refined oil annually.[23]

But the new developments do not lessen the anxiety of the oil barons over the security of their Middle Eastern sources and the troublemaking potential of the Soviet Union in that area. At the European Institutional Investor Conference, David H. Barran, managing director of the Royal Dutch Shell group, recently argued that "the Soviet interest in the Middle East is oil for its own sake." The high cost of developing the new Russian fields on Siberia and Central Asia and of piping oil to the industrial centers of European Russia would cause the Russians to become oil-buyers for the first time, he predicted.[24] If that happened on a large scale, the Western nations, with half of their oil presently coming from the Middle East, might be badly upset by losing their buyers' market, by having to pay more or having to look elsewhere for the bulk of their imports.

17.

Images and Realities

Late in the 1960's Americans began to suspect, once again, that the oil industry was prospering inordinately at the expense of the rest of the country. The industry's standard response was institutional advertising, publicity campaigns and other image-polishing devices designed to convince the public that the oil business and its methods of operation are a prime necessity to the nation's health. In the same blanket-sized ads placed in newspapers throughout the country, with the theme "our business is *your* business," there was a hint of poor-mouthing over the industry's burden and its low recompense for toting all its responsibilities.

The advertising pointed out that the United States was using 550,000,000 gallons a day, which rate would rise to 1 billion gallons by the year 2000. Even while shouldering the burden of supplying this increasing demand, "drastic changes are being proposed which could greatly weaken the oil industry's ability to serve you," based on the "misconception" that "prices and profits are too high; that oil taxes are too low; that the flow of foreign oil into the country could be greatly increased without harmful results . . ." The industry's response to such allegations was that retail gasoline prices before taxes have gone up at a much lower rate than other consumer goods; that "the oil industry has paid a higher share of its gross revenue in direct taxes than the average for other industries"; that if "an over-supply of imported oil" was permitted "many of the small domestic wells would be forced to shut down" and by the early 1970's the United States "would be depending on foreign sources for about half its petroleum," upon which we would be "at the mercy of other countries" and "it would be too late to revive our domestic industry." The oilmen's information bureau begged the public to ponder the calamity of "America without a healthy oil industry."[1]

One got the impression that the oil companies were resting on the slenderest props, that oil was almost a marginal enterprise like strip mining or manufacturing buggy whips.

The fact is that the giants are getting more gigantic, that the old oil families are becoming wealthier and more powerful than ever, that the "big seven" internationally includes Standard Oil of New Jersey, Royal Dutch Shell, Mobil Oil, Texaco, Gulf, Standard Oil of California, British Petroleum; three of them Rockefeller companies, one Mellon. The Rockefellers and Mellons, through the processes of conglomeration, are not quiescent tribes content with fondling their objets d'art and overseeing their philanthropies. The Rockefeller, Mellon and Morgan interests, according to one alarmed observer, are still expanding and engrossing, are being "extended and consolidated to control coal and uranium — in short, moving to corner the entire fuel market in the country."

The observer explains the process in terms harshly unsympathetic: "Through the coal companies they now control, the families are back in the old game of raping the poor, especially the miners of Eastern Kentucky and West Virginia. The United Mine Workers sold out to the coal interests twenty years ago. Mechanization has spurred production, reduced costs, and increased the incidence of the incurable black

396

lung disease." He cites a "sporadic guerrilla warfare" going on in the coalfields for several years between the mining companies and the miners, adding, "This may all come back rather hard on young John D. Rockefeller IV, the new Secretary of State in West Virginia, who wants to make a political career for himself in the state. He pretends his family has nothing to do with West Virginia. In fact through the Rockefeller Foundation they own huge investments in Continental Oil, which in turn owns Consolidation Coal, the largest mining operation in West Virginia."[2]

The destinies of the immense Rockefeller fortune may be guided by corporate managers, just as the public impression of the family itself has been assiduously shaped and reshaped for the last three generations by their corps of public relations experts, but it is still as compact as it was in the old trust-building days. The public has been encouraged to believe that the Rockefellers are really out of the oil business, that they are completely divorced from such mundane considerations as the continued accumulation of wealth (at a geometric rate), and that they are dedicated to various cultural and humanitarian projects, as well as liberal and reformist politics in New York, West Virginia and Arkansas, while the various Standard Oil companies and their subsidiaries go clickety-click on their own, on a less elevated plane. As Ferdinand Lundberg remarked, however, the "Rockefeller foundations are instrumental in keeping in being and under family control the Standard Oil empire that the Supreme Court ordered dissolved in 1911." Similarly, the various Mellon foundations, with assets totaling almost $300 million, "do not diminish by much the personal Mellon holdings of today . . . The family, all lovers of the oldtime capitalism will be cheered to note, does not appear to be dissipating its fortune in riotous charity."[3]

A study titled *Tax-Exempt Foundations and Charitable Trusts: Their Impact on Our Economy*, published by Representative Wright Patman's Select Committee on Small Business, bluntly sets forth the fact that the Rockefeller empire is intact and still firmly under family control:

"At the close of 1960, seven Rockefeller-controlled foundations owned 7,891,567 shares of common stock of Standard Oil of New Jersey with a market value of $324,946,110. The same seven foundations owned 602,126 shares of the common stock of Socony Mobil Oil Co. with a market value of $23,610,770. Two Rockefeller foundations owned 306,013 shares of Continental Oil capital stock with a market value of $17,060,224 (the Rockefeller Foundation itself held 300,-000 of these shares with a market value of $16,725,000); four Rockefeller foundations owned 468,135 shares of Ohio Oil common stock with a market value of $17,998,495; five Rockefeller foundations owned 1,256,305 shares of the common stock of Standard Oil Co. of Indiana with a market value of $59,736,991; and the Rockefeller Foundation itself owned 100,000 shares of the capital stock of Union Tank Car Co. with a market value of $3,100,000.

"If Standard Oil Co. (New Jersey) were to attain substantial ownership in its competitors, it would certainly tend to eliminate competition and again tend toward monopoly, and engage the Department of Justice in inquiry.

"The use of a subterfuge — in the form of Rockefeller-controlled foundations — in effect produces the same result as if Standard Oil Co. (New Jersey) owned substantial stock interest in Continental Oil, Ohio Oil, Standard Oil Co. (Indiana), *et al.*"

In his introduction to the study, Representative Patman adds that "It is a well-known fact that the Rockefeller family controls Standard Oil Co. (New Jersey), and the Rockefeller-controlled foundations own a substantial part of the corporation."[4] Through its foundations, in fact, the Rockefeller family holds unshakable control over the companies first organized by John D. Sr. and all their subsequent proliferation. Just how the foundations operate to protect that control was demonstrated forty years ago when Colonel Robert W. Stewart, board chairman of Standard of Indiana, tried to wrench it away. Stewart appealed to the mass of stockholders in opposing his will to the Rockefellers. An avalanche struck him when the Rockefellers rolled up the proxies of all their foundations and those of the old Standard Oil satraps' families and voted Stewart down. In the clutch, the Rockefeller foundations' stockholdings obey the family will.

Occasionally a curious conflict of interest arises between the family's financial holdings and its devotion to public service. In the summer of 1969, for instance, Governor Nelson Rockefeller was dispatched to South America on an ill-defined mission by the Nixon Administration. Whatever goodwill or fact-finding was supposed to have been accomplished by the descent of Rockefeller and his party on Latin American capitals was made impossible by riots and demonstrations, which in some places were so violent that the American proconsul was either received at remote and well-guarded airfields or asked not to come at all. This despite Rockefeller's sincere and long demonstrated interest in Latin American welfare.

One cause of the hostility, undoubtedly, was the controversy over the expropriation by Peru of a Rockefeller subsidiary. The confiscated property was the International Petroleum Corporation, a subsidiary since 1924 of Standard Oil of New Jersey. According to Jon Basil Utley, writing in a conservative magazine not at all unfriendly toward the oil industry, the IPC concession rests on shaky legal ground. It was originally granted to a Peruvian with the understanding that he would be working a "tar-mine." Standard, of course, acquired it after oil was discovered on the property, regardless of the fact that under Peruvian law the concession did not include underground mineral (or oil) rights. The Standard subsidiary, in other words, had been extracting oil for forty-four years when, by the letter of the Peruvian laws, it was entitled only to take out tar. The seizure, coupled with the

399

threat of American countermeasures through the Hicken-looper Amendment, caused a wave of anti-American feeling. "Even moderate Peruvians," Utley observed, "think that IPC, with its enormous economic power, abused Peru's hospitality by continually obtaining special privileges, and by failing to take advantage of past opportunities to renegotiate its legal position under more favorable circumstances than today. It is generally believed that IPC used to find it cheaper and easier to buy off politicians than to negotiate a fair settlement."[5]

Nationalization or expropriation, as the cases of Iran and Mexico proved, is usually a losing game when the opponent is a combination of the world's oil companies with their ability to shut off markets, financing and transportation. Possibly emboldened by the Peruvian example, Bolivia a short time later expropriated the Gulf Oil subsidiary. Within months, she began suffering from the effects of that decision, and the Bolivian Minister of Mines was clamoring that an "international conspiracy" was operating against him. The surprised tone was unwarranted, but the Bolivians quickly learned that a major oil company can reach many shutoff valves. A natural-gas pipeline being built from Santa Cruz to the Argentine border by an American company was suddenly abandoned. International financing became unavailable. Tanker fleets and refineries which might handle Bolivian oil, knowing that they might lose out on a Gulf contract, were proving reluctant to transport or process Bolivian crude.[6]

Neither the Mellon (Gulf) nor the Rockefeller interests have lost their ability to defend themselves. In their relatively unostentatious way the Mellons retain all the generative power of their accumulated wealth. Some indication of the size of the Mellon fortune was indicated recently on the death of Mrs. Ailsa Mellon Bruce, the daughter of Andrew Mellon, whose personal fortune of $500 million made her the richest woman in the United States.

In Europe as well as America "old" oil maintains its supremacy, even when political upheaval has separated it from its former bases. Royal Dutch Shell, its original concessions long ago swept away by Indonesian independence, is the largest of all the European industrial combines. Shell's annual income is larger than Switzerland's and years ago it outgrew both Britain and the Netherlands and became a truly international company. It is still divided by the two parent companies, with Royal Dutch holding sixty percent of the shares, Shell forty percent, and has five managing directors, two British, two Dutch and one American, the last apparently acting as referee.

"It operates in nearly every country in the world," Anthony Sampson reports, "with largely autonomous marketing companies in every country in Europe — Shell Italiana, Deutsche Shell, Belgian Shell, etc. Shell is one of the companies that claims to be the most 'geocentric' in Europe and it certainly has very international managers; but the problems of Anglo-Dutch cooperation are not easy. Two drastic reorganizations in ten years have tried to cut out overlapping and muddle between the two centres, London and The Hague. The Dutch remain touchy about their national interests, but they have admitted an American to the board. One of their directors said, 'The great thing about the Dutch is that they put one thing above everything — making money. I wish I could say the same of the British.' "[7]

In Royal Dutch's old barony of Indonesia, it has been taught a severe lesson in neocolonial behavior. Indonesian oil is now a state monopoly. When offshore drilling concessions were offered in a rich new field off the Java coast with rumors of a "billion-dollar pool," American, Canadian, French, Italian and Japanese companies were allowed to bid. Even the Japanese. But not the old colonial masters. The onshore Sumatran fields are operated by Caltex (a company jointly organized by Standard of California and Texaco) where once red-faced

Dutchmen bellowed orders at the natives. The wonders of oil technology have been demonstrated for those same natives at the Sumatran village of Pakanbaru, where Caltex began operating late in the 1950's. It is now a city of eight hundred thousand. What was once the preserve of Royal Dutch is now the government-owned Pertamina monopoly headed by an Indonesian general. It is run in a hard-headed way the colonial Dutch might have admired. Foreign firms bidding for leases have to pay "signature bonuses" ranging from $100,-000 to $7 million; the concessionaire is allowed forty percent of production to cover the costs, but of the remaining sixty percent must hand over two-thirds to Pertamina. All imported movable equipment becomes Pertamina's property and is rented back to the importer.[8]

British Petroleum, the old Anglo-Persian, later Anglo-Iranian, has been slimmed down from its fat years in the Iranian monopoly and almost miraculously revitalized. Now coming up fast on Shell's heels, it is the fourth largest European industrial organization and growing fast with its stake in the Alaskan North Slope discoveries. BP is still half-owned by the British government, thanks to that mysterious deal engineered by Churchill more than a half-century ago, possibly with the help of the Secret Service. "BP have been less agile than Shell," according to Anthony Sampson, "in adapting themselves and they are now busily trying to acquire a more international image; they are sensitive, above all, about their name, and in their subsidiary companies they call themselves simply BP; they are run by a Frenchman in France, a German in Germany, a Belgian in Belgium, but they keep a discreet eye through a 'shareholders' representative.' " Just like Shell before World War I, BP is rejuvenating itself partly by an invasion of America.[9]

The survival of the old Burmah Oil Company, which antedates Shell and British Petroleum, would be an oddity in any but the oil business. It lost its long-worked wells in Burma, first to the Japanese army of occupation and then to Burmese independence. But Burmah hangs on, antique designation and all. It has oilfields in the Far East and Latin America, marketing agencies throughout the Orient, refineries in Britain, and other relatively minor enterprises. Burmah's ace in the hole, however, is its holdings in Shell and British Petroleum dating back to the beginnings of those companies. It owns three percent of Shell, almost twenty-five percent of British Petroleum, and two of its directors sit on BP's board.[10]

"Old" oil companies, it seems, rarely die and seldom fade away. Similarly oil fortunes seem to have a generative power of their own. There is the startling instance of Howard Hughes and his father. The senior Hughes was a Texas wildcatter who had a modest success in the post-Spindletop era before World War I. Then he invented a special "roller" bit for drills designed to chew through Texas rock and shale. It was a revolutionary device with 166 cutting edges which drillers found very useful whenever they struck hard rock strata. The elder Hughes founded the Sharp-Hughes Tool Company, a steady source of income to his son, who used it to build eccentric financial pyramids, plunging into motion picture production, aircraft manufacture, space and electronics technology, running a major airline in a highly individualistic fashion, and eventually buying up part of Las Vegas and much of the surrounding territory.

There is a fabulous quality about oil money which Midas would have envied. The chauffeur of the late Michael Benedum, for instance, often told his employer that his sole ambition was to be guaranteed a $50 weekly pension on retirement. Instead Benedum gave him bits and pieces of some of his deals, and the chauffeur wound up with a $17 million fortune. A New Orleans surgeon, Dr. Martin Miller, dabbled in oil investments as an avocation and ended up with an income estimated at between $7 and $8 million a year. The late Hugh R. Cullen, who single-handedly endowed the University of Houston, once gave the school a $2,225,000 bonus when its football team beat Baylor's. The Texas gold-dust twins, Clint

403

Murchison and Sid Richardson, raised $20 million between them to help Robert R. Young gain control of the New York Central Railroad in 1958. So casual were they in such ventures that Richardson, it turned out, thought he was contributing $5 million instead of $10 million to the project. He was not at all irked over the misunderstanding, but did call Murchison to ask, "Say, Clint, what was the name of that railroad?"

Given the public concept of the oil industry and its beneficiaries as standing under a perpetual shower of gold, it is a political and economic miracle that the industry has occupied so privileged a position for decades, particularly in regard to taxes. Certainly the industry in its worldwide operations has used more than its share of government services. The State Department has often seemed an overseas branch of the oil industry, and the Department of Defense, particularly the navy, has often been concerned in its problems. The Interior Department, as well as Commerce, must devote much of its budget to regulating and refereeing oil production and transportation. But it is the industry's relations with Treasury, its grip on Congress, which has excited so much controversy and speculation. The oil-depletion allowance, late in the 1960's when less privileged citizens and corporations were taxed and surcharged to the point of exhaustion, became a canker of injustice and inequity.

The tax position enjoyed by the industry has been estimated to have cost the Treasury approximately $2 billion dollars annually under the time-honored depletion allowance and other tax breaks. "This prodigious drain on the federal Treasury," notes Philip Stern, "is frequently defended as an indispensable incentive to the costly and high-risk exploration for oil and gas. Some find this argument less than convincing in view of the deliberate policy of restricting Texas oil wells to less than thirty percent of their production capacity, and, more especially, in view of the acknowledgment by a leading

404

depletion *proponent* that we already 'have enough oil' to meet our 'requirements for the next hundred years,' not to mention 'potential fuel in the known [oil] shale reserves [sufficient] to last this nation a thousand years.' "[11]

Down through the years politicians publicly decried the tax preferences given the oil industry, but somehow the votes could never be mustered in Congress to eliminate the sacred loophole. Opposition to the depletion allowance has cut across party lines and divided both conservatives and professed liberals. Often, ironically, the conservatives have registered their opposition, and voted accordingly, while liberal Democrats who proclaimed themselves the tribunes of the public interest, inheritors of the New Deal, have quietly worked to keep the loophole open for the oilmen. It undergoes contraction and expansion, depending on the political climate, sometimes a pinhole, sometimes a "truckhole" as former Senator Paul Douglas of Illinois characterized it, but always a firing slit through which the oil industry peers defensively, as though standing watch on the walls of the Alamo.

The history of the industry's preferential treatment is exactly as old as the federal income tax, which was enacted in 1913. Congress, in passing the new revenue laws, allowed certain "extractive industries" — oil and mining among them — to be allowed five percent of their gross income tax free, the principle being that they should be compensated for the decline in their capital assets as the fields they were working were gradually depleted by production.

Cynical godfather of that tax break was Senator Boies Penrose, the political boss of Pennsylvania and close collaborator of Andrew Mellon of Gulf Oil, Alcoa and the Mellon bank. He was a whale of a fellow, literally, a 350-pounder who rivaled his contemporary, Diamond Jim Brady, as a gourmand. Once, according to a Washington historian, he stifled his appetite on a dozen oysters, chicken gumbo, terrapin stew, two ducks, six kinds of vegetables, a quart of coffee, and a number of cognacs; another time he engorged nine cocktails, five highballs, twenty-six reed birds in a monstrous chafing dish, wild rice, and a bowl of gravy.

Senator Penrose inherited a fortune and did not have to accept bribes for himself, but acted as a conduit for slush funds which he passed on to his liege men. Thus he received and disposed of $25,000 from John Archbold of Standard Oil. He was no hypocrite but openly proclaimed that his primary responsibility was maintaining the protective tariff and otherwise guarding corporate interests.

Late in 1918 he succeeded in widening the pinhole depletion allowance by presenting the Senate with his Finance Committee's proposal that depletion for oil wells and mines be based "on market value instead of cost." As he explained it, under the new provision, when a ton of coal was sold part of the excess of the price over cost must be treated as "a repayment of what was invested." Only seven enlightened senators opposed him.

The oil companies, and other beneficiaries of Senator Penrose's gimmick, began profiting enormously from 1918 onward. In one year, 1919, Mellon's Gulf Oil had a depletion allowance 449 percent larger than its net income. This was revealed several years later, after Senator Penrose had selected President Harding's Secretary of the Treasury for him — Andrew Mellon. Naturally Mellon, holding the same post through the Coolidge and Hoover administrations, did nothing to halt the triumphal progress of the depletion allowance. It was greatly enlarged during the 1920's on the claim of industry spokesmen that the nation faced a serious oil shortage following the heavy exports of the World War I years.

The most serious opposition to that enlargement came from Senator James Couzens of Michigan, a multimillionaire who had been Henry Ford's original partner. Conducting an investigation into the profits being absorbed by the major oil companies, Senator Couzens studied 13,671 claimants of the depletion allowance and found that only thirty-five of them had discovered new oil-bearing properties, that only three and one-half percent was going to wildcatters. But big business was in the saddle and riding hard. In 1926, Congress raised the depletion allowance from five to twenty-seven and one-half percent, despite the protest of Senator William King of Utah that "I cannot understand this great solicitude for the Standard Oil Company, the Shell Oil Company, the Sinclair Company, and the other great organizations, whose annual profits are many hundreds of millions of dollars." During the Harding, Coolidge and Hoover administrations, Gulf Oil more than doubled its assets, and the growth of the other majors was on a comparable scale.[12]

Under the depletion clauses, which similarly favor all minerals (though uranium and platinum received only a twenty-three percent write-off), farm crops, coal, sand and gravel, oyster and clam shells, the oil industry received an immediate deduction for most capital assets in developing a project, plus continuing write-offs. Philip Stern provided a simple diagram of the way the depletion allowance worked, cutting through the dense verbiage of the tax laws which confound the non-expert: "Suppose you invest $100,000 in drilling an oil well. Roughly $25,000 of this pays for the derrick, the pipe in the ground and other immovable material and equipment. The other $75,000, called 'intangible drilling expense,' goes for wages and salaries, fuel, machine and tool rental. Now this $100,000 is . . . a 'capital' cost. In any other industry, the entire $100,000 would be deducted gradually, over the 'useful life' of twenty years." Oilmen, however, would be permitted a first-year deduction of $75,000, with the other $25,000 to be written off through the years as in any other industry. "As a sensible businessman," Mr. Stern continues, "you know that a dollar in hand is worth far more than the expectation of a dollar at some future date." Thus "you have a splendid opportunity to use Uncle Sam's money to parlay your first well into still others . . . If you're smart you'll follow in the footsteps of many an oil operator before you, and you'll take your tax-free $75,000 and 'drill it up' . . . drilling more wells and generating still more depletion-sheltered income . . ."[13]

For all the obvious inequalities sanctified by most of the presidential administrations and all the Congresses since 1926, the depletion allowance was something to be orated against but not acted upon until mid-1969 when a congressional committee bravely suggested reducing the percentage to twenty percent. In his 1950 message to Congress, President Harry Truman asserted that "no loop-hole in the tax law is so inequitable." The only echo that came from Congress was uttered by Truman's opposition leader in the Senate, the conservative Republican Senator Robert A. Taft, who declared that "The percentage depletion allowance is to a large extent a gift, a special privilege beyond what anyone else can get." No one, however, seemed able to summon up the outrage to denounce the loophole in even so stirring a manner as Senator Dirksen orating on the glories of the marigold. The oil industry had been treated reverentially ever since the rumpus created in the early 1930's by hot oil, the NRA and Harold Ickes. Certainly the Eisenhower Administration did not bestir itself on the issue; no one loved Ike more than the oilmen, and the feeling apparently was mutual.

The liberal instincts of John F. Kennedy, both as a Senator and as a presidential candidate, were aroused by the issue. As a Senator he favored an amendment to the tax laws which would have provided a sliding scale, and a juster rate of depletion write-offs. In 1960 he ran on a platform which pledged a Democratic administration to "close the loopholes in the tax laws by which certain privileged groups legally escape their fair share of taxation," adding more specifically that "among the more conspicuous loopholes are depletion allowances, which are inequitable." Somehow the New Frontier never got around to redeeming that promise. The Kennedy abstention may have been traceable to the weighty influence of the vice-president, Lyndon B. Johnson, and the Democratic leader of the House, Sam Rayburn; both Texans were regarded as walking delegates from the supranational state of Petrolia.

Campaign contributions from the oil companies indicated where their sympathies lay and their expectations resided. Officials of twenty-nine of the largest contributed, in sums of $500 or more, $344,997 to Republicans during the Eisenhower reelection campaign of 1956 and a mere $14,650 to the Democratic ticket headed by Governor Adlai Stevenson. That same year three of the great oil families — the Mellons of Gulf Oil, the Pews of Sun Oil, the Rockefellers of Standard Oil — gave almost a half-million to the Eisenhower-Nixon campaign effort. During the 1960 contest between John F. Kennedy and Richard M. Nixon, officers and directors of the American Petroleum Institute that year gave the Republican campaign a recorded total of $113,700 against $6,000 to the Democrats. Four years later, when Lyndon B. Johnson headed the ticket against Senator Barry Goldwater, the balance tipped toward a greater parity, $48,310 to the Republicans, $24,000 to the Democrats.

Generally, it appears, the Republicans are regarded as the more reliable protectors of the oil industry's privileged position. Yet the industry has always felt comfortable with certain representatives of the oil states — Johnson and Rayburn of Texas, Senator Russell Long of Louisiana, chairman of the Finance Committee and presently its most vigorous defender in the Congress — in the seats of power. During the 1960 national campaign, no knowledgeable Texan expected that, in the event of a Democratic victory, the oilmen's loophole would be closed or even tightened. As a writer for the Houston *Post* reassuringly advised its readership, "The Democrats have Lyndon Johnson. Furthermore there is Speaker Sam Rayburn. These two men have stood like Horatio at the bridge for years defending depletion against all comers. Almost any oilman knows that without Lyndon and Mr. Sam, there might be no depletion provision today."[14] And when Johnson succeeded Kennedy as President, of course, there came no trumpeting from the White House for reforming the tax laws even when the budget situation grew so critical in 1968 that the President had to plead for a ten percent surcharge on the federal income tax.

The ani-depletion pressure began to build almost the moment President Johnson left office. But why should Nixon move when Coolidge, Hoover, Roosevelt, Truman, Eisenhower, Kennedy and Johnson were content to stand pat, well knowing how generous oilmen were when campaign funds were solicited? Reportedly (and the reports were not denied) Nixon's campaign was heartily supported by the oilmen. While he was choosing the members of his Cabinet at the Hotel Pierre in New York, he was visited by Robert O. Anderson, Secretary of the Treasury under Eisenhower and now board chairman of Atlantic-Richfield, which as one of the developers of the North Slope (Alaska) field, with incoming proceeds from that strike expected to run into the billions, has a keen interest in any tax-law changes. The appointment of a Secretary of the Interior was also on Mr. Anderson's mind, and one Washington columnist reported that as a result of Anderson's counseling President-elect Nixon switched his choice from Governor Tim Babcock of Montana to Governor Walter Hickel of Alaska, formerly board chairman of Anchorage Natural Gas, who harbored no grudges against the oil industry.[15]

Later the *Washington Post* reported that during the presidential campaign Nixon "promised a group of Houston oilmen that he would protect the 27½ percent depletion allowance . . . In appreciation, the oil tycoons contributed heavily to the GOP cause."[16] Nixon did promise to eliminate the Johnson surcharge, and when he broke that pledge a few months after taking office he refused to couple a plea for the surcharge's extension with recommendations for any tax reforms despite plentiful evidence that the electorate was becoming restive over the inequal burdens borne by its various sectors. The groundswell of demands for tightening the oilmen's loophole rose to the level of the Capitol, the floor of

Congress, but without any encouragement from the White House.

In a thoroughgoing analysis of the industry's profits and the means by which they have steadily increased, Ronnie Dugger, one of those hard-nosed Texas journalists that state is now producing in greater quantity than oil millionaires (one possibly the result of the other), has shown that more and more oil billions have been placed beyond the reach of the Internal Revenue Service. "Early in World War II the estimate was $80 million — then $200 million. By 1950 it was half a billion; by 1960 $2 billion; by 1962, the Treasury estimates, the total depletion allowances for all minerals were close to $4.5 billion, $2.3 billion of that for oil and gas companies . . . It seems conservative to estimate that depletion will have placed $20 billion of pre-tax oil income beyond the reach of U.S. income taxation during the 1960's. This means that other taxpayers have forked over an extra $10 billion or so in one decade . . . If the government doesn't get the money it needs out of one hide, it has to take it out of another."[17]

Mr. Dugger came up with the kind of proposal that makes insomniacs out of otherwise well-adjusted tycoons and coupon-clippers. "The nation," he boldly suggests, "should be producing its own oil from its naval reserves or offshore. This would give us an independent standard by which to evaluate the performance of the subsidized oil industry. The nation, through a public oil company, should be planning to produce oil for the public treasury from the publicly owned oil-shale reserves in the West." (There are an estimated 2,000 billion barrels of shale oil, most of it in government reserves, which could be extracted at a viable price once American technology tackles the extractive problem. Those deposits constitute a sleeping bonanza of almost unimaginable proportions. Their value has been estimated as high as $8 trillion. Located in parts of Colorado, Utah and Wyoming, they are believed to contain ten times more than the world's total petroleum reserves. Early in the century prospectors began staking claims on those lands until Congress, in the 1920's, declared the whole area a U.S. naval reserve. Despite their enormous potential value, despite the fact that the shale reserves have been described as "the greatest package of potential energy on the face of the globe," and are rightly a heritage of the whole American people, legislation has been introduced in Congress to lease them at a pathetic $2.50 an acre to the oil companies.) "How else," Mr. Dugger continues, "can the growing concentration of the industry in a few companies be stopped? How else can the public equities in public property be preserved?" Questions like that — suggesting the virtual nationalization of oil resources not yet snatched up by corporate entities — will probably be asked in louder and more insistent tones during the coming decade.

Well-drilled battalions of oil industry publicists deploy their arguments for retention of the depletion allowance, of course, whenever it is threatened. The bulwark of the oilmen's defensive position is, simply, that their product is essential to the national well-being and that a protected domestic supply is of crucial importance to the military establishment. The United States, following the British lead, has always agreed that the industry is entitled to a large measure of protection.

The industry also maintains that it needs a tax break in order to support the high-risk enterprise of searching for oil. It argues that, though the depletion allowance benefits alike the major companies and the wildcatter with a broken-down rig, the real concern is for the small operator. In a hypothetical discourse between a taxpayer and an oilman, Philip Stern has the former protest, "If it's the small wildcatter who's taking the risks and needs the help, let's by all means give it to him. *But let's make sure the help really goes to him*, and not to a lot of people who take no risk and need no relief."[18]

A succinct argument on behalf of the allowance was entered by H. E. Tolle, a Humble economist, shortly before it appeared to be doomed to congressional reduction. He argues that "(1) production depletes a wasting asset that cannot be replaced by man; (2) the search for oil is characterized by great uncertainty and a long time lag between the outlay of funds and eventual recovery of capital; (3) oil production is subject to the principal of diminishing returns and increasing costs . . . Even after a field is discovered, much exploratory work involving unusual risks remains to be done."

Mr. Tolle adds: "Unlike his counterpart in manufacturing or farming, the petroleum producer cannot predict what it will cost him to replace his productive facilities. The more he finds, the harder it is to find more. The shallower, larger, and richer resources are always easier to locate and develop. Consequently, most of the 'easy' oil and gas fields have already been found. Drilling costs increase extremely rapidly with depth and inaccessibility of location.

"The petroleum industry, by its very nature, requires large sums of capital for its operation and expansion. However, the unique nature of the risks involved in petroleum production constitutes a serious handicap in attracting capital. Only through the existing petroleum tax treatment have investors been encouraged to make the tremendous capital outlays that petroleum production requires. Without the percentage depletion allowance the necessary inflow of capital might well cease, and petroleum exploration would suffer a severe setback."[19]

The industry insists that neither its tax shelter nor its ultimate profits are out of line with the rest of the economy. As of 1969 it maintained that "Oil's return on investment during the last ten years averaged 11.5 percent as compared with 12.1 percent for all other manufacturing companies. Reasonable profit levels are absolutely vital if the oil industry is to raise the tremendous capital needed to meet America's soaring energy needs." As far as taxes are concerned, it takes the position that "In recent years, the oil industry has paid a higher share of its gross revenue in direct taxes (federal, state and local) than the average for other industries. And this doesn't include taxes collected from consumers, which add up to a far bigger dollar amount than is generated by any other industry."[20]

With some justification, it argues that "horrible examples" cited from studies of Internal Revenue files are not at all typical. One famous citation was that of a Houston oilman whose return was analyzed by the Treasury Department; his name, as required by law, was withheld. The Houston man had an income of $2,035,000 in one year but paid not a cent in federal income tax because of legitimate deductions. In three following years his income totaled $1,703,000, $1,443,000 and $2,945,000, none of which was subject to federal taxation. Over a ten-year period he paid a total of less than $44,000 on income of $10,583,000; a rate of 0.4 percent. Another Treasury study centered on an oilman identified only as 'Individual D,' who in 1960 reported an income over $26,000,000 and not only paid no income tax but listed a loss of $846,330. Much of his year's income came from the sale of an oil reserve, on which he received a down payment of $10,872,449, listed as a long-term capital gain. Other write-offs included the expense of drilling a large number of dry holes and "farming losses" of $276,368.[21]

The rather touching figure of the lone, wandering, often penniless wildcatter is pointed out by the industry as a worthy beneficiary of tax shelter. The majors by themselves produce only about half of the oil extracted in the United States, the rest coming from nine thousand independents. Some of the latter, of course, are lordly figures in their own right: H. L. Hunt with his billion-plus, John Mecom, James Ambercrombie, and others in the multimillion class.

The wildcatters, the real risk-takers, who usually are bought out by the majors immediately after making a sizable find, are indeed in a precarious situation. Their lot has been increasingly difficult. Oil is rarely found near the surface now, and their crews have to drill three times as deep as formerly. In addition, the costs of drilling a well in Texas, still the wildcatter's favorite territory, have increased by twenty-eight percent since 1959. The "wellhead" price of oil meanwhile has risen only a little. Because of this squeeze between costs and profits (if any), the number of wildcat wells had declined from 16,200 in 1956 to 8,900 in 1968, which partly accounts for the fact that American domestic production is estimated to be rising at the relatively low rate of 1.8 percent.[22] It has also become harder for the wildcatter to obtain profitable leases. The landowners once were satisfied with a one-eighth share of the profits, now they demand a larger percentage plus bonuses. Finding backers for their enterprises is made more difficult by the added expense of making seismic surveys, which investors now insist upon before they will gamble on a prospective new field. One leading wildcatter's fortunes may serve as an example. Carl W. Van Wormer of Houston, formerly worth $300,000 and headquartered in a suite of four offices, now operates out of a cubbyhole and contemplates his sorry recent record of twenty consecutive dry holes.

The decline of the wildcatter may also be studied in Kilgore, Texas, once one of the three leading boomtowns of the East Texas field. Kilgore, as one of the wildcatting centers, has gone rapidly downhill. The wildcatters stare down on the streets from their dusty offices. Keegan Carter, a veteran operator, grumbles that it has been three years since he drilled a producing well. Risk money, he says, is almost impossible to obtain. Another wildcatter, Jim Clark, agrees, explaining, "People who don't understand the business become angry after a series of dry holes. An oilman will shrug it off if he can, put an X in his book, and go to the next one." One gets the impression that the pine scrub is growing daily closer to the oil boomtown. It all seems a million miles away from the skyscraper offices of the big oil companies, which point to the

415

Carters and Clarks and Van Wormers as one of the reasons the whole industry must be protected from the very real specter of "depletion."

While the oil-depletion allowance was being battled out in Congress, and in the byways and water holes where lobbyists and their prey gather, the matter of import quotas was also being considered in a quiet hearing room presided over by Senator Philip Hart of Michigan. That summer and fall of 1969 was a bad one, in the legislative and public relations sense, for the oil industry. The exhaustive hearings before the antitrust and monopoly subcommittee should have produced some sensational television news segments and newspaper headlines: Americans were paying between $5 and $7 billion a year in excess costs for fuel oil and gasoline because of the protectionist quotas which keep cheaper foreign crude off the market; in the past ten years Americans had been tapped for at least $50 billion. This would represent the cost of a full antiballistic-missile system, which was then agitating the public. Yet those hearings went unreported by the usually vigilant *New York Times*, were buried by the rest of the daily press and were ignored by television, perhaps because of journalism's notoriously brief attention span.

The whole record of those hearings, however, constituted a tale that would have inflamed the temper of the bulk of the nation's homeowners. In essence, the summer-long proceedings before the mild-mannered but staunchly liberal Senator Hart developed the picture of a protectionist policy which enriched the oil companies at the expense of the consumer. The oil-import controls were instituted in 1959 by the outgoing Eisenhower Administration and limited imports to 12.2 percent of domestic production; supposedly this was in the interests of national security. In case the supply of foreign crude was suddenly cut off, it was theorized, there would always be enough U.S. production, sheltered by import controls, to satisfy the nation's requirements. Since foreign-produced crude sells at about $2 a barrel against $3-plus a barrel for the American produced, the government has supplied a "captive market" for domestic producers. The import controls are administered by the Interior Department, which generally acts as the oil industry's defender, a historic role dating back to the scandals of the Harding Administration.

Senator Hart's subcommittee exhaustively studied the consequences of the quota system, particularly as they affected New England, the Southeast and Great Lakes regions, Hawaii and the petrochemical industry. Refineries are mostly located, naturally, in the oil-producing states. There the quotas are generous. Elsewhere they are niggardly. New England, for instance, has no oil refinery and therefore no petrochemical industry. Yet 8 million of its 10 million people use a light fuel oil for heating, most of it supplied by thirty-eight hundred independent dealers, many of whom are being bought out by the major oil companies.

The situation of New England consumers, compared with that of Canadians, is almost ludicrously unbalanced. There is no quota system in the provinces, and there fuel oil is 3 cents a gallon cheaper. If the quota were abolished, and oil from Venezuela and Libya or other parts of the Middle East were processed in New England, it would save the region's users $140 million a year. If, that is, prices were reduced. Often enough, they are not, certainly not in proportion to the profits taken by oil-importers and processors. Even if proposed refining facilities were installed at Machiasport, Maine, and a free port established or the quota system abolished, there is no guarantee the savings inevitable from refining Caribbean or Middle Eastern crude would be passed along to the consumer. Under the quota system, in fact, foreign crude has been brought to Portland, Maine, and piped 230 miles to Montreal. Portland has the mess, the occasional pollution resulting from transfer from tanker to pipeline head, while Canadians benefit from the cheaper fuel oil. Maine users were forced to pay, instead, for more expensive oil shipped by tanker from the Gulf Coast while the pipeline to Canada gurgled taunt-ingly, and worse yet on at least two occasions fuel-oil supplies in New England have given out during hard winters.

Hawaiians may not suffer the same kind of distress in their balmier climate, but they are part of Standard Oil of Cali-fornia's fiefdom. As it was testified before Senator Hart's sub-committee, Standard of California operates the only refinery in the islands. All seven of the oil companies with retail dis-tribution in Hawaii must buy their gasoline from that refinery. Since they belong to the brotherhood of the major producers — Texaco, Shell, Union and others — they reciprocate in other parts of the world, where they have oil and California Standard doesn't.

Thus Hawaiians are forced to use gasoline refined from crude produced in Saudi Arabia, Iran and Indonesia, where Standard of California has a share of the production. Iranian and Indonesian oil is the cheapest in the world, and despite shipping costs oil refined in Honolulu should be only two-thirds as expensive as crude refined in California, yet Hawaiian con-sumers pay 3.5 cents more per gallon than those in Los An-geles. The surplus produced by California Standard's Honolulu refinery is shipped back to the West Coast and even with the expense of sending it by tanker it sells for about 3 cents per gallon less in Seattle than in Honolulu.

Obviously the construction of a second refinery in Hawaii would reduce costs to the consumer and prove that California Standard was not operating as a monopoly in the islands. True competition — as demonstrated in the price warring of Shell and Standard Oil before World War I, to cite the classic prec-edent — is not in the best interests of the oil industry, which are not to be confused with those of the public at large. What Hawaii needed, and the delicately balanced noncompetitive system established by the majors would abhor, was a relaxa-tion of the quota system. That was sought by William Sum-mers Johnson, the Honolulu finance director, in testifying before the Hart subcommittee. "The main criticism of the oil import quota system, as it applies to Hawaii," he told the subcommittee, "is not that it keeps foreign oil and oil products out of the state. On the contrary, substantially all of the oil products used in the state are from foreign sources anyway. The fault to be found with the oil import quota program in Hawaii is that it only has the effect of imposing arbitrarily high prices for foreign oil. The program has the practical effect of restricting the business of importing foreign oil — and most particularly the products of foreign oil — to a relatively few favored companies."

The hearings also developed the unusual situation of one corporate giant criticizing another *in public*. Usually such skirmishes are conducted in boardrooms and around private conference tables. Yet a representative of nine of the most powerful petrochemical companies appeared before Senator Hart to complain of oil industry practices. He was Kenneth Hannan, vice-chairman of Union Carbide, representing his own company as well as Dow, DuPont, Kodak, Monsanto, Olin Mathiesen, Celanese, National Distillers, and Publicker Industries. Hannan pictured them all as an "unintended victim" of the oil-import quotas. As one commentator noted, "For DuPont to criticize Standard Oil is as unthinkable as for General Motors to bitch openly about the prices of U.S. Steel. But recently both have. In the case of the chemical companies it has finally dawned on them that the oil industry has uniquely used the government. While other industries hoped the government would simply stop bothering them, oil lobbied for itself a gold mine in oil-depletion allowances and oil-import quotas."

A certain despair therefore was indicated in the chemical companies' public opposition to oil quotas. The reason for that corporate anguish was revealed in the testimony before the senatorial inquiry. Petrochemical manufacturers depend upon natural gas and petroleum for their raw materials in making everything from vitamin pills to synthetic-fibered raincoats. They are victimized, like the homeowner, by the restrictions on foreign oil. With the import quotas as their umbrella, the oil companies have been entering the petrochemical field on advantageous terms. They are enabled to compete by the lower costs of their raw materials, and DuPont, for instance, has nervously taken note of the fact that Standard Oil of New Jersey already has a petrochemical division one-third the size of its own.[23]

And the acquisition of raw material is where the crunch comes for the petrochemicals. Natural gas is priced low enough for them to compete with foreign firms, but the industry is growing much faster than the domestic production of that element, forcing the chemical industries to rely more on oil itself. By 1975, under present conditions, they claim that their prices will no longer be on a par with those of their foreign competitors. If the quota system was eliminated, if refinery complexes were built elsewhere than the Gulf Coast (Texas and Louisiana), by processing the cheaper crude from South America, the Middle and Far East, the petrochemical companies could continue to prosper.

If not, they threaten to migrate, move their plants overseas, and manufacture their synthetics from an unrestricted supply of foreign crude.

"We could turn our backs on the domestic situation," Kenneth Hannan told the committee in his role as industry spokesman, "and move ahead with plans for overseas plants — built with foreign equipment, manned by foreign employees, and supplied with foreign oil free of import restrictions — and plan to supply the U.S. market with their output." His emphasis on "foreign" suggested that congressmen might be feeling political heat if a sizable industry were forced to migrate. "I don't believe," he added, "the industry wants to do that. Frankly, I do not believe that would be in the national interest, and it is hard to see why our government would wish to continue a policy that would encourage this result."[24]

The paradox of that tough talk, which did not escape the subcommittee because it was remarked upon by a witness hostile to both corporate giants, was that the petrochemical companies demand a similar protectionist policy for their own products against foreign synthetics. It was obvious that the only party to the hearings with fairly clean hands was the inarticulate mass of American consumers.

18.

The North Slope Discoveries

A quick glance at an oilman's map of the world late in the 1960's would have convinced the casual observer that the United States was certain to lose its position in the vanguard of oil-producers. The map, showing both major established fields and major new explorations, indicated that in all of the United States, except Alaska, there was no large new development. Along the west coast of Africa, along the Persian Gulf, in Australia, in Indonesia, in the western Siberia region of the Soviet Union there were clusters of major exploratory efforts. Statistically, too, the United States has lagged behind the Middle East, producing 9 million-plus barrels a day to the Middle East's 12 million-plus. The Oklahoma and Kansas fields are on the downgrade, and Louisiana, Texas and California will pass their peak production late in the 1970's. It was apparent that the old union of forty-eight states would be thirsting for heavier and heavier imports in the coming decades, with the gap between domestic production and consumption widening every year — except for the new state of Alaska.

What an exception. The giantism, the explosive wealth and

corporate energy of the oil industry, has been astounding the world for more than a century, but the discoveries made on the North Slope of Alaska, around Prudhoe Bay, have summoned up a new array of superlatives. Ironically, the huge Alaskan discoveries came just when the industry, adjusting its sackcloth, was pulling a poor mouth and pleading it needed depletion allowances and import quotas to insure its survival in the world market.* Maintaining that pauperish posture became difficult, however, as even the most conservative industry spokesmen estimated the Alaska field would produce from 5 to 10 billion barrels; others (such as Walter Levy, an international oil consultant) more objectively came up with a 20-billion estimate, and Secretary of the Interior Walter Hickel raised the ante to 100 billion barrels. By comparison, the East Texas field, previously the biggest U.S. strike, has produced 5 billion barrels. The North Slope discoveries, an Anglo-American enterprise, undoubtedly will double American reserves and rank us with Kuwait (70 billion barrels) as the greatest source of oil.

The North Slope oil rush began when a joint venture of Atlantic-Richfield and Humble paid off in the spring of 1968 and a well named Prudhoe Bay State No. 1, drilled ninety-five hundred feet through the permafrost, started producing. Other companies had also started operations in the district, having acquired leases at an auction conducted by the state of Alaska three years before. Soon other wells were brought in. British Petroleum, which had made its first strike in the hot sands of Iran, now found vast new resources in the frozen tundra of the Far North; its leases are believed to contain at least 5 billion barrels.

With almost incredible speed, cooperating whenever corporate wisdom dictated, the oil companies proceeded to de-

---

* The oil industry, of course, has maintained that the North Slope find would have been impossible without the exploration money set aside through the depletion allowance. It also contends that a sharp reduction of that allowance would preclude any more such costly explorations.

423

velop the North Slope field. An immense airlift brought supplies to the bleak, treeless, icebound coast between the Arctic Ocean and jagged Brooks Range to the south. A 429-mile "winter road" from Fairbanks was rushed to completion over the tundra. The power of modern technology to operate in any environment, the driving force of industrial enterprise, the ability of the major oil companies to mobilize the men and equipment required for swift exploitation were never more strikingly illustrated. It was an industrial epic to rival the military-scientific accomplishment, also an Anglo-American enterprise, which resulted in the manufacture of the atomic bomb.

Just as the first wells on the North Slope began producing, early in the fall of 1969, Alaska conducted an auction of the land surrounding the discovery wells which brought in just under a billion dollars (exactly $900,220,590) during a day of frantic bidding in an Anchorage auditorium. It was a game for billionaires. It also demonstrated the oil industry's curious habit of consolidating interests, which elsewhere may be in vigorous competition, to attain a certain goal, and the fact that only giant corporations may now play for high stakes (despite the industry's professedly tender regard for wildcatters and other independents). The consortium is simply a fact of corporate life; it enables the giants to become more gigantic. Thus the first tract offered — land which several years before had gone begging at $15 an acre — was sold to a combination of Gulf Oil and British Petroleum for $15,528,960: a frozen nugget of land on the Colville River delta. The next two tracts, at $20.7 million and $31 million, went to the same consortium. So did the next three, for a total of $97 million, while other bidders muttered resentfully.

The bidding rose even higher when tracts lying southwest of Prudhoe Bay, closest to the discovery wells, were offered to the assemblage of oil company executives, some of whom carried their bids in envelopes wrapped in aluminum foil to guard against X-ray camera eyes. Tract 37 was sold to a combination of California Standard, Mobil Oil, and Phillips Petroleum for $41.2 million. Another consortium, including the surprise appearance of H. L. Hunt and J. Paul Getty, with Amerada Hess and Louisiana Land, walked off with Tract 56 after depositing $43.6 million with the state's auctioneer. For Tract 57, the Gulf–British Petroleum group bid $47.1 million, was topped by an offer of $72.1 million from the California Standard–Mobil-Phillips combination, and listened in astonishment to the successful bid of a Getty–Amerada Hess combine of $72.3 million, the highest of the auction. The state of Alaska had profited from an event that broke all records for oil-lease auctions, but the Eskimos and Indians who claimed that land as a birthright were left out, as usual, in the cold. While they pondered their situation in shacks which constitute an Arctic Appalachia, the victorious oilmen celebrated at Anchorage's Petroleum Club, where the glass breakage topped any New Year's Eve in living memory.[1]

The problem then confronting the consortiums which had taken over the North Slope was how to get the billions of gallons of crude to the refineries in the most economical manner. The main question: tanker or pipeline or both?

While they worked on that problem, British Petroleum, one of the big winners, dealt with disposing of an embarrassment of riches. It would have an enormous input of crude oil without a market large enough to absorb it. Earlier in the year BP had acquired Sinclair Oil and its network of eastern filling stations. To expand that market, it was only logical to acquire a similar system of distribution nearby. Standard Oil of Ohio seemed the best bet for a merger since it has thirty-five hundred filling stations in the Midwest, and by a combination of Sinclair's and Ohio Standard's outlets BP could compete with such fellow titans as Gulf, Jersey Standard, Mobil and Texaco for a large share of the American market. Before World War I, Shell had similarly invaded the United States with the aid of American financing; now BP would be enabled to do the same, by merger, with oil extracted from U.S. territory. Standard Oil of Ohio was more than willing to merge because it has a redoubtable refining and marketing organization but no longer has access to large supplies of crude oil. Under that arrangement Ohio Standard would market BP's crude, with BP eventually obtaining a fifty-four percent interest in the company for about $1 billion. But that cozy arrangement still had to be approved by the U.S. Attorney General, whose antitrust division took a jaundiced view of the fact that a monopolistic situation would be created.

Understandably the British were bemused by the convolutions of American antitrust laws. "The tragedy is that antitrust legislation was devised to encourage competition in the United States," as one British financial journal commented. "Yet the manner in which it is being implemented is having the effect of deterring European countries from entering the U.S. and so bringing with them a completely fresh wind of change."[2]

Professor Edith Penrose, a leading British expert on the international oil industry, also entered a brief for British Petroleum. As she analyzed the situation for a British periodical: "The problems and capital cost of producing and transporting Alaskan oil are formidable; but for a company without an established position in the United States market, the profitability of its entire enterprise depends in the last analysis on the conditions under which it will be able to enter the market and sell its oil. If the company is forced to sell all or most of it as crude oil, the operation will in general be less profitable than it would be if the company could itself refine and sell most of the oil in the form of oil products. For a variety of reasons, including monopolistic elements in the market, price competition is very much less prevalent in product markets than in crude oil markets. Moreover, a company with large amounts of crude oil to sell in the U.S. market might find itself faced with only a few large buyers taking advantage of their position to force down prices. On the other hand, to

426

build refining facilities and a distribution network from scratch is very expensive indeed and takes a long time."

Professor Penrose affirmed that she did not believe the American government was "prejudiced" against a British invasion; its actions were dictated by an antitrust policy "very much stricter" than in most other countries. Yet, she pointed out, "To most people it seemed absurd that the entry of BP into the U.S. market in this way would be likely to increase monopoly there, and in any case it is obvious that many U.S. firms abroad have obtained much stronger monopolistic positions in other people's markets by similar acquisitions.

"Consequently, the action of the Department of Justice raised serious suspicions that the United States was discriminating against BP because it is foreign, and perhaps also because the British government owns nearly half of it. Certainly there were voices raised in the United States, particularly in Congress, which reinforced these suspicions, and the British Foreign Secretary saw fit to underline officially the British government's interest in BP's success."[3]

What the British apparently did not care to take into account was that BP enormously increased its leasehold on the North Slope through financial assistance from its consortium partner Gulf Oil, and that it was after all American crude oil that enabled BP to mount the invasion of the American market. In any case, BP and its majority shareholder, the British government, could congratulate themselves on the fact that BP, via North Slope, moved up to third place among the world's crude-oil producers.

Getting the oil out of northern Alaska, under conditions never before confronted, was the immense problem which the stakeholders tackled immediately after the who-gets-what question of leases was settled in the usual manner. Corporate like military luck favors the bigger battalions and heavier artillery. Jersey Standard and its subsidiaries, Gulf, British Petroleum, Getty, and Hunt all raked in the gold chips, but the

427

chips couldn't be cashed in until an economical way of transporting North Slope crude was found.

The economics of transporting Alaskan oil to the "lower forty-eight" were cost analyzed by the oil expert for a Boston brokerage firm after he made an inspection tour of the North Slope "moose pasture" and its possible supply routes. He came up with the conclusion that the oil companies involved would rake in healthy profits even after the expense of transportation was deducted. Out of the $3 a barrel price that producers are expected to command, even with the influx from Alaska, would come 35 cents per barrel for tanker charges, another 15 cents for pipeline charges to the port, 30 cents for development, 20 cents for royalties and direct taxes. The total was $1 a barrel, leaving the producer with $2 a barrel. If North Slope produces 50 billion barrels, the oil companies will share take-home pay of $100 billion.

The happy conclusion of the brokerage's oil expert was that "any mutual fund manager who doesn't have Atlantic-Richfield, Standard of Ohio or British Petroleum in his portfolio will look just as silly in five years as they have in the past without IBM and Xerox."[4]

With profits like that dancing on the horizon like northern lights, the S.S. *Manhattan*, a huge tanker equipped with an ice-breaking bow, the largest commercial ship ever built in the United States, was sent on what newspapers persistently termed an "epic" voyage around the top of the continent through the Northwest Passage in the early fall of 1969. Epic it would have been in the sailing-ship days, but not really with a 1,005-foot ship with reinforced bows, powered by 43,000-horsepower engines, with planes constantly overhead and Canadian icebreakers to help out whenever the *Manhattan* got stuck in ice-jammed straits. Epic, though, in the $40 million cost of pioneering a tanker route through the Northwest Passage.

The Northwest Passage venture undertaken by Humble Oil was a luxury cruise, three hearty meals with fresh fruit daily,

428

compared with the ordeals of earlier voyagers hoping to find a short trade route to China over the top of the world. Nothing like Sir John Franklin and his crew, in 1845, driven to cannibalism when they were stranded in polar ice; Henry Hudson set adrift after his crew discovered that he had been pilfering from the ship's stores; or Robert McClure traversing the final two hundred miles of the passage in a dogsled in 1854. The *Manhattan*'s mission was more humdrum, to collect scientific data on the feasibility of the route and determine whether it would be easier and cheaper to bring the oil out by tanker to a deep-water port in Maine, which would be closer to the North Slope than Seattle. The question wasn't whether a super-tanker suitably fitted and equipped with the most powerful engines could negotiate the passage, but whether such a vessel could operate on that run through most of the year without requiring the assistance of a fleet of ice-breakers.

The *Manhattan* had all the help that could be supplied, including a corps of specialists, a survey plane which scouted ahead and dropped photographs of the ice hummocks in its path, and the constant services of the Canadian icebreaker *John A. MacDonald*. Captain Roger A. Steward charted the toughest possible course for the *Manhattan*. Whenever the rock-hard ice, some of it in chunks the size of a bus, closed in around the *Manhattan*, the Canadian icebreaker came steaming up to clear a passage. The tanker charged into the hitherto impenetrable McClure Strait guarding the comparatively ice-free Beaufort Strait. It ran into a series of ridges of thickly compressed ice, and once again the signal went out to the *John A. MacDonald*, "Would you please come along our flanks and nibble some ice?" The passage through McClure Strait finally had to be abandoned in favor of the less difficult Prince of Wales Strait; once through that last stretch of pack ice there were only five hundred miles of open water to the oil rigs of Prudhoe Bay.

Evidently the results of that first voyage were inconclusive, and further test runs were scheduled in hope of soon determining whether tankers could make it the year around under their own power. There was another unanswered question: whether tankers could dock off Prudhoe Bay. The water is very shallow off the Alaska coast, and oil from the North Slope field would apparently have to be piped at least ten miles over the continental shelf to shipboard. One imaginative solution would be to build underwater storage and piping facilities manned by crews living and working beneath the surface of the Arctic Ocean.

The *Manhattan* voyage could not supply the definitive answer to what has been called the greatest technological challenge ever faced by the oil industry or any other private enterprise. Moving North Slope oil to market by tanker would cost an estimated $2 billion to $3 billion. The alternative, a pipeline from Prudhoe Bay to the "lower forty-eight," would run an estimated $3 billion to $6 billion, but once built it would be less subject to the hazards of wind, weather and ice than the sea route.

A partial pipeline is already under construction. Called the Trans-Alaska Pipeline System (TAPS), it will cost an estimated $1 billion, using 48-inch pipe and running from Prudhoe Bay eight hundred miles south to the warm-water port of Valdez. The huge pipeline, taking two years to build, will be in two sections, one between Valdez and the Yukon River, a distance of 430 miles, and the northern part from the Yukon to Prudhoe Bay. Pushing that line over permafrost and tundra will present problems never before encountered, particularly north of the Yukon.*

Both building and maintaining a pipeline in the intense cold over terrain that tends to buckle and heave will present serious difficulties, according to Richard C. Dulaney, chairman of the management committee of TAPS. "People tend to

---

* The Russians have recently completed an eight-inch pipeline running one thousand miles into Siberia, but it never goes above the Arctic Circle.

emphasize the difficulties a little too much, however," he said. "The technology is available for construction. Steel capable of resisting the climate is available. The problem is one of scale because an oil line forty-eight inches in diameter has never been built before . . . What must be avoided at all costs are the permafrost areas where the water content is high. In summer it could melt and cause a quagmire and in winter it could collect in one spot and freeze, causing upheaval that might rupture the pipe." To avoid permafrost areas with heavy moisture, the pipeline will cross the Brooks Range at Dietrich Schandler Pass at an elevation of four thousand feet. TAPS will cross the Yukon at a place where it can be built under the riverbed. Part of the line will be constructed on wooden A-frame pilings above the ground, but much of it will be buried, TAPS officials say, to avoid interfering with the migratory habits of the caribou and other Arctic animals.[5]

Optimism about the pipeline was considerably dampened in the summer of 1970 when legal and legislative obstacles cropped up. Conservation groups had obtained a temporary injunction blocking construction of the pipeline. Even if that roadblock were removed, there was still a dispute with the Alaska state legislature to be resolved. The legislature had voted to finance a 370-mile highway to the North Slope. The legislation, however, contained what the oil companies considered a flaw fatal to their interests. There was no guarantee that the road would parallel the proposed pipeline and be useful in hauling the pipe and heavy equipment. Thanks, but no thanks, the oil companies replied to the legislature's proposed financing. Thus there was deep gloom over the tundra as hundreds of construction workers, $40 million worth of heavy equipment, and two hundred miles of pipeline stood idle while attempts were being made to resolve the controversy.

Even when all the legal and legislative obstacles are overcome, the TAPS operation faces tremendous challenges in attempting to pump viscous crude, deep in the frozen earth in places, over mountains, below Arctic rivers, and through swamps. And even with that partial pipeline system the crude would have to be transported from Valdez by tanker to the western states. Yet the less expensive alternative is even more awesome, sending ships over the top of the world through ice packs sometimes twenty feet thick in Arctic gales and partly in the three-month-long Arctic night. A choice between tankers and a full pipeline system will obviously have to be made unanimously by all participants in the North Slope field. Using both would simply be too expensive. And the decision will have to be made in the next year or two, before the flow from North Slope reaches floodtide.

But there are other problems connected with the venture which are of wider concern. Ecologists and biologists, Eskimo and other Indian natives living in a threatened environment are also vitally interested. To conservationists there were causes for alarm, for one thing, because an oil spillage from a tanker going through the Northwest Passage would take decades, possibly centuries, to dissipate in the low temperature of the Arctic waters.

Such professionals have pointed out that the Arctic Ocean, a vast bowl of 2.5 million square nautical miles, greatly expanded during the winter months when it sucks in warmer water from the surrounding seas, influences the climate and atmosphere of other parts of the world. Regarding that all-important and easily disturbed bowl of the Arctic, a science writer recently has warned: "Considering their importance as a remote control on civilization, the processes that go on in this strange receptacle of life are far too little known to science. Except for the superficial pokings of explorers and adventurers, almost no attention has been paid to the Arctic by comparison, say, to the moon . . . The chasm of remaining ignorance is frightening, for a temperature rise of only a few degrees would melt all the polar ice within a decade or less, with certainly distressing and perhaps disastrous consequences for modern man.

"One way to raise the temperature is to darken the surface of the ice and so capture solar energy that is now reflected back to the sky. The most effective darkener would be a substance that would float on water and consequently would spread quickly and widely." Oil, in other words. "The delicate flowering of the polar summer bespeaks the eternally fragile state of Arctic life, which cannot find deep rooting anywhere. Mutilation tends to be permanent, for the workings of biology go slowly in the cold. Ever since men invaded the North with machines, the dimensions of violence done to the environment have been growing.

"The number of scars has multiplied in the past few years, all the way from the northern slope of Alaska through the site of the magnetic pole and well beyond that toward the geographic pole. Yet, only in the past few months have thoughtful people become worried enough to consider means of forestalling potential tragedy on a grand scale."[6]

To investigate ways to head off such consequences, greatly increased by the exploitation of the North Slope, the Arctic Institute of North America was engaged by the Interior Department. It was assigned the problem of deciding how oil could be extracted from the Alaskan tundra and marketed without destroying the delicately balanced ecology of the Arctic. At one session of polar scholars, Secretary of the Interior Walter Hickel, not hitherto renowned as an apostle of conservation, startled everyone by urging the necessity of protecting that region from the consequences of exploitation before it was too late. "The North Country," he said, "is beginning to undergo the most rapid and profound changes ever seen in any wilderness region. We must find new ways to meet this unprecedented challenge. We need new ideas, new techniques, perhaps even new institutions." He continued by emphasizing that the Alaska natives must be "given every opportunity to take part in decisions involving the Arctic" and that "all developmental problems be considered in terms of their effects on peoples." Stewart Udall, his predecessor, had stopped construction of the pipeline, however, until native land claims could be settled, and he prohibited any further leasing of federal lands. That "freeze" order has been lifted to allow construction while the claims are being adjudicated.

Once TAPS is installed, of course, it will be too late to do anything about it. And construction proceeds while such questions as those raised by the science writer quoted above go unanswered. "No pipeline of this size has ever been laid through permafrost. Consequently, no one knows what damage to expect from the heat of the oil itself, let alone the heat generated by pumps that will be required at intervals to drive the oil along. Two ranges of the Rocky Mountains must be crossed. What mutilation of natural beauty — one of Alaska's strongest allures — will be wrought? Will the wildlife be restored? Will the countryside be polluted by oil leaks?"

Such considerations do not seem to be occupying the oil companies as much as the technical problems of extracting and transporting the source of their new wealth under conditions that admittedly absorb their time and energy and ingenuity. An aroused public might, however, persuade them to bend their efforts also in the direction of preserving the environment for their own sakes as well as ours. A melting icecap should distress them as much as the rest of us. So far the companies have given little indication of being distracted from their pursuit of new billions. Three liberal Democratic senators, Edmund S. Muskie (Maine), Thomas J. McIntyre (New Hampshire) and William Proxmire (Wisconsin), have jointly charged the companies with withholding all information on the size of the estimated Alaskan reserves, coolly turning aside all requests through their National Petroleum Council.[7] That such *hubris* might cost them dearly in the end, through legislative counteraction, was indicated in the senators' implied threat they demand revocation of import quotas in the wake of the expected flood of oil from Alaska.

434

19.

Oil in Troubled Waters

The encroachments of the oil industry on the lives of all of us, from participation in wars partly traceable to international oil rivalry to breathing the smog of our cities, often seem inexorable, inevitable, irresistible, as though ordained by forces which can't be controlled by any earthly power. In the big picture, as viewed on their maps and charts by executives and boards of directors, the invasion of the Maine coast by the oil industry would seem a small matter. They're bringing "industrial development" to an undeveloped section, promising cheaper fuel oil, providing jobs, opening up opportunities, aren't they? The fact that they were planning to establish themselves (as on Whiddy Island in Ireland's Bantry Bay) on a lovely unspoiled stretch of coast, one of the few left on the whole American littoral, and possibly would despoil it in the process, is only something for the sentimentalists and softheaded nature-lovers to blubber about.

The sense of doom along the Maine coast, the feeling that no one can deny the oil industry anything it demands, was conveyed in a weekly newspaper published in the region with an editorial that read in part: "Oil is coming to the Coast of

435

Maine. It is coming whether the State is or is not ready with laws and methods to meet the pollution hazard . . . The prospect that arises in the mind is like a bad dream — that of a 2,500 mile coast, once the scene of a flourishing fishing industry and the delight of millions of residents and summer visitors, dotted with oil offloading depots and refineries coated with oil scum and debris, reeking with the odors of the petrochemical industry. It is a gloomy prospect even if the descendants who live in this miserable environment will be fully employed, well-paid and highly educated with the profits that are returned to the community . . ."[1]

Within the space of the year 1969 the state of Maine was confronted by plans for large-scale exploitation by the oil industry. A legally controversial offshore drilling concession was granted; a Denver firm, King Resources Company, announced plans for building an offshore oil dock capable of unloading the new super-tankers in Casco Bay, for generations the haunt of sailing enthusiasts and other summer vacationers; and Occidental Oil proposed to build a $145 million refinery, storage complex, and deep-water port at Machiasport further up the coast near the Bay of Fundy. In one bound, it seemed, the oil industry would gobble up the whole rugged coast; nightmarish visions arose of another *Torrey Canyon* disaster, of another Santa Barbara incident, of polluted coastal waters and the crisp Maine air sulfurized, of poisoned fish and dead seabirds and dying vegetation along the intertidal flats.

There seemed to be little that conservationists and many other Maine citizens, both summer residents and year-around people, could do but protest, investigate, and hope that effective laws could be found to protect them from the prospective despoliation, the conversion of Maine, one of the few remaining "clean" states, into another sumplike New Jersey.

For confirmation of their fears that Casco Bay, on which Portland is located, would be ruined by the King Resources venture, they had only to look down the coast at the wasteland created by the Bayonne to Trenton, New Jersey, complex and superimpose the plans for a steel pier stretching the distance of five football fields into the waters of Hussey Sound and for a huge tank farm on coastal Maine's Long Island, "as visually appropriate," it was said, "as an oil derrick in the reflecting pool near the Washington Monument in the nation's capital." The latter project would call for the reactivation and expansion of the U.S. navy tank farm built during World War II to refuel the North Atlantic fleet, which the accommodating Portland City Council rezoned in June 1969 for industrial use. The City Council presumably was influenced by the developer's propaganda that "there will be broad implications both for Arctic development and for international trade . . . For New England and western Canada, the new sources and supplies of fuel could be expected to have major impact."[2]

At the rather emotional hearing held on the matter of rezoning, it was apparent that two sectors of American opinion were well and effectively represented. One group, sort of neo-Babbitt, the college-bred businessman, was interested in present profits, a booster shot for the faltering New England economy. The other appeared more idealistic, more concerned for the future America, but many of its representatives admittedly were those who had it made, who were more interested, really, in sailboats and summer homes than jobs and tax revenue. A Chicago lady who summered in Casco Bay indignantly cited the noisome Jersey meadows ruined perhaps forever by the nearby oil refinery complexes. The member of a citizens' committee demanded that an independent survey be made to determine whether the lobster-fishing and recreational facilities could be preserved in the shadow of a storage depot, with monstrous tankers lying out in Casco Bay and discharging their cargoes with inevitable spillage. He and others voiced suspicions that on the heels of the Long Island development would come petrochemical companies eager to build factories there. Anyone who has toured along the Ship Canal between Houston and Galveston knows, of course, how a petrochemical industry can mush-room overnight.

Ironically the Long Island tank farm and allied facilities became an attractive site largely because the navy had left its World War II depot there after burying it under hillocks of sand, while another government agency, the Interior Department's Bureau of Outdoor Recreation, recommended in a report released on December 29, 1967, that the surplus Navy Fuel Annex and the surrounding area be preserved for fishing and recreation. The annex, it proposed, would be converted into administrative headquarters of a training center for future recreation and conservation leaders. The study, part of a survey of all the country's coastal islands, noted that Casco Bay was "dotted with many wooded islands and even more rock protrusions and is one of the outstanding scenic areas found along the Atlantic Coast." It also declared that efforts should be made to "protect the recreation and conservation value of Casco Bay and to plan the orderly de-velopment of the islands in a method that will be compatible with the existing resources present."[3]

King Resources, for all the protests, not only obtained the Long Island facility from the navy for a bargain price of $203,000 but secured the necessary rezoning. The *Boston Globe* was prompted to observe that "if the Federal govern-ment does not change its past and present policies toward abandoned and derelict seaside military installations, there will be less and less access to the shoreline for the public and more and more of its development for private industry — industry such as King Resources' oil terminal in scenic Casco Bay."

Up the coast, or "down east" as Maine puts it, Machiasport became the focus of vigorous competition after Occidental announced its plans to develop a "foreign trade zone" there and import foreign oil, mostly from Libya, to be refined in a 100,000-barrel-a-day plant and distributed mostly in New England, where fuel-oil prices are high. Occidental could bring in foreign oil at $1.25 to $1.46 a barrel less than the price in Texas, but would need permission from the Foreign Trade Zones Board, comprised of the Secretaries of the Treasury, Commerce and Defense, who were under pressure from the major oil companies not to grant it, at least until several of the majors announced their own plans to build refineries at Machiasport. If that happens, of course, the pristine forested coast east of Bar Harbor will soon resemble the tarry desolation of the beach between Long Beach and Wilmington, California.

The Natural Resources Council and other interested groups held a conference at Portland in the summer of 1969, at which the centerpiece was Senator Edmund Muskie. The senator evidently was trying to balance two possibly conflicting roles. In the Senate he has been the most vigorous exponent of controlling air and water pollution. Outside the Senate he was regarded that summer as a leading candidate for the Democratic nomination for the presidency. Thus he urged that the citizenry devise and push through local and state regulations which would eliminate the possibility of pollution — though there are no known devices to accomplish that entirely — and declined to declare himself opposed to the establishment of the proposed facilities at Machiasport or elsewhere. Any knowledgeable candidate knows that most recent Presidents have been elected with oil industry support, whether or not this is a coincidence. His own senatorial committee, he explained, was working on a bill to regulate the transfer of oil from ship to shore and provide penalties in case of spillage; such penalties, of course, could be shrugged off by the offending company and would hardly alleviate conditions on an oil-drenched coastline.

Other speakers at the day-long conference were unable to supply any comforting information for those concerned with the air and water pollution they feared. In a way it served as a time capsule for all communities and areas which will be confronted by the expansion of oil-distribution and oil-re-

439

fining facilities, along with their allied chemical industries, and the atmospheric pollution they bring. The lesson of the conference was that, as of 1969, no effective methods of control had been found. The U.S. Attorney at Portland, Lloyd La Fountain, admitted that the Federal Pollution Control Act of 1966 had been found to be unenforceable regarding smaller tankers already calling in at Portland Harbor, that in prosecuting cases of spillage the city had to base its case on an 1899 ordinance prohibiting the dumping of "refuse" in the harbor, that regulating pollution could not be left to the federal government, and that each locality had to depend on its own legal resources.

The sessions were really chilling in their import, though the tone of the experts and other participants was moderate. James A. Fay, professor of mechanical engineering at the Massachusetts Institute of Technology, told the conference that the present means of cleaning up oil spills were ineffective. Booms and other mechanical means of containing an oil slick did not work when even a moderately choppy sea was running. Detergents, emulsifiers, and other chemicals used to break up oil slicks did more damage to marine life than the oil itself. Professor Fay could only suggest that laws be enacted to regulate and improve the design of the facilities used to transfer oil from ship to shore and make certain they couldn't malfunction, that other laws pin down the financial liability of the companies involved in any spillage, that a hundred-million-dollar research program be instituted by the federal government to find ways of mopping up after the damage is done.

Gardiner C. Means, who had been charged with drawing up the regulations under which an oil port would function at Machiasport, had thoroughly researched the difficulties of other communities coexisting alongside similar facilities. Air pollution, he had learned, could be controlled but only by the use of complex and expensive devices. As an example of absolute control he cited the Hess Refinery in the Virgin Islands

440

where there is no odor or discoverable pollution of the atmosphere. Water pollution he had found to be an insoluble problem. It would occur, he said, under four sets of circumstances: "(1) those arising from refinery operations, (2) those originating in clearing barges and dumping ballast, (3) those due to operational spills, and (4) those coming from disasters like the *Torrey Canyon*." The regulations being drawn up for the Machiasport project, he said, included a prohibition on dumping effluents from refining processes into the bay, on pumping out the bilges of the tankers within a hundred miles of shore. But there were no safeguards against accidents or disasters. Booms to contain spillage wouldn't work with the rough seas off Machiasport. And if one of the new 300,000-ton super-tankers went aground off the port, a strip of oil twenty-four feet wide and an inch deep would carpet the coast from Halifax to Boston.

It was Senator Muskie's opinion, at the conclusion, that the encroachments of the oil industry could only be met with a kind of fatalism. "We cannot lock up our resources and preserve them in their pristine state," he said. "Neither can we permit their exploitation by methods that incur needless risk."

It was bad news to Maine and the tradition of salty self-reliance, the willingness to keep out of the mainstream of "progress" that has always governed its citizens, that somehow their happy isolation had been breached and they could no longer control their own environment.

About the same time, through 1968 and 1969, the world's largest oil company, Standard of New Jersey, began running double-page, full-color advertisements in the national magazines. In a Madison Avenue campaign designed to convince people that the industry could operate in a manner that does not foul up things for everyone else, Esso devoted part of its ad budget to demonstrating the joys of coexistence with oil-extracting and oil-refining.

With the expertise that recently had been bent to persuad-

441

ing people around the world to "put a tiger in your tank," Standard of New Jersey in gorgeous color spreads showed a Louisiana oilfield operating next to a bird sanctuary and cowhands rounding up cattle on the King Ranch in Texas against the background of a Humble (a Standard subsidiary) installation gleaming monstrously on the horizon.

An impressive verbal effort was made to prove how harmless such operations were to the surrounding environment. In the ad headed "Coexistence on the King Ranch," in the folksy, condescending prose of the copywriter, the reader is informed that the King Ranch, biggest in the nation, is "a hunk of pure Americana." On the ranch are twenty-eight oil and gas fields, thirty thousand head of cattle, one thousand miles of pipeline, the world's largest gas plant. "Good housekeeping," says the ad, is responsible for the fact that all those oil and gas operations haven't harmed the environment. "They have been drilling for oil and gas on the ranch for forty-five years. If running an oil field were the noisy, messy business some people think it is, how come wild geese, wild turkey and bobwhite quail elect to stay and multiply by the thousand? If pipelines and gas plants pollute the water, how come deer, nilgai and javelinas guzzle it? And thrive. One more point about this precious water. The King Ranch gas plant uses thousands of gallons an hour for cooling purpose. When this water is returned to the ponds and creeks, the cattle drink it."

The ad titled "This bird sanctuary is an oil field" pictures a dreamily peaceful island in the Louisiana bayous which accommodates the Tabasco Sauce factory, "over a hundred oil wells," and the Avery Island Bird Sanctuary. "Here you find irises from Siberia. Grapefruits from Cochin. Evergreens from Tibet. Bamboo from China. Lotuses from the Nile. Soap trees from India. Daisies from Africa's Mountains of the Moon. And the world's most complete collection of camellias . . . Now, over 100,000 [egrets] nest around its man-made lake every year. To see these alabaster birds sharing their Eden with herons, ducks, coots, swans, cormorants, turtles, deer and alligators is almost a primeval experience. It seems to put the clock back to the beginning. And, wherever you wander on this peaceful island, you have to look hard to spot the oil wells. Many are hidden by grandfatherly oak trees bearded with Spanish moss. Others are screened by banks of azalea and rhododendron. To Jersey's affiliate, Humble Oil & Refining Company, this respect for environment is only right and proper. The oil industry provides Louisiana with one-third of its total revenue. But even this contribution would be a poor excuse for defiling beauty or disturbing wildlife. Amen say the egrets."

Why all this sudden, nationally advertised infatuation with wildlife from a company previously given to promoting the Esso tiger?

Several shocking events had occurred which impressed on the public mind the dangers associated with the oil industry's varied operations.

On March 18, 1967, the tanker *Torrey Canyon* grounded on a reef off the Cornish coast and spilled much of its 36 million gallons of Kuwaiti crude, and a month later beaches as far away as New Jersey and Cape Cod were polluted. Eight days later the tanker *Desert Chief*, unloading crude at Yorktown, Virginia, accidentally poured out tons of oil through an open sluice pump, polluted twenty miles of the York River, and several weeks later the beaches of summer resorts on Cape Cod and the New Jersey coast were also polluted, leaving "long ridges of oil and hundreds of dead waterfowl," according to a congressional report. And less than a year later, in March 1968, the Liberian tanker *Ocean Eagle* broke in two outside San Juan, Puerto Rico, and the Greek tanker *General Colocotronis* struck a reef in the Bahamas, causing wide spread pollution on the Puerto Rican and Bahaman coasts. Then, even more alarmingly to Americans, an offshore oil well in the Santa Barbara Channel early in 1969 sprung a leak and covered miles of white California beaches with a deadly black slime. On March 17, 1969, a barge broke loose off the

443

Louisiana coast and knocked the control valves off an offshore well just completed. The well was capped within forty-eight hours but only after it had gushed out ten thousand gallons of oil. The incident persuaded the federal government to investigate other offshore wells along the Louisiana coast and resulted in the indictment of the Chevron Oil Company for failure to provide safety devices on ninety of its wells. Even more alarmingly, early in 1970, three tankers exploded and sank off the African coast for undetermined reasons. It was little wonder that in the summer of 1970 mariners began reporting that even remote stretches of ocean, well off the regular sea lanes, were being covered with oil slicks.*

It was the *Torrey Canyon* disaster that demonstrated humanity's growing helplessness before the runaway tendencies of technology. Overnight it became a symbol of mankind's unpreparedness in confronting oil pollution and awakened it to the dangers presented by the giant tankers. The *Torrey Canyon* is still the starting point for all discussions of the hazards presented by giant oil tankers. It served as a warning for legislatures and bureaucrats of the necessity of developing oil-cleanup methods and made the citizens of all advanced nations uncomfortably aware of the dangers to ecological balance, recreational facilities and other amenities long taken for granted along their coastlines. "Essentially," as one authority observed, "the *Torrey Canyon* disaster revealed ignorance. Man had figured out how to move enormous quantities of oil but not how to cope when the system fails on a grand scale."[4]

The oil companies and the tanker tycoons, it should be noted, were undeterred by that disaster from making any es-

* There was also a growing suspicion that the outsized tankers may have serious flaws in their construction, possibly inherent in their sheer size. The Japan Marine Association announced in June 1970 that it had discovered twenty cracks, some of them nineteen inches wide, in the *Shosei Maru*, one of five tankers built in 1965 under a government-assisted program. Two of the other five tankers in that group had sunk — the *Bolivar Maru* in January 1969 and the *California Maru* in February 1970 — in the Pacific. Two other tankers in that class were also reported to have developed structural defects (Associated Press dispatch, June 9, 1970, from Tokyo).

444

sential changes in their plans. Gulf Oil continued full speed ahead on operating six 312,000-ton tankers between the Persian Gulf and Bantry Bay, Ireland, where its transshipment terminal for western Europe is located. And Professor G. S. Sturmey, an expert on oil transportation at the University of Lancaster, has forecast an upswing in building giant tankers at least for another generation because "there is no reason to expect other than a doubling of world oil consumption every ten years, certainly for the next two or three decades."[5]

Obviously the rest of humanity was more shocked and appalled by the *Torrey Canyon* disaster than the industry involved. Its magnitude, in fact, took several years to measure. For one thing, the *Torrey Canyon*, 974 feet long, a third longer than any World War II aircraft carrier, was the biggest ship ever to be wrecked. It was one of three intercontinental tankers built for the Union Oil Company of California, an organization noted in Los Angeles (its home base) for the influence it has wielded on local and state politics and for the awed respect its top executives command at the California Club, a bastion of privilege and privacy which required newspapermen summoned for an infrequent audience to use the service entrance.

The management and ownership of the *Torrey Canyon* was a diffuse international setup of the type which often characterizes the industry. Its operator was Union Oil. It flew the Liberian flag, however, and its registered owner was the Barracuda Tanker Corporation. Barracuda, for all the maritime power it represented, was a paper whale (or shark). Its headquarters was a filing cabinet in Hamilton, Bermuda, where it was represented by a firm offering tax-free accommodation, though it was incorporated under the laws of Liberia. The company was one of those cobwebs created by Wall Street lawyers and financiers: operator in California, files in Bermuda, flags from Liberia, brains in Wall Street.

Barracuda Tanker was organized, as the *Wall Street Journal* learned in an investigation six years before the *Torrey Can-*

yon went aground, by the investment banking house of Dillon Read & Company, which has supplied more than its share of Secretaries of State and Treasury. It was one of seven companies set up by Dillon Read on behalf its client, all of them owning facilities, tankers, pipelines, service stations, chemical plants, even Union Oil's headquarters building, which they in turn leased to Union Oil. Barracuda itself, as was revealed by the *Journal's* investigation and disclosures to the SEC, was organized by twenty-seven persons connected with Dillon Read, whose then-president, Frederic H. Brandi, was also a director of Union Oil. The twenty-seven persons put up a total capital of $20,000, and on that base — such are the miracles of corporate financing — three tankers including the *Torrey Canyon* and costing a total of more than $50 million were built. The key to all this, of course, was Dillon Read's ability to obtain bank financing on such a modest investment by Barracuda's organizers. In a period of twenty years, it was estimated, Barracuda would produce a net of $1 million.[6]

The *Torrey Canyon*, with an Italian master and crew, had been chartered from Union Oil by British Petroleum to carry the cargo of Kuwaiti oil to Milford Haven, Wales. Instead she piled up on a granite reef sixteen miles off the southwest coast of England. Thousands of tons of crude oil immediately flooded out of her torn bottom into the sea and eventually slimed the beaches of Cornwall as well as the coast of Brittany across the Channel. The definitive account of the grounding of the *Torrey Canyon* has been provided by Edward Cowan, a *New York Times* correspondent, in *Oil and Water*, which also tells of the heroic efforts to staunch the flow, to control it with plastic booms, to mop up the mess on land and sea with emulsifiers.

It took months to eliminate the worst effects of the disaster, particularly along a 140-mile stretch of the Cornish coast. The damage may never be entirely undone, however, as Dr. Anthony Nelson-Smith, a British zoologist, warned. His warning, quoted by Mr. Cowan, should counteract the general belief that the ocean is a huge pool infinitely capable of handling wastes. Dr. Nelson-Smith pointed out that "everyone thinks of the ocean as being limitless; but if it is, by and large, dependent on the coastal strip then its apparently huge capacity as a sink for all sorts of pollutants is, in fact, illusory — especially when most of those pollutants are poured into it across or just offshore from the all-important strip," by which he referred to the intertidal bands which serve as the nursery for all sorts of marine life.

"People also talk about the tides and currents washing pollutants away — but where to? For example, water from Cornwall passes either up the Channel or into the Irish Sea. Passing northwards from Land's End, the tidal stream swishes past Westen-super-Mare and Bristol, then back past here, Swansea, and around the corner into St. Bride's Bay and Cardigan Bay. Having received, shall we say, emulsified oil from the north coast of Cornwall, the same block of water gets domestic sewage from Weston, industrial effluents from Avonmouth, steel-mill wastes from Newport, coke washings from the Welsh valleys, more industrial waste from Swansea, oil spillage from Milford Haven — yet everyone is, of course, merely allowing their poisons to be dispersed by the 'infinite dilution' of the sea . . . What keeps seaweed off rocks is limpets and winkles — what keeps slime off sand is sandhoppers and similar creatures — what keeps scum from rock pools is other small marine animals. These animals can be killed off a lot more rapidly than the plants. The chances are that the clean beaches of today will be the slippery, slimy, smelly beaches of tomorrow — because the animals are gone."[7]

An enormous effort was launched by the Royal Society for the Prevention of Cruelty to Animals and other groups which cleaned, fed, and cared for thousands of birds disabled when they touched down on the oil-slicked waters. Thousands died horribly. The committee formed at Prime Minister Wilson's request by his chief scientific adviser, Sir Solly Zuckerman, to investigate various aspects of the *Torrey Canyon* disaster

447

and its long aftermath estimated that twenty thousand guillemots and five thousand razorbills lost their lives. Of the 7,849 birds picked up at sea and from the shore and given emergency care and treatment, only 450 — less than one percent — survived and were freed. You don't have to be a zoologist to be sickened by those statistics.

In concluding his vivid account of the *Torrey Canyon* incident, Edward Cowan noted a tendency to condemn industrial progress for such destruction but suggested that the blame really rests with the human impulses responsible for devising new techniques without waiting to develop safeguards against the inevitable hour they malfunction. "But the fault lies not with technology," he observed, "even though it may seem to have a will of its own. It lies with man's habit of lunging for the benefits of new inventions and failing to ask what the hazards may be, of being too much the consumer and too little the political animal activated by a sense of community responsibility." Union Oil and Barracuda Tankers late in 1969 agreed to pay $7.2 million damages for their share in the responsibility for the disaster.

Less than two years later, on its Pacific shore, the United States was visited with the same sort of catastrophe. On January 28, 1969 an offshore well, Platform A, five and one-half miles offshore from Santa Barbara, began leaking a thousand gallons an hour. Four hundred square miles of ocean were coated with oil, forty miles of the most elegant beaches on the Pacific Coast were fouled along the Santa Barbara Channel. It took a dozen days for the leak to be sealed, except for a slight continuing seepage, with a plastic sealant and cement.

There was a national outcry, a search for villains.

Oddly and ironically enough, the corporate responsibility fell upon the Union Oil Company as in the *Torrey Canyon* case. Until then the company had known a modest but satisfactory profit margin, starting before the turn of the century when it was organized to work the Torrey Canyon field seventy miles northwest of Los Angeles. In 1966 its profits were rising faster than the industry average and reached $142,000,000. Until 1964, however, it had been a regional company. That year Fred L. Hartley, a chemical engineer who worked his way up the executive ranks, attained the presidency and inaugurated a new and more competitive policy. Realizing that Union had to expand or would be swallowed up in a merger, he voted for expansion and a year after becoming president engineered the acquisition of the Pure Oil Company, which provided a chain of service stations in the South and Midwest.[3]

Hartley thrived on the competition of the marketplace, but understandably was less comfortable when the floodlights of publicity were focused on him during the Platform A crisis. With Union Oil losing considerable sums in stopping the leak, Hartley was being badgered by conservation and wildlife groups about the hundreds of cormorants, grebes and other birds who were dead or dying along the tarry stretches of beach. His manner was something less than apologetic when he appeared before Senator Muskie's subcommittee to testify on the Santa Barbara situation. A national hubbub arose, in fact, when the *Wall Street Journal* quoted him as saying, "I'm amazed at the publicity for the loss of a few birds."[9]

Union Oil took a full-page ad in the *New York Times* to protest under Hartley's signature, that he had been misquoted. What he had actually said was, "I think we have to look at these problems relatively. I am always tremendously impressed at the publicity that the death of birds receives versus the loss of people in this country in this day and age." He also affirmed that on the third day following the leak a bird-cleaning station was established "with appropriate scientists and cleaning chemicals to try to do our best to save our feathered friends."[10]

Contrary, undoubtedly, to the company's hopes and expectations, the furor over the Santa Barbara leak did not die down. The community was not greatly mollified when the

449

Nixon Administration asked Congress to cancel twenty federal leases on 198,000 acres in the Santa Barbara Channel, where a marine bird sanctuary was to be established, and to compensate the oil companies by selling them crude from the naval reserve near Bakersfield. Drilling would continue at fifty sites near the proposed sanctuary under leases left in effect.

Santa Barbara is renowned for its wealthy estates, its top-drawer resort facilities, but conservatives, liberals, radicals and intellectuals all banded together, acronymously, in an organization called GOO (Get Oil Out) to circulate petitions calling for a stop to offshore drilling. Aside from the possibility of further pollution, Santa Barbarans pointed to the fact that the region had suffered sixty-eight minor earthquakes in the past year and that further drilling might make the area even more unstable.

And there was considerable national support for GOO and the conservationists when a national magazine ran a striking color spread showing oil-stained baby sea lions on San Miguel Island, thirty-five miles from Platform A, most of them doomed. "At the water's edge," the magazine's investigator reported, on San Miguel Island, "on the channel beaches the blight of oil extended in both directions as far as the eye could see. [This was 118 days after the first leakage from Platform A.] Scattered through the mess were the living and the dead creatures whose bright habitat this once had been. Until we became weary and sick of the tally, we counted over a hundred dead sea lions and elephant seals in the immediate area . . . There was much evidence of sickness . . . Here and there, we came upon oil-drenched pups that cried weakly and thrashed about like scalded rats, their eyelids gummed shut, umbilicals stained and caked . . ."[11]

Reflecting on the moral, economic and ecological lessons of the Santa Barbara incident, Garrett Hardin, professor of biology at the University of California's Santa Barbara campus, expressed an understandable cynicism over the efforts of humanitarians to deal with the activities of oil companies long experienced in riding out storms of adverse public opinion. "I don't think it will do much good to dwell on the fate of the poor sea birds and all they symbolize. As a member of the Sierra Club, I am moved by their plight — but I know I am in the minority. Indignation over the rape of the environment is an avocation of many people who are paid to do other things. Making money is the full-time occupation of the oil drillers. They can be patient. They can ride out the storm. Sooner or later, emotional fatigue overcomes the viewers-with-alarm. Even the worst news ultimately becomes a bore. Apathy and anomy set in, and the drillers take over . . ."

The sophistry of the oil industry's arguments in favor of its enterprises must be exposed, Hardin declared. "Spokesmen for the oil interests tell us that the 'resources' of the world must be 'developed' to meet the 'needs' of a growing population. The quotation marks are essential to sensitize us to the assumptions hidden in the words. As conclusions can be loaded into premises, so can reflex responses be incorporated into these words. To speak of a 'resource' is to imply it must be used up, destroyed. To 'develop' something is to somehow help it to realize the full potential for which it was predestined . . . There are men who desecrate the landscape with hundreds of ticky-tacky houses and boastfully call themselves developers, but would never dream of living in their own developments. Natural resources that are destroyed are also said to be developed. Possibly the trickiest word of all is 'needs.' Few men are so rich that they don't feel they 'need' more. Informed that the population is growing — and accepting as gospel that such growth is inevitable — few people question the legitimacy of the 'needs' of a growing population. Seldom is it asked: 'Is this growth necessary?' How often is the question raised as to the possibility that what we really 'need' is a smaller population?"

The Santa Barbara experience led Hardin to believe that humanity would have to put up a better fight to protect its

451

environment from pollution. "A man may own the land on which his smelter, tannery or television station stands: he does not own the media that surround us. When the population was sparse, what a man did to the media could be safely ignored. Now it is time to say, 'Let the polluter pay the cost of pollution'; better still, let him be enjoined from polluting in the first place." Somewhat optimistically, at least for the short run, Hardin concluded, "The heresy that no one has a right to pollute the media of the world is changing to orthodoxy. Sooner or later the ecological ethic will prevail."[12]

Even before the Santa Barbara incident Congress had been working on ways to enforce that "ethic" by legislation. The Senate's Committee on Public Works had reported: "Of the various threats to our environment from oil pollution, the most serious occurs during transport of oil. [The *Torrey Canyon* disaster was then fresh in senatorial minds.] This includes movement, loading, unloading, transfer and cleanup. It includes bulk movement by vessel, river, and lake barge, pipelines, road and rail tank cars, terminals, pump stations and bulk marketing. Accidents, poor maintenance, carelessness, shortcutting and cleanup operations, the apparatus and methods used — all contribute to the problem." A Senate bill sponsored by Senators Muskie and Clifford P. Case would provide a maximum $10,000 fine for spillage due to negligence, one year in jail and a $2,500 fine for "willful" violations.

The adversity of public and legislative opinion was, of course, countered by the industry in its traditional fashion: the doctrine of "need" cited by Professor Hardin.

A special task force charged with studying ways of preventing spillage in offshore drilling operations made its report through the American Petroleum Institute, leading off with the wry acknowledgment that "To pour oil on troubled waters originally meant to calm the water. Today, pouring oil on water won't calm anything; it will only cause trouble."

It also acknowledged there is no sure way of preventing leakages that may accidentally occur, but the institute pointed

452

out that in 1967 and 1968 the petroleum industry paid the federal government more than $2 billion just for the right to explore for oil on the continental shelf. "An overall investment approaching $10 billion since the 1950's has led to domestic offshore production in excess of one million barrels a day. This output is expected to increase fifteen percent annually through 1975."

It's all a question of "need," as the American Petroleum Institute sees it; the spiraling increase in consumption that forces the industry to undertake offshore drilling at a cost of $1 million a well against the average $68,000 for an onshore well. That trend will continue despite sterner government regulations on the practice. Thomas D. Barrow, a geologist and senior vice-president of Humble Oil & Refining, was quoted in the institute's report: "Despite the difficulties of accurate financial predicting, industry continues to go offshore because it must. This is where the potentially large reserves are to be found."

The biggest strikes are now being made offshore not only around the American coastline but in the Persian Gulf and elsewhere. Total proved reserves are approximately 350 billion barrels, but geologists believe another 700 billion barrels may be found in offshore areas. These are generally close to onshore oilfields, such as those in Louisiana and California. The institute cites the fact that "demand for oil has risen forty-four percent in the past ten years while proved reserves have gone up only fifteen percent . . . This makes the situation quite clear; we are not finding domestic reserves commensurate with the increase in demand." (The Alaskan discoveries, the oil industry contends, will only lessen, not eliminate our dependence on the Middle Eastern sources. Consumption continues to rise almost as fast as new fields are found and exploited. The margin between is indeed narrow enough to cause alarm.)

Barrows pointed to the high bonuses paid at federal sales of offshore drilling rights on the continental shelf as evi-

453

dence of a "long-term need to replace dwindling crude oil reserves even if present conditions indicate low or marginal return on investment." What particularly tantalizes the industry, he said, is discovery of an offshore field with 100 million barrels or more. "There are very few places in the inland United States where we feel this can be done at any price."[13]

Thus the federal government, in a somewhat schizophrenic fashion, actively participates in the oil industry as a financially interested partner even while it regulates and sometimes punishes the same industry. It protects the domestic industry through import quotas to encourage oil exploration within the United States at the expense of the consumer. It is also true, of course, that such policies tend to make the United States use up its own reserves when much cheaper foreign oil is available. How can the United States be "safer" while depleting a strategic resource at the fastest possible rate rather than using up the Middle Eastern reserves? "National security" is endangered rather than cosseted by burning up our own, more or less sheltered continental supply. As Senator Edward Kennedy has remarked, the industry is saying in effect that "our reserves will be conserved if we consume them first."

Beyond the continental shelf, another senator has pointed out, the competition for natural resources is also accelerating. The foreseeable danger of that undersea collision was outlined by Senator Claiborne Pell of Rhode Island: "In the no man's land of the seabed, a scramble for minerals and oil, for new underwater empires secured by advancing armies of technology, could well set a newer and wider stage of world conflict."

Senator Pell, who is chairman of the subcommittee on ocean space, has disclosed that offshore drilling already extends fifty miles out to sea. "In the twelve years between 1955 and 1967, offshore production of crude oil increased from 7 million to 222 million barrels. Estimates of known reserves of

454

natural gas have more than tripled in the past fifteen years, and each advance of scientific exploration of the ocean beds brings to light new finds that would gladden the eye of the most hardened veteran of the California gold rush."

The rush to exploit the oil and mineral resources beneath the ocean floor is outpacing by far any attempts to regulate it under international law. The potential political hazards are apparent to Senator Pell. "Parts of the Gulf of Mexico became such a forest of drilling rigs that an agreement was necessary to clear shipping lanes. This spring, the Dominican Republic granted a single oil concession covering some three-quarters of a million acres of offshore seabed, and many other small coastal nations are looking for an economic bonanza in the leasing of drilling rights. Under what safety and pollution regulations will such developments take place? How far out may any nation grant such leases or undertake such exploitation?

"In short, diplomats and politicians who five years ago looked backward to the slow evolution of mining the sea and found nothing to engage their immediate concern have been overtaken, as is frequently the case in this day, by the less stately pace of technological change. If the know-how of ocean exploitation has gathered momentum of its own, the same cannot be said for any reasoned approach to orderly development under a regime of law."[14]

There is some hope that the government will be required to control the exploitation as well as prevent the environment from being irrevocably damaged. A vocal and articulate bloc pushing for regulatory programs includes Senator Gaylord Nelson of Wisconsin, who believes there is a growing, mostly youthful constituency determined to deal with environmental problems. He has noted that a study of student publications showed that young people were more engrossed by that subject than any other except the Viet Nam War, that

455

the next "youth crusade" might well be directed at preserving the environment. "They do understand what's happening," he added, "and they do understand what they're going to inherit."

He spoke, fittingly enough, at the annual Congressional Conference on the Environment, where a number of frightening bulletins in the losing war against pollution were issued. Estimating that elimination of water pollution alone would take between $100 and $150 *billion*, Senator Nelson pointed out that only $3.7 billion had been appropriated in the 1970 federal budget for environmental use, less than two percent of the total, the lowest percentage ever allotted for that purpose. Obviously there were many of Nelson's colleagues who refused to share his apprehensions. The justification for such fears for the near future were underlined by the report of Barry Weisberg, director of San Francisco's Bay Area Institute, that this country alone throws 133 billion tons of pollutants into the atmosphere every year, equal to the annual tonnage of steel produced by the United States.

The world, except for a relatively few dissidents and malcontents, willingly accepts the price in human suffering in return for being allowed to drive automobiles in greater and greater numbers and heat homes more conveniently. Everyone accepts the price of "progress," even though automotive traffic in the cities moves closer to total paralysis and the smog grows denser and the danger to the shorelines increases daily. We accept an annual death toll of more than fifty thousand in traffic accidents with hardly a blink. The Dow-Jones averages are of greater consideration than the statistics of the President's Science Advisory Committee (published as *Restoring the Quality of Our Environment* in 1965) or its warning that the extra heat induced by fuel-produced carbon dioxide accumulated in the air by the year 2000 might melt the Antarctic ice cap. The results would not be pleasant: "The melting of the Antarctic ice cap would raise sea level by 400 feet. If 1,000 years were required to melt the ice cap, the sea level would rise about four feet every ten years, forty feet per century." Many of the world's major cities would be inundated.

Even worse results may be anticipated from the heating of the earth's atmosphere. Neither the atmosphere nor the sea are endlessly efficient sewer systems for the waste products of civilization. The atmospheric warning comes from Dr. Barry Commoner, director of Washington University's Center for the Biology of Natural Systems, the first environmental health institution to be established by the U.S. Public Health Service. "Each ton of wood, coal, petroleum or natural gas burned contributes several tons of carbon dioxide to the earth's atmosphere. Between 1860 and 1960 the combustion of fuels added nearly 14 percent to the carbon-dioxide content of the air, which had until then remained constant for many centuries . . .

"Carbon dioxide plays an important role in regulating the temperature of the earth because of the 'greenhouse effect.' Both glass and carbon dioxide tend to pass visible light but absorb infrared rays. This explains why the sun so easily warms a greenhouse on a winter day. Light from the sun enters the greenhouse glass. Within, it is absorbed by soil and plants and converted to infrared heat energy which remains trapped inside the greenhouse because it cannot pass out again through the glass. Carbon dioxide makes a huge greenhouse of the earth, allowing the sunlight to reach the earth's surface but limiting reradiation of the resulting heat into space. The temperature of the earth — which profoundly affects the suitability of the environment for life — is therefore certain to rise as the amount of carbon dioxide in the air increases."[15]

Will such reasonable predictions of ultimate suffocation persuade one man to give up one of his family cars, motorboats, power mowers or snowmobiles, or one oilman to forgo

457

drilling one well anywhere in the world? The record of mankind indicates that it won't. The slagheap of misery will grow, until the birds start dropping out of the sky, and life slowly withers, and the green earth turns brown. This is the throne of the oil barons.

Appendixes

A.

Standard Oil and Nazi Germany

During World War II, Standard Oil of New Jersey was accused of having supplied Germany, in the prewar years, with technical information invaluable to the Nazi war machine. The *Petroleum Times* on December 25, 1943, published an article titled "American Business and Standard Oil's Blueprint for World Trade" and written by R. T. Haslam, an Esso official, which defended the prewar agreement with Germany and declared that "the secrets brought to America from Germany fifteen years ago by American scientists have been turned into mighty weapons against Germany."

The charges, laced with innuendo, have often been cited since as evidence of the cooperation of various cartels above and sometimes against their national interests. They are explored here on the basis of captured Nazi documents published by a subcommittee of the Senate Committee on Military Affairs, Seventy-ninth Congress, 2nd session, in 1946. The subject of the investigation was "Elimination of German Resources for War." The relevant documents were published in the subcommittee's report, pages 1302 to 1305.

The most important was a memorandum compiled for the

461

Central Committee of I. G. Farbenindustrie's Board of Managing Directors, which was among those captured by the U.S. army at Heidelberg, to which they had been removed from I. G. Farben's headquarters at Ludwigshafen at the end of the war.

Regarding the memorandum, the army's investigators wrote in an introduction, "In this studied and technical answer to the Haslam article it is set forth that I. G. Farben gained from America information far more important to Germany's war effort, through the medium of the Agreement with Standard Oil of New Jersey, than Standard Oil was able to obtain for the American war effort from Germany. This conclusion was reached after a detailed analysis of the development of four technical fields which Mr. Haslam has referred to as the 'miracles' which Standard Oil received from I. G. Farben; namely, Iso-octane, Toluol, Oppanol and Buna. [Buna was an artificial rubber process.]

"The I.G. article goes on to describe the 'many valuable contributions' which were received 'as a consequence of our contracts with the Americans . . . above and beyond the Agreement . . . which just now during the war are useful to us'; namely, lead-tetraethyl; polymerization; de-waxing and de-asphaltizing of lubricating oils, and Paraflow; and finally assistance in purchasing a large reserve stock of aviation gasoline and aviation lubricating oil, which I.G. obtained 'on the basis of its friendly relations with Standard Oil,' but acting in fact as 'trustee to the German government.' "

The memorandum dated May 30, 1944, thus constitutes a defense by I. G. Farben officials of their exchanges with Standard Oil on the grounds that Germany got more out of the deal than the United States did. It read in part:

"The closing of an agreement with Standard was necessary for technical, commercial and financial reasons: *technically*, because the specialized experience which was available only in a large-scale oil industry was necessary to the future development of our process, and no such industry existed in

Germany; *commercially*, because in the absence of State economic control in Germany at the time, I.G. had to avoid a competitive struggle with the great oil powers, who always sold the best gasoline at the lowest price in contested markets; *financially*, because I.G., which had already spent extraordinarily large sums for the development of the process,* had to seek financial relief in order to be able to continue development in other new technical fields, such as Buna.

". . . By reason of their decades of work on motor fuels, the Americans were ahead of us in their knowledge of the quality requirements that are called for by the different uses of motor fuels. In particular, they had developed, at great expense, a large number of methods of testing gasoline for different uses. On the basis of their experiments they had recognized the good anti-knock quality of Iso-octane long before they had any knowledge of our hydrogenation process. This is proved by the single fact that in America fuels are graded in octane numbers, and Iso-octane was entered as the best fuel with the number 100. All this knowledge naturally became ours as a result of the Agreement, which saved us much effort and protected us against many errors . . . we were also kept currently informed by the Americans on the progress of their production process and its further development . . . it must be noted that particularly in the case of the production of aviation gasoline on an Iso-octane basis, hardly anything was given to the Americans, while we gained a lot.

"The conditions are such in the Buna field that we never gave technical information to the Americans, nor did technical cooperation in the Buna field take place . . . the Americans had only the right to reach a technical cooperation with I.G. at some undetermined date. Even the agreement reached in September 1939 . . . did not give the Americans any technical information, but only that which was contractually their due, i.e., share in the patent possession . . . The Americans did not

* The process referred to was, evidently, the lead-tetraethyl (antiknock) developed by Standard in the early 1920's.

463

at that time receive anything important to war economy, besides, they could have procured the patents without our Agreements in wartime, for during war a State will never be kept from production by enemy patents . . ."

Regarding the ethyl process, the memorandum stressed that "without lead-tetraethyl the present method of warfare would be unthinkable. The fact that since the beginning of the war we could produce lead-tetraethyl is entirely due to the circumstances that shortly before the Americans had presented us with the production plants complete with experimental knowledge. Thus the difficult work of development [one need only recall the poisonous property of lead-tetraethyl, which caused many deaths in the United States] was spared us, since we could take up the manufacture of this product together with all the experience that the Americans had gathered over long years."*

The memorandum to the I. G. Farben directorate concluded with the statement that the reserve stock of $20 million worth of aviation gasoline and lubricating oils, bought from Standard and Royal Dutch Shell, was made possible "only through the aid of the Standard Oil Co."

The bitter criticism of Jersey Standard just after the war, though its relations with I. G. Farben had predated the war by twenty years, convinced Frank Abrams, board chairman from 1946 to 1954, that the corporation as well as the Rockefeller family itself needed a public relations program. Until

* Ethyl itself had a rather fascinating corporate history and understandably was much resented by other oil companies. The Ethyl Corporation, owned by Standard Oil of New Jersey and General Motors, "served to police the pricing of all gasoline companies except Sun, which had its own process, through a monopoly of an anti-knock compound that it sold to refiners" (Robert Engler, *The Politics of Oil*, p. 55). The company operated up to 1940, with one of the conditions of its franchises being the maintenance of a 2-cent differential on the sale of premium (Ethyl) gasoline over regular. Eight years ago control of Ethyl Corp. was obtained by Floyd D. Gottwald and his two sons, formerly manufacturers of blotting paper and paperbags. In 1970, the value of their holdings plummeted from $33 million to $21 million when General Motors and other automakers blamed Ethyl-type, leaded gasoline for much of the pollution from automobile exhaust. (*Wall Street Journal*, March 17, 1970.)

464

then Jersey Standard did not even have a public relations department. He saw that the public-be-ignored, if not public-be-damned, was a shortsighted policy. As he explained in an interview with L. L. Golden (published in the *Saturday Review*, September 8, 1969), it was necessary to explain the company's actions to journalists, educators, legislators and stockholders alike. He had decided that "no business exists in economic isolation. It is part of the social climate of the time." Thus Jersey Standard, as a direct result of the congressional investigation into the I. G. Farben affair, ended (to an extent dictated by discretion) its isolation from the public.

B.

A Defense of the Rockefellers

The most reasonable, clearly stated and scholarly defense of Standard Oil's operating methods and the Rockefellers' business ethics was composed by Allan Nevins. A little more than a dozen years after publishing a sympathetic biography of John D. Rockefeller, Sr., he produced the two-volume *Study in Power* (New York, 1953). Unlike other investigators, Mr. Nevins was permitted the use of the Rockefeller and Standard Oil papers. He was intent on making it clear, however, that he was not otherwise beholden.

"I can protest my disinterestedness," he stated in the preface. "On the one side I have scrupulously kept myself free from financial obligation, and have in fact accepted heavy penalties in devoting so much time and toil to a book whose royalties can hardly meet my personal costs of research. On the other side I have kept myself free from any temptation to prove an artificial 'courage' by pelting wealth with moral objurgations."

Up till then, in fact, big business had been objurgated endlessly in the works of Matthew Josephson (*The Robber Barons*), Harvey O'Connor (biographer of the Mellons, Guggen-

466

heims and others), Gustavus Myers (*History of the Great American Fortunes*), and other adverse witnesses. Mr. Nevins believed it was time for a healthy, well-balanced revisionism. "In our own history it was long easy to write the story of railroads, financiers, and industrial aggregations out of the innumerable state and federal investigations and prosecutions. This was an important part of the story, but only part."

The growth of giant corporations and trusts was inevitable, is Mr. Nevins' plea, and besides "without our powerful industrial units . . . the free world might have lost the First World War and most certainly would have lost the Second." As Mr. Nevins saw it, "A business world of small, weak, highly competitive units gave way to a world of concentration, efficiency, and highly organized power. This transformation involved a long process of destruction and reconstruction. Great business aggregations are not built without frustrating, crushing, or absorbing multitudinous small enterprises. To many caught in the midst of the transformation, its destructive and exploitive aspects seemed paramount. The leaders in the process appeared as 'robber barons' and the process itself the 'great barbecue.' This is one facet of the truth, but there are others . . ."

In Mr. Nevins' view, the rapid industrialization following the Civil War made combinations into trusts both inevitable and salutary, and Rockefeller Sr. merely led the way. "Great manufactories could make larger use of cost-saving machinery; could arrange for the subdivision and specialization of labor; could buy materials at wholesale prices; could set up branch plants at advantageous points for serving specialized markets; could utilize by-products; and could establish research departments quite beyond the reach of small companies." Standard simply "fashioned the mould in which much of American industry was reshaped . . ."

Mr. Nevins did not attempt to defend monopoly as a socially desirable outcome, but he explained: "Rockefeller's aim, when pushed to almost complete monopoly, was and is repug-

467

nant to believers in social and economic freedom and was certain to involve him in opprobrium. We must be sufficiently objective, however, to keep in mind a basic fact: that in industry after industry at this time the chaos and cruelty of over-competition bred a resort to monopoly as a natural cure. To every element in the oil industry . . . the excesses of competition seemed absolutely insufferable . . ."

He asks himself, "Did the deadweight the Standard Oil hung upon business ethics (for though it would be hard to prove that it depressed the current code, it certainly did nothing to raise it) outweigh the great constructive innovations of the combination, and the example set by its efficiency and order?" His reply is that "the oldtime black-and-white antithesis between monopoly and 'perfect competition' is as dead as the view that industrial concentration can or should be destroyed." Mr. Nevins held that the Standard Oil type of monopoly was "in the long run intolerable; but . . . not so intolerable as the 'perfect competition' contemplated by the makers of the Sherman Act would be." As for the hundreds of millions accruing to Rockefeller, Mr. Nevins believed that "gratitude is really due" him and his associates for seeing to it that "the gold was used to do the utmost possible good."

C.

Statistics

The latest statistical size-up of the American oil industry, as of 1969, has been produced by the Committee on Public Affairs of the American Petroleum Institute. It includes the following nuggets:

With twenty-five percent of the world's production, the United States is the largest oil-producing country. In excess of 3.2 billion barrels of crude are produced annually. The U.S. Geological Survey estimates 500 billion barrels may yet be discovered in the United States and on its continental shelf. Such discoveries would barely keep pace with the rising demand, projected at 80 billion barrels between now and 1980. That figure almost equals all the oil produced in the United States since 1859.

There are 218,000 miles of pipeline in the United States compared with 211,000 miles of railroad.

There are 270 oil refineries operating in thirty-nine states, with capacities ranging from one hundred barrels a day to over four hundred thousand. Combined, they can process 11 million barrels of crude daily, or thirty percent of the world capacity.

469

Improvements in processing have resulted in a 42-gallon barrel of oil now yielding 19 gallons of gasoline against 11 gallons in 1920. Gasoline is only one of about three thousand products processed from petroleum.

There are about 219,000 gasoline service stations in the United States, one for every 380 automobiles.

More than sixteen thousand U.S. companies are engaged in exploration for and production of petroleum.

Notes on Sources

Introduction

1. Harriet Van Horne, *New York Post*, February 21, 1969.
2. *New York Times*, April 16, 1969.
3. *New York Post*, March 20, 1969.
4. *Time*, April 18, 1969.
5. *Washington Post*, December 8, 1968.
6. Associated Press dispatch from Washington, April 15, 1969.

1. "Strong Men Go Mad"

1. Quoted in Hildegarde Dolson, *The Great Oildorado*, 15.
2. J. H. A. Bone, *Petroleum and Petroleum Wells*, 35.
3. Quoted in Stanley Vestal, *Short Grass Country*, 289.
4. Quoted in Dolson, *The Great Oildorado*, 65.
5. Quoted in *Ibid.*, 183.
6. Andy Logan, *The Man Who Robbed the Robber Barons*, 79–83.
7. Joseph Millard, *The Wickedest Man*, 77–78.
8. See Herbert Asbury, *The Golden Flood*, 114–137; John W. Steele, *Coal-Oil Johnny, His Book*, privately printed, 1902.
9. Titusville (Pa.) *Herald*, December 21, 1866.
10. Quoted in Jules Abels, *The Rockefeller Billions*, 58.
11. Allan Nevins, *Study in Power: John D. Rockefeller, Industrialist and Philanthropist*, Vol. I, 4.
12. Quoted in John T. Flynn, *God's Gold*, 132–133.
13. Stewart H. Holbrook, *The Age of the Moguls*, 66.
14. Quoted in Asbury, *The Golden Flood*, 301.
15. Cleveland *Plain Dealer*, February 21, 1872.
16. Flynn, *God's Gold*, 177.
17. *New York Times*, March 25 and 26, 1872.
18. Quoted in Flynn, *God's Gold*, 177.
19. Holbrook, *The Age of the Moguls*, 70.
20. H. L. Mencken, *Prejudices: Fourth Series*, 146.

471

2. "Individualism Is Gone, Never to Return"

1. Flynn, *God's Gold*, 248–249.
2. Samuel C. T. Dodd, *Combinations: Their Uses and Abuses*, 22.
3. Flynn, *God's Gold*, 200.
4. Ida M. Tarbell, *History of the Standard Oil Company*.
5. The aide, William Warden, is quoted in Abels, *The Rockefeller Billions*, 210.
6. Henry Clews, *Fifty Years in Wall Street*, 77.
7. New York *Tribune*, February 28 to March 5, 1888.
8. Caro Lloyd, *Henry Demarest Lloyd*, 87.
9. Henry Demarest Lloyd. "The Story of a Great Monopoly," *Atlantic Monthly*, March 1881.
10. Caro Lloyd, *Henry Demarest Lloyd*, Vol. I, 259–260.
11. Henry Demarest Lloyd, *Wealth and Commonwealth*, Vol. I, 44–45.
12. John J. McLaurin, *Sketches in Crude Oil*.
13. S. S. McClure, *My Autobiography*, 237–238.
14. Ida M. Tarbell, *All in a Day's Work*, 202.
15. Quoted in Thomas Lawson, *Frenzied Finance*, 190.
16. McLaurin, *Sketches in Crude Oil*.
17. Flynn, *God's Gold*, 245.

3. The Lessons of Spindletop

1. New York *Herald*, May 2, 1898.
2. Carl Coke Rister, *Oil! Titan of the Southwest*, 52.
3. C. A. Warner, *Texas Oil and Gas Since 1543*, 19.
4. Mody C. Boatright, *Folklore of the Oil Industry*, 83.
5. Quoted in Ruth Sheldon Knowles, *The Greatest Gamblers*, 28.
6. *Ibid.*, 31–32.
7. Rister, *Oil! Titan of the Southwest*, 55–56.
8. Beaumont (Texas) *Daily Enterprise*, January 10, 1901.
9. Quoted in Holbrook, *The Age of the Moguls*, 212–213.
10. Quoted in Knowles, *The Greatest Gamblers*, 37.
11. R. T. Hill, "The Beaumont Oil Field," *Journal of the Franklin Institute*, August–October 1902.
12. *Ibid.*
13. *Ibid.*
14. Robert Henriques, *Bearsted: A Biography of Marcus Samuel*, 341–347.
15. Quoted in Knowles, *The Greatest Gamblers*, 43.
16. Rister, *Oil! Titan of the Southwest*, 63.
17. *Ibid.*, 96–99.

4. Gentlemen, Start Your Engines

1. The race is described in John Bentley, *Great American Automobiles*; T. R. Nicholson, *Adventurer's Road*; Gerald Rose, *A Record of Motor Racing*; and Antonio Scarfoglio, *Round the World in a Motor Car*.

2. Glyn Roberts, *The Most Powerful Man in the World*, 117–118.
3. Quoted in Henriques, *Bearsted*, 527.
4. The Samuel family background and the inception of Shell Oil is covered in Henriques, *Bearsted*; and Isaac Marcosson, *The Black Golconda*.
5. Henriques, *Bearsted*, 65.
6. *Ibid.*, 151.
7. *Ibid.*, 217.
8. *Ibid.*, 293.
9. Henri Deterding, *An International Oilman*, 83–84.
10. Deterding's early career is described in Roberts, *The Most Powerful Man in the World*.
11. *Ibid.*, 88.
12. Henriques, *Bearsted*, 367–370.

5. A Chinese Interlude

1. Alice Tisdale Hobart, *Oil for the Lamps of China*, 13.
2. *Ibid.*, 36.
3. *Oil Magazine*, February 17, 1911.
4. Roberts, *The Most Powerful Man in the World*, 100–101.
5. Deterding, *An International Oilman*, 57.
6. Henriques, *Bearsted*, 521–523.

6. An Ailing Octopus

1. Clews, *Fifty Years in Wall Street*, 210, 223–224.
2. Abels, *The Rockefeller Billions*, 220–221.
3. Justin Kaplin, *Mr. Clemens and Mark Twain*, 321–323.
4. Quoted in Knowles, *The Greatest Gamblers*, 78.
5. Flynn, *God's Gold*, 417–418.
6. Chicago *Tribune*, July 2 to August 14, 1907.
7. Richard O'Connor, *The Scandalous Mr. Bennett*, 44.
8. W. A. Swanberg, *Citizen Hearst*, 228–229, 257–264.
9. New York *World*, November 20, 1908.
10. Christopher Tugendhat, *Oil: The Biggest Business*, 43.
11. Roberts, *The Most Powerful Man in the World*, 111–112.
12. *Ibid.*, 115.
13. Deterding, *An International Oilman*, 271–272.
14. Henriques, *Bearsted*, 523–524.
15. *Time*, November 29, 1968.

7. Oil as the Aztecs' Revenge

1. Richard O'Connor, *Pat Garrett*, 209–211.
2. Quoted in Knowles, *The Greatest Gamblers*, 59.
3. Frank C. Hanighen, *The Secret War*, 56–57.
4. Jack London, "Our Adventures in Tampico," *Collier's Magazine*, June 27, 1914.

5. Joseph C. Hergesheimer, *Tampico*, 12–13.
6. Anton Mohr, *The Oil War*, 209–212.
7. *Revolutions in Mexico*, Report on the Senate Foreign Relations Committee, Sixty-sixth Congress, 2nd session, 1921, 104, 462.
8. Burton J. Hendricks, *The Life and Letters of Walter Hines Page*, Vol. I, 218.
9. *Revolutions in Mexico*, 255–256.
10. *Ibid.*, 284.
11. Jack London, "The Trouble Makers of Mexico," *Collier's Magazine*, May 23, 1914.
12. Quoted in Hanighen, *The Secret War*, 69.
13. Edgcumb Pinchon, *Viva Villa*, 338.
14. Deterding, *An International Oilman*.

8. The Man from Mount Morgan

1. Essad Bey, *Blood and Oil in the Orient*.
2. Martin Arafelian quoted in Ralph Hewins, *Mr. Five Per Cent*, 49.
3. Roberts, *The Most Powerful Man in the World*, 52.
4. *Ibid.*, 54.
5. *Ibid.*, 60.
6. Henry Longhurst, *Adventure in Oil: The Story of British Petroleum*, 20–22.
7. Winston Churchill, *The World Crisis, 1911–1914*, 133–141, 179–181.
8. Roberts, *The Most Powerful Man in the World*, 412–413.
9. Hanighen, *The Secret War*, 24–32.
10. Sidney Reilly, *Britain's Master Spy*, which was completed and edited by his wife Pepita after Reilly was presumed to have been executed in the Soviet Union.
11. Robin Bruce Lockhart, *Ace of Spies*, 40–44.
12. Quoted in Longhurst, *Adventure in Oil*, 24.
13. *Ibid.*, 36.

9. The Kaiser's Pilgrimage

1. Quoted in Virginia Cowles, *The Kaiser*, 165.
2. Henry Morgenthau, Sr., *Ambassador Morgenthau's Story*, 7.
3. Elizabeth Spafford Vester, *Our Jerusalem*, 74–75.
4. Harold Armstrong, *Turkey in Travail*, 18.
5. Hewins, *Mr. Five Per Cent*, 27–30.
6. Armstrong, *Turkey in Travail*, 214–215.
7. Admiral Mark Bristol's War Diary, Box 16, Bristol Papers, Manuscript Division, Library of Congress.
8. Gulbenkian quoted in Hewins, *Mr. Five Per Cent*, 72–75.
9. *Ibid.*, 81.
10. Quoted in E. H. Davenport and S. R. Cooke, *The Oil Trusts and Anglo-American Relations*, 27.

10. A Tale of Two Admirals

1. Armstrong, *Turkey in Travail*, 198.
2. The story of the siege of Kut has recently been recounted in stirring fashion by Russell Braddon, *The Siege* (New York, 1970).
3. Cyril Falls, *Armageddon: 1918*, 166.
4. Armstrong, *Turkey in Travail*, 214–215.
5. Falls, *Armageddon*, 173.
6. French note to the United States, December 15, 1917.
7. Essad Bey, *Blood and Oil in the Orient*, 80–81.
8. Quoted in Robert Dunn, *World Alive*, 283.
9. John A. De Novo, *American Historical Review*, July 1956, 854.
10. *Sperling's Journal*, September 1919.
11. Senate Document 272, Sixty-sixth Congress, 2nd session, 1921.
12. Davenport and Cooke, *The Oil Trusts and Anglo-American Relations*, 120.
13. Dunn, *World Alive*, 293.
14. Admiral Bristol's War Diary, entry of October 8, 1919, Box 16.
15. *Ibid.*, entry of July 10, 1921, Box 20.
16. *Ibid.*, entry of August 2, 1922, Box 20.
17. *Ibid.*, entry of May 4, 1922, Box 20.
18. Dunn, *World Alive*, 283.
19. Admiral Bristol's War Diary, entry of June 3, 1922, Box 22.
20. *Ibid.*, entry of April 20, 1923, Box 24.
21. Armstrong, *Turkey in Travail*, 265.
22. Richard Washburn Child, *A Diplomat Looks at Europe*, 91–92.
23. Quoted in Waldo H. Heinrichs, Jr., *American Ambassador: Joseph C. Grew and the Development of the American Diplomatic Tradition*, 80.
24. *Ibid.*, 81.
25. *New York Times*, December 18, 1927.
26. *United States Daily* (Washington, D.C.), April 11, 1928.
27. Henri de Jouvenal, *Foreign Affairs*, July 1927.
28. Quoted in Hewins, *Mr. Five Per Cent*, 133.
29. *The Lamp* (Standard Oil of New Jersey publication), April 1926.
30. London *Financial Times*, October 28, 1927.
31. Ludwill Denny, *We Fight for Oil*, 155.
32. Admiral Bristol's War Diary, entry of February 25, 1924, Box 25.
33. Quoted in Hewins, *Mr. Five Per Cent*, 163.
34. *Ibid.*, 141.

11. The Sinclair Follies

1. C. B. Glasscock, *Then Came Oil*, 198. The story was originally published in an Oklahoma City *Times* series, April 1924.
2. *Ibid.*, 199.
3. M. R. Werner and John Starr, *Teapot Dome*, 41.
4. *Ibid.*, 79.

5. *Ibid.*, 86.
6. Senate Document 97, Sixty-eighth Congress, 2nd session, 113–116.
7. New York *Herald Tribune*, September 27, 1924.
8. Louis Fischer, *Oil Imperialism*, 81–82.
9. *Ibid.*, 128.
10. *Ibid.*, 155–156.
11. Francis Russell, *The Shadow of Blooming Grove*, 635.
12. Hanighen, *The Secret War*, 223.
13. Fischer, *Oil Imperialism*, 154.
14. *Ibid.*, 230–231.
15. London *Morning Post*, January 5, 1926.
16. Francis Delaisi, "Oil and the Arcos Raid," *Foreign Affairs*, October–November 8, 1927.
17. Quoted in Roberts, *The Most Powerful Man in the World*, 269–270.
18. G. P. Whaley, *Current History*, September 1927.
19. *Living Age*, September 15, 1927.

12. The Little Wars of Calvin Coolidge

1. Richard O'Connor, "Mr. Coolidge's Jungle War," *American Heritage*, December 1967.
2. New York *World*, April 4, 1928.
3. *Foreign Relations* (Pamphlet published by the Republican National Committee), 1924, 56.
4. *Ibid.*, 58.
5. Quoted in Denny, *We Fight for Oil*, 61–62.
6. Kenneth S. Davis, *The Hero*, 253–261.
7. *New York Times*, December 14, 1927.
8. Davis, *The Hero*, 259–260.
9. Harold Nicolson, *Dwight Morrow*, 270, 282.
10. *Ibid.*, 398.
11. *Wall Street Journal*, December 6, 1927.
12. Denny, *We Fight for Oil*, 86.
13. Release from Mexican News Bureau, October 22, 1927.
14. *El Universal* (Mexico City), quoted in the New York *Herald Tribune*, April 1, 1928.
15. *Excelsior* (Mexico City), quoted in New York *Herald Tribune*, April 1, 1928.
16. Denny, *We Fight for Oil*, 93.
17. Roscoe B. Gaither, *Expropriation in Mexico*, 8–9.
18. *Ibid.*, 18.

13. Dad Joiner Blows the Roof Off Texas

1. Samuel W. Tait, Jr., *The Wildcatters*, 142–143.
2. Tait, *The Wildcatters*, 141; Knowles, *The Greatest Gamblers*, 25–253.
3. Tait, *The Wildcatters*, 145.
4. Quoted in Knowles, *The Greatest Gamblers*, 258.

5. *Oil and Gas Journal*, October 20, 1930.
6. Quoted in Tait, *The Wildcatters*, 146.
7. George Sessions Perry, *Texas: A World in Itself*, 169–170.
8. Knowles, *The Greatest Gamblers*, 262.
9. *Ibid.*, 263.
10. Tom Buckley, "Just Plain H. L. Hunt," *Esquire*, January, 1967.
11. Dallas *Morning News*, March 29, 1947.
12. Perry, *Texas: A World in Itself*, 171.
13. Quoted in Samuel B. Pettengill, *Hot Oil*, 47.
14. *Ibid.*, 80–82.
15. Knowles, *The Greatest Gamblers*, 266.
16. Pettengill, *Hot Oil*, 151.
17. *Ibid.*, 154.
18. Dallas *Morning News*, November 15, 1934.
19. *Oil Weekly*, November 19, 1934.
20. Perry, *Texas: A World in Itself*, 179.
21. John Bainbridge, *The Super-Americans*, 2.
22. Perry, *Texas: A World in Itself*, 9.
23. Bainbridge, *The Super-Americans*, 197–198.
24. Edna Ferber, *Giant*, 9, 10, 223.
25. Quoted in Bainbridge, *The Super-Americans*, 108.
26. Knowles, *The Greatest Gamblers*, 326.
27. Quoted in Bainbridge, *The Super-Americans*, 96.

14. The New Arabian Nights, Revised American Edition

1. Tugendhat, *Oil: The Biggest Business*, 112.
2. Harold L. Ickes, *Fightin' Oil*, 132.
3. *Ibid.*, 115–116.
4. *Elimination of German Resources for War*, Report of the Senate Committee on Military Affairs, Seventy-ninth Congress, 2nd session, 1946, 1302–1306.
5. Ickes, *Fightin' Oil*, 14.
6. *Ibid.*, 71–75.
7. Tugendhat, *Oil: The Biggest Business*, 116.
8. Knowles, *The Greatest Gamblers*, 338.
9. Hanighen, *The Secret War*, 196.
10. Quoted in Tugendhat, *Oil: The Biggest Business*, 89.
11. Michael Sheldon Cheney, *Big Oil Men from Arabia*, 35. Cheney went out to Saudi Arabia as a public relations man for Aramco early in the 1950's and brought back a very lively and informative book on his experiences.
12. St. John Philby, *Arab Jubilee*, 164–177.
13. Quoted in Benjamin Shwadran, *The Middle East: Oil and the Great Powers*, 348.
14. Cheney, *Big Oil Man from Arabia*, 3–4.
15. Shwadran, *The Middle East: Oil and the Great Powers*, 309.
16. *Time*, April 3, 1944.

17. Quoted in Hewins, *Mr. Five Per Cent*, 219.
18. Philby, *Arab Jubilee*, 182–183, 232.
19. Shwadran, *The Middle East: Oil and the Great Powers*, 364–365.
20. James Morris, *Islam Inflamed*, 183.
21. Cheney, *Big Oil Man from Arabia*, 124–125.

15. Portraits in Oil: Wendell Phillips and J. Paul Getty

1. Wendell Phillips, *Unknown Oman*, 219.
2. *Ibid.*, 240.
3. *Ibid.*, 241.
4. *Ibid.*, 242–243.
5. Stephen H. Longrigg, *Oil in the Middle East*, 317–318.
6. Phillips, *Unknown Oman*, 243.
7. J. Paul Getty, *My Life and Fortunes*, 27.
8. *Ibid.*, 218–219.
9. *Ibid.*, 220.
10. *Ibid.*, 220–221.
11. "The Fifty-Million Dollar Man," *Fortune*, November 1957.

16. Fifty-Fifty or Fight

1. Tugendhat, *Oil: The Biggest Business*, 135–136.
2. Longrigg, *Oil in the Middle East*, 154–157.
3. Anthony Eden, *Full Circle*, 219.
4. Shwadran, *The Middle East: Oil and the Great Powers*, 151.
5. Longrigg, *Oil in the Middle East*, 172–173.
6. Eden, *Full Circle*, 230.
7. *Ibid.*, 234–235.
8. *Ibid.*, 235–236.
9. Allen W. Dulles, *The Craft of Intelligence*.
10. David Wise and Thomas B. Ross, *The Invisible Government*, 110–113.
11. Eden, *Full Circle*, 241.
12. *Ibid.*, 478.
13. Willi Frischauer, *Onassis*.
14. *Ibid.*, 212–214.
15. Tugendhat, *Oil: The Biggest Business*, 187.
16. Robert Engler, *The Politics of Oil*, 197–198.
17. *New York Times*, April 15, 1969.
18. "The Youth Movement," *Newsweek*, October 20, 1969.
19. "Nigerian Sacrifice," *New Statesman*, October 31, 1969.
20. Nigel Calder, "Opening Up the Arctic," *New Statesman*, June 6, 1969.
21. "Oh, What a Lovely War!" *Newsweek*, September 15, 1969.
22. *Wall Street Journal*, May 19, 1970; *New York Times*, June 1, 1970; *Time*, June 15, 1970.

23. *New York Times*, March 28, 1970.
24. *New York Times*, December 6, 1969.

17. Images and Realities

1. The advertisements were placed in the nation's press by the Petroleum Industry Information Committee, July 22, 1969.
2. James Ridgeway, "The Conglomerates Take Over, " *New Statesman,* March 28, 1969.
3. Ferdinand Lundberg, *The Rich and the Super-Rich,* 479.
4. *Tax-Exempt Foundations and Charitable Trusts: Their Impact on Our Economy,* Report of the House Select Committee on Small Business, Vol. I, 1969, v.
5. Jon Basil Utley, "Second Thoughts," *National Review,* July 1, 1969.
6. *National Review,* December 16, 1969.
7. Anthony Sampson, *Anatomy of Europe,* 93–94.
8. "BP Strikes Again," *Newsweek,* June 16, 1969.
9. Sampson, *Anatomy of Europe,* 94.
10. Tugendhat, *Oil: The Biggest Business,* 219.
11. Philip M. Stern, *The Great Treasury Raid,* 21.
12. Ronnie Dugger, "Oil and Politics," *Atlantic Monthly,* September 1969.
13. Stern, *The Great Treasury Raid,* 24–25.
14. Houston *Post,* October 10, 1960.
15. *New York Post,* December 23, 1968.
16. *Washington Post,* May 7, 1969.
17. Dugger, "Oil and Politics."
18. Stern, *The Great Treasury Raid,* 39.
19. Memo supplied the author by Mr. Tolle following an interesting and argumentative discussion August 17, 1969.
20. Display ad taken by the Petroleum Industry Information Committee and appearing in various U.S. newspapers on July 22, 1969.
21. *Congressional Record,* December 12, 1963, 23230.
22. "Bad Days for Wild Ones," *Time,* July 11, 1969.
23. David Stanford, "Jousting with Oil," *New Republic,* August 30, 1969. See also "A Dry Hole," *Newsweek,* August 4, 1969.
24. Stanford, "Jousting with Oil."

18. The North Slope Discoveries

1. "The Great Oil Hunt," *Newsweek,* September 22, 1969.
2. London *Financial Times,* October 12, 1969.
3. Edith Penrose, "BP and the Yankee Market," *New Statesman,* November 21, 1969.
4. William C. Bradstreet of Reynolds & Co., quoted in the *Boston Globe,* June 25, 1969.
5. *New York Times,* December 1, 1969.
6. John Lear, "Northwest Passage to What?" *Saturday Review,* June 25, 1969.
7. Washington dispatch to Bangor *Daily News,* July 11, 1969.

19. Oil in Troubled Waters

1. Ellsworth (Maine) *American*, July 23, 1969.
2. *Boston Sunday Globe*, June 29, 1969.
3. *Ibid.*
4. Edward Cowan, *Oil and Water: The Torrey Canyon Disaster*, 223.
5. G. S. Sturmey, *Shipping: The Next Hundred Years*, 127.
6. *Wall Street Journal*, June 13, 1961.
7. Quoted by Cowan, *Oil and Water*, 154–155.
8. *Ibid.*, 66.
9. *Wall Street Journal*, February 7, 1969.
10. *New York Times*, February 20, 1969.
11. David Snell, "Iridescent Gift of Death," *Life*, June 13, 1969.
12. Garrett Hardin, "Finding Lemonade in Santa Barbara's Oil," *Saturday Review*, May 10, 1969.
13. Associated Press dispatch under Houston dateline, April 27, 1969.
14. Claiborne Pell, "The Oceans: Man's Last Great Resource," *Saturday Review*, October 11, 1969.
15. Barry Commoner, *Science and Survival*, 10–11.

Selected Bibliography

Abels, Jules. *The Rockefeller Billions.* New York, 1965.
Armstrong, Harold. *Turkey in Travail.* London, 1925.
Asbury, Herbert. *The Golden Flood.* New York, 1942.
Bainbridge, John. *The Super-Americans.* New York, 1961.
Bates, J. Leonard. *Origins of Teapot Dome.* New York, 1965.
Bentley, John. *Great American Automobiles,* New York, 1957.
Bey, Essad. *Blood and Oil in the Orient.* New York, 1932.
Boatright, Mody C. *Folklore of the Oil Industry.* Dallas, 1963.
Bone, J. H. A. *Petroleum and Petroleum Wells.* Philadelphia, 1865.
Braddon, Russell. *The Siege.* New York, 1970.
Cheney, Michael Sheldon. *Big Oil Man from Arabia.* New York, 1958.
Child, Richard Washburn. *A Diplomat Looks at Europe.* New York, 1925.
Churchill, Winston. *The World Crisis, 1911–1914.* New York, 1949.
Clark, J. Stanley. *Oil Century.* Norman, Okla., 1958.
Clark, James A., and Halbouty, Michael T. *Spindletop.* New York, 1952.
Clews, Henry. *Fifty Years in Wall Street.* New York, 1908.
Commoner, Barry. *Science and Survival.* New York, 1966.
Cowan, Edward. *Oil and Water: The Torrey Canyon Disaster.* Philadelphia, 1968.
Cowles, Virginia. *The Kaiser.* New York, 1963.
Davenport, E. H., and Cooke, S. R. *The Oil Trusts and Anglo-American Relations.* London, 1925.
Davis, Kenneth S. *The Hero.* New York, 1959.
Denny, Ludwill. *We Fight for Oil.* New York, 1928.
Deterding, Henri. With Stanley Naylor. *An International Oilman.* New York, 1934.
Dodd, Samuel C. T. *Combinations: Their Uses and Abuses.* New York, 1888.
Dolson, Hildegarde. *The Great Oildorado.* New York, 1959.
Dulles, Allen W. *The Craft of Intelligence.* New York, 1963.
Dunn, Robert. *World Alive.* New York, 1956.
Eden, Anthony. *Full Circle.* Boston, 1960.
Engler, Robert. *The Politics of Oil.* New York, 1961.
Falls, Cyril. *Armageddon: 1918.* Philadelphia, 1964.
Ferber, Edna. *Giant.* New York. 1943.
Finnie, David H. *Desert Enterprise: Middle East Oil Industry in Its Local Environment.* Cambridge, Mass., 1958.

481

Fischer, Louis. *Oil Imperialism*. New York, 1926.

Flynn, John T. *God's Gold*. New York, 1932.

Fox, A. F. *World of Oil*. London, 1964.

Frankel, P. H. Mattei. *Oil and Power Politics*. New York, 1966.

Frischauer, Willi. *Onassis*. New York, 1968.

Gaither, Roscoe B. *Expropriation in Mexico*. New York, 1940.

Getty, J. Paul. *My Life and Fortunes*. New York, 1963.

Gibb, George Sweet, and Knowlton, Evelyn H. *Resurgent Years: 1911–1927*. New York, 1956.

Glasscock, C. B. *Then Oil Came*. Indianapolis, 1938.

Gould, Charles N. *Covered Wagon Geologist*. Norman, Okla., 1959.

Hamilton, Charles W. *Americans and Oil in the Middle East*. New York, 1962.

Hanighen, Frank C. *The Secret War*. New York, 1934.

Harter, Harry. *East Texas Oil Parade*. San Antonio, 1934.

Hartshorn, E. J. *Politics and World Oil Economics*. New York, 1962.

Heinrichs, Jr., Waldo H. *American Ambassador: Joseph C. Grew and the Development of the U.S. Diplomatic Tradition*. Boston, 1966.

Hendricks, Burton J. *The Life and Letters of Walter Hines Pages*. New York, 1922.

Henriques, Robert. *Bearsted: A Biography of Marcus Samuel*. New York, 1960.

Hergesheimer, Joseph C. *Tampico*. New York, 1926.

Hewins, Ralph. *Mr. Five Per Cent*. New York, 1958.

Hobart, Alice Tisdale. *Oil for the Lamps of China*. Indianapolis, 1932.

Hofstadter, Richard. *The Age of Reform*. New York, 1955.

Holbrook, Stewart H. *The Age of the Moguls*. New York, 1953.

House, Boyce. *Oil Boom*. Caldwell, Idaho, 1941.

Howard, Harry N. *The Partition of Turkey*. Norman, Okla., 1931.

Ickes, Harold L. *Fightin' Oil*. New York, 1943.

Kaplan, Justin. *Mr. Clemens and Mark Twain*. New York, 1966.

Knowles, Ruth Sheldon. *The Greatest Gamblers*. New York, 1959.

Larson, Henrietta M., and Porter, Kenneth W. *History of the Humble Oil and Refining Company*. New York, 1959.

Lawson, Thomas. *Frenzied Finance*. New York, 1905.

Lenczowski, George. *Oil and State in the Middle East*. New York, 1960.

Levorsen, A. I. *Geology of Petroleum*. San Francisco, 1956.

Lloyd, Caro. *Henry Demarest Lloyd*. 2 Vols. New York, 1912.

Lloyd, Henry Demarest. *Wealth and Commonwealth*. New York, 1894.

Lockhart, Robin Bruce. *Ace of Spies*. New York, 1967.

Logan, Andy. *The Man Who Robbed the Robber Barons*. New York, 1965.

Longhurst, Henry. *Adventure in Oil: The Story of British Petroleum*. London, 1959.

Longrigg, Stephen H. *Oil in the Middle East*. 2nd Edition. London, 1961.

Lundberg, Ferdinand. *The Rich and the Super-Rich*. New York, 1968.

McClure, S. S. *My Autobiography*. New York, 1914.

McLaurin, John J. *Sketches in Crude Oil*. Harrisburg, Pa., 1896.

Marcosson, Isaac. *The Black Golconda*. New York, 1924.

Mencken, H. L. *Prejudices: Fourth Series*. New York, 1924.

Millard, Joseph. *The Wickedest Man*. New York, 1954.

Mohr, Anton. *The Oil War*. New York, 1925.

Morgenthau, Sr., Henry. *Ambassador Morgenthau's Story*. New York, 1918.

Morris, James. *Islam Inflamed*. New York, 1957.

Myers, Gustavus. *History of the Great American Fortunes.* New York, 1936.

Nevins, Allan. *Study in Power: John D. Rockefeller, Industrialist and Philanthropist.* 2 Vols., New York, 1953.

Nicholson, T. R. *Adventurer's Road.* New York, 1956.

Nicolson, Harold. *Some People.* London, 1927.

———. *Dwight Morrow,* New York, 1935.

Noggle, Burt. *Teapot Dome.* New York, 1965.

O'Connor, Richard. *Pat Garrett.* New York, 1960.

———. *The Scandalous Mr. Bennett.* New York, 1962.

Perry, George Sessions. *Texas: A World in Itself.* New York, 1942.

Pettengill, Samuel B. *Hot Oil.* New York, 1936.

Philby, St. John. *Arab Jubilee.* London, 1952.

Phillips, Wendell. *Unknown Oman.* New York, 1966.

Pinchon, Edgcumb. *Viva Villa.* New York, 1933.

Pratt, Wallace. *Oil in the Earth.* Lawrence, Kans., 1942.

Reilly, Sidney. *Britain's Master Spy.* New York, 1932.

Rister, Carl Coke. *Oil! Titan of the Southwest.* Norman, Okla., 1949.

Roberts, Glyn. *The Most Powerful Man in the World.* New York, 1938.

Rose, Gerald. *A Record of Motor Racing.* London, 1909.

Rostow, E. V. *National Policy for the Oil Industry.* New Haven, 1948.

Russell, Francis. *The Shadow of Blooming Grove.* New York, 1968.

Sampson, Anthony. *Anatomy of Europe.* New York, 1968.

Schackne, Stewart, and Drake, N. D'Arcy. *Oil for the World.* New York, 1960.

Shwadran, Benjamin. *The Middle East: Oil and the Great Powers.* New York, 1955.

Stern, Philip M. *The Great Treasury Raid.* New York, 1964.

Tait, Jr., Samuel W. *The Wildcatters.* Princeton, 1946.

Tarbell, Ida M. *History of the Standard Oil Company.* New York, 1904.

———. *All in a Day's Work.* New York, 1939.

Tugendhat, Christopher. *Oil: The Biggest Business.* New York, 1968.

Vestal, Stanley. *Short Grass Country.* New York, 1941.

Warner, C. A. *Texas Oil and Gas Since 1543.* Houston, 1939.

Werner, M. R., and Starr, John. *Teapot Dome.* New York, 1959.

Wise, David, and Ross, Thomas B. *The Invisible Government.* New York, 1964.

483

Index

485

487

493

497